Promotion of Mental Health
Volume 1, 1991

Edited by

DENNIS R. TRENT

Director, Mental Health Promotion Unit
University of Keele
and
The Mental Health Foundation of
  Mid Staffordshire NHS Trust

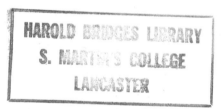

Avebury

Aldershot · Brookfield USA · Hong Kong · Singapore · Sydney

Published by
Avebury
Ashgate Publishing Limited
Gower House
Croft Road
Aldershot
Hants GU11 3HR
England

Ashgate Publishing Company
Old Post Road
Brookfield
Vermont 05036
USA

A CIP catalogue record for this book is available from the British Library and the US Library of Congress.

ISBN 1 85628 307 0

Printed and bound in Great Britain by
Billing and Sons Ltd, Worcester

Contents

Section Three: Research

Section Four: Programmes

List of contributors

Baily, Heather. Shropshire Centre for Health Promotion

Barry, Margaret, Ph.D. University College of North Wales

Borthwick, Alexander, B.A., M.Sc. West Lambeth Health Authority

Broad, Penny, M.A., M.Sc. South Warwickshire Health Authority

Childs, Kath, B.Sc., P.G.C.E. South Derbyshire Health Authority

Chiu, Herbert. City Polytechnic of Hong Kong

Chwedorowicz, Aleksandra. Academy of Music, Lodz

Clarkson, Petruska, M.A., Ph.D(Clin Psych). A.F.B.Ps.S. Metanoia Psychotherapy
   Institute, London

Crosby, Charles, Ph.D.

Davies, Robert, B.A. Shropshire County Council

Elliott, Sandra. North Staffordshire Health Authority

Gerrard, Janice. North Staffordshire Health Authority

Gilbert, Paul, B.A. (Econ).,M.Sc., Dip. Clin. Psych.. Southern Derbyshire Health
   Authority

Goodbody, Louise. Southern Devon Healthcare

Gordon, P. Kenneth, B.A., M.Psychol., Ph.D., C.Psychol., A.F.B.Ps. Winchester
   Health Authority

Graham, Helen, B.A., M.Phil. University of Keele, Staffs

Harris, John. South East Thames Regional Health Authority

Harvey, John, M.B., B.Chir., M.Sc., M.F.P.H.M., D.T.M. & H. Newcastle upon Tyne Health Authority

Henden, John, B.A.Hon. West Somerset Health Authority

Holroyd, Graham. Salford Health Authority

Hopkins, Jeffrey. University of Keele, Staffordshire

Jenkins, Anne. National New Parent Infant Network (NEWPIN), London

Kappler, George, B.A., M.S.W. Fife Regional Council

Keir, Norman, B.Sc., Ph.D., C.Chem., F.R.S.C. Ex-Chairman of the Samaritans

Loumidis, Konstantinos, B.Sc., M.A. University of Keele, Staffordshire

MacDonald, Glenn, B.Ed. Shropshire Centre for Health Promotion

McAdoo, Patricia, B.A., Dip. Clin. Psych. Northumberland Health Authority

Milne, Derek, B.Sc., M.Sc., Dip. Psychol, Ph.D., A.F.B.Ps.S. University of Newcastle Upon Tyne

Mitchell, David, Ph.D. University College of North Wales

Mooniaruch, Fiona, R.M.N. Shropshire Mental Health Services

Moore, Gordon, R.M.N. Northumberland Health Authority

O'Neill, Elizabeth, M.A., M.B.I.M. ChildLine, London

Olsen, Rolf, Ph.D., M.Sc., Dip.M.H., Dip.Soc.Admin. Prof. Emeritus, Birmingham University

Price, John, D.M., M.R.C.P., F.R.C.Psych., D.P.M. Milton Keynes Health Authority

Robinson, Jill, B.Sc. (Hons). Suffolk & Great Yarmouth College

Roulston, Rea, O.B.E. Fife Regional Council

Sartorius, Norman, M.D., M.A., D.P.M., Ph.D., F.R.C. Psych. World Health Organization

Sloboda, John, Professor, Department of Psychology, University of Keele, Staffordshire

Such, John, B.Sc.(Hons). Suffolk County Council

Sunderland, Margot, M.A., B.Ed(Hons), F.Coll.P.,A.H.P.P. The Institute for Arts in Therapy and Education

Swallow, Brian, B.Sc. Director of MIND

Trent, Dennis, BA., M.A., Ph.D., C.Psychol, A.F.B.Ps.S. The University of Keele, Staffordshire

Tudor, Keith, B.A., M.A.(Social Work), C.Q.S.W. Senior Research Fellow, King's College, University of London

Waring, Anthony, M.A., M.Sc. Vice-Chair of MOVE, Bolton

Wilson, J. Chair of MOVE, Bolton

White, Jim, B.A.(Hons), M.App.Sci., PL.D., C.Psychol. Lanarkshire Health Board, Hairmyres Hospital, Glasgow

Introduction

The Mental Health Promotion Unit (MHPU) was established in 1988 through the efforts and foresight of the Unit General Manager of St. George's Hospital in Stafford. Throughout its history, the unit has maintained a commitment to the promotion of mental health in both conceptual and practical terms. Its purpose has been to raise the awareness of mental health and the issues surrounding it within the professional and general populations. In the spring of 1990, a partnership with the University of Keele was established.

The field of mental health promotion was beginning to take an upswing throughout the health care professions and numerous authorities were beginning to take a closer look at the subject. Health education officers as well as other professionals were tasked with coming up with a mental health promotion strategy. Frequently the individuals tasked had the requirement added on as an extra area of responsibility to the positions they already held. As a unit dedicated specifically to the promotion of mental health, the MHPU became the first of its kind within Britain and established itself as a leader within the field.

Shortly after the creation of the partnership it became apparent that there was a lack of facilities for individuals and groups to get together on a national and international basis to explore and discuss the ideas and efforts to promote mental health. There appeared to be no lack of issues and programmes, only the mechanism for their exploration. Not since the national one day conference at Salford University in 1986* had there been an attempt to get people together. Additionally, there had been no follow-up process at Salford to continue the process. The members of the MHPU decided that the time had come to make the attempt again.

The management structure of St. George's Hospital has a long history of innovative involvements. When approached on the idea of a national conference they immediately agreed to underwrite the project. Additionally, the Department of Psychology at the University of Keele, through which the unit is managed at the university end, added its unconditional support without hesitation. The stage was now set to see if there would be enough interest to make the project effective.

The conference was envisioned as an annual two day event and a call for papers was issued in January, 1991. Papers were elicited from psychiatry, psychology, social work, nursing, health education, education, religious and volunteer sectors in an attempt to gain the widest possible perspective on current interests and efforts. It was determined that if sixteen papers of an appropriate level of quality could be elicited, the conference could proceed.

The response was beyond the expectations of any of us in the MHPU. We received over fifty abstracts all of which surpassed the quality standards which we had set. Of these, thirty-two were selected for presentation. Additionally, three guest speakers were invited. Again in an attempt to represent as wide a group as possible, the speakers came from psychiatry, social work and the volunteer sector.

While a number of presenters at the conference have had wide experience of presenting to academic conferences throughout the world, many were involved with the provision of mental health services and had never presented to an academic conference before. Recalling my first presentation to a large group, I take my hat off to them. It took courage and without them the conference would have been much the poorer.

To say that the conference was a success would be an understatement. The comments we received on the conference evaluation sheets were highly supportive and gratifying. We are already looking toward the conference in 1992 and have plans well under way. The psychology department of the University of Keele continues to provide academic support. The management of St. George's continues to look toward new horizons. In April 1991 it became The Mental Health Foundation of Mid-Staffordshire NHS Trust, one of the first NHS trusts in the nation. Without either there would be no MHPU.

D.R.T., November, 1991

xiv

SECTION ONE
GUEST SPEAKERS

1 ChildLine and the voices of children

E. O'Neill

Introduction

Mental health is not the absence of mental illness. Health is more than simply not being ill -it is a state of physical, mental and social well being, and is influenced by many factors, including life style and the social and physical environments in which people live.

My presentation today is about the work of ChildLine and about what children and young people have told ChildLine about their lives, and about the factors which affect their physical, mental, and social well being. It is unique in that it is not an account of children's lives shaped by adult or professional priorities or interests. It represents the children's perspective. It is what THEY want us to hear.

The ChildLine service

I would like to tell you first about ChildLine, how it works and how it is different from the ways in which others work. I would like to tell you about ChildLine's volunteers. Since children talk to ChildLine in their thousands I would like too, and most importantly, to tell you something of what they tell us - about sexual abuse, about fears about telling about sexual abuse, about being in care, about bullying and about what can happen to children in schools, and, perhaps most sadly, about children who are abusers. The focus of the work of most of us here who strive to promote mental health is that of promoting positive development, a sense of individual worth and well being, an empowering of those children, families and individuals with whom we work, so that they can have choice, decision making power, and a sense of control over their own lives. At ChildLine this is what we do in our work with children and young people - but with very great differences from the ways in which many of you work.

Your work is often to do with the child in his/her environment - you can see the child, you can place the child in a setting, you can touch the child. At ChildLine we have only a child's voice on the telephone. There is no distraction - there is only the child. We are therefore in no danger of overlooking the child. We do not focus on the family, the home, the school, or the adult perception of what is the problem. **The child is our focus.** We are able above all to follow the recommendation in the Cleveland report - that we listen to the children.

The body of information gathered by ChildLine is unique in that it is child-led. Children and young people identify their own problems to counsellors, and it is their definition which is recorded. The voices of the children are heard by us and through us by others who need to hear what children and young people feel about the services which are there for them. They tell us about the supports they want to enable them to achieve that state of physical and mental well being which we have defined as health. They talk to ChildLine, the free, 24 hour, national, confidential telephone counselling service for children and young people. Calls are free to the children who call the 0800 1111 number and children know this number and use it. ChildLine has counselled more than 170,000 children, and given advice and help to 27,000 adults since its launch in 1986. The service operates 24 hours a day, every day; we never close. As you can imagine, our callers don't recognise office hours, 5 day weeks, or public holidays. It is a national service: calls from all over the U.K. are answered in the London office. At peak times, ChildLine's two other centres in the Midlands and Scotland, are open to take calls from children in those areas. At other times calls from those areas come to the London office. We hope to expand and open centres in other areas, including Wales and Northern England.

The demand

We need to expand because British Telecom tell us that over 10,000 attempted calls are made every day on our lines. Many of these calls are children trying repeatedly to get through - but there are still more calls than ChildLine can answer. The pressure on the lines is continuous. On the night that ChildLine launched BT told us of the noise of the whirring of the machinery that was children trying to reach ChildLine - that noise continues.

In common with many other mental health services we cannot give the kind of service that we would like. We are a charity so we must also work to raise the money to provide that service. We answer 1500-2000 calls a day and of those 200 are written up as significant interactions. Think what it would be like to have 2000 children at the doors of the office or clinic, 2000 children every day. Many of our calls are silent. Many children when they are finally able to talk to us tell us that they tried 8 or 9 times before they actually plucked up the courage to speak.

Children test us out sometimes, which seems an appropriate way of trying a service before perhaps trusting the people there with your fears and your anxieties, *but children don't lie about sexual abuse or about their distress.* People often ask how many of our calls are hoax calls, which suggests to us that people resist accepting the degree and extent of distress among our children and young people and are sometimes deaf to the voices of children.

Working for ChildLine

ChildLine is a confidential service - we work at the child's pace, we assure them that anything they tell us will remain confidential to ChildLine unless they give us permission to pass it on. We offer options, we work hard to take a child forward, and to support them in making their lives different and safer for them. We are often able to work to a point where the child decides that he/she will, with us, talk to another service. For the record we do refer, on average, 25 - 30 children a month to the statutory services. We will break confidentiality if a child is in a dangerous situation - but only after careful discussion, usually involving the youngster.

Our counsellors are volunteers - selected, trained and supervised by professional staff. The volunteers are ChildLine. Volunteers do not have to have specific qualifications or prior experience. They come however with a wide range of experience and from a variety of cultural and ethnic backgrounds: they range in age from 20 to over 70. ChildLine welcomes the richness and diversity which this brings to the service we offer. A quote from a ChildLine volunteer perhaps describes best what work at ChildLine is like: 'Working for ChildLine for me means a regular commitment to a cause that sadly exists. Children are the adults of the future and by trying to help them now we are also helping them for the future. Doing this work means a growing understanding of myself, and a growing respect for children and their courage.'

The callers and their needs

Most of the callers are between 11 and 15, though younger children and adults also call. The adults who call often do so because of experiences in their own childhoods - and they tell us of their need then, and now, to talk about those experiences. It is rare for any of us at ChildLine to talk to an outside group about our work without someone in the audience wanting to talk to us afterwards about their experiences of abuse in childhood and their need to talk to someone at that time. Sadly, and usually, there was no-one that they felt they could talk to.

Children call ChildLine about a wide range of problems and concerns. Unlike many of the relationships which children have with adults, in this telephone counselling relationship **the power is in the hands of the child.** He/she can put the phone down at any time, can speak or not, can decide what they will tell or will not tell you.

Children call about bullying, pregnancy, drug and alcohol abuse, parental divorce, running away from home - and, during the Gulf crisis, about their fears about war and being bombed. Since the service began the largest categories of calls have consistently been those about physical and sexual abuse. We have learned much from the children and young people who call us about abuse in their lives. They tell us of their fears of not being believed, of their feeling that in some way they are responsible and to blame for what is happening to them.

Children need to be heard: they need to hear that it is not their fault; they need to be believed and accepted for themselves. When this happens children may then be ready to work with us to look at their options and to consider what they can do. Sometimes this means identifying a trusted adult to whom they can talk, and who may be their ally if they do disclose. This may be essential if they do tell - in the next stage of the system they

5

may well desperately need an ally. Children talk to us about their fears of the system - of their worries about what will happen if they do tell: 'I want my Dad to stop, but I don't want you to take him away - I don't want him to go to prison - I want to get help to make it stop - I don't want to break up my family - I don't want to go into care, to leave my school, my dog, my friends.'

We hear from children that many of them, having told, find the system fails them. At present only a very small proportion of children who report abuse go to court and only a very small proportion of those finish up with any satisfactory resolution. We have listened to what the children have told us and are working with other children's organisations, for example in relation to the recent Criminal Justice Bill, to make changes, to push for the use of screens, and of videos and taped evidence. Of course perpetrators must have proper justice, but at present the scales of justice are very weighted against the child.

We are working to produce material which will prepare children for court appearances. We are also working to advocate more support and services for families, and more support for children who are in care.

ChildLine's experience of counselling children in care leads us to the unsurprising conclusion that they are particularly pained and troubled children, needing greater access to sources of assistance, comfort, welfare and nurture. The overriding features which distinguish children and young people in care, as a group, from the other children who call us are the range, extent and complexity of the difficulties with which they struggle. They use ChildLine to talk to someone independently about their worries, their feelings and their confusion. As with other callers sexual and physical abuse predominate, usually abuse by fathers and stepfathers though also abuse in care by staff, foster parents, or other children. When children in care talk of this re - abuse there is an impression that they feel that they may already have used up their quota of adult belief in their stories, and a strong sense of defeat.

Our experience leads us to believe that children in care, like other children, need to be able to talk about their troubles, privately, to someone outside their own network so that they can voice their worries, and talk through the best ways of finding help from the people who care for them. These are among the most troubled and needy children we talk to - they need to be cared for by highly trained, skilled and gifted staff, and those staff also need recognition, status and remuneration.

Children have conflicts of loyalty over parents, carers and workers and they have feelings for them and about them. These can confuse young people and lead them to voice things in order to please, placate, comfort or anger. It can help to deal with a non - partisan service like ChildLine as a source of independent assistance to children in care.

What we hear from children in care may sound old fashioned - they want to be heard, to have continuity and connections in their lives - in short to be loved. The love they need has to be combined with skill, understanding and maturity of judgement - a formidable challenge for everyone involved in caring for children in residential care. A quote from a letter written by one caller talks about this; 'I was really glad when I found out about ChildLine because otherwise I don't think I could ever have started talking about my problems, not with someone who knew me, or even with someone who could look at me when I was talking.'

6

Sometimes that breakthrough of talking and being accepted is enough to enable a young person to work out how to deal with a problem: sometimes it is the first step in a process which leads to a child making contact with another adult, or another face to face service.

Special problems

From time to time ChildLine sets up **special lines** to deal with particular issues. We became aware through our calls that bullying was a major concern for many of the children who called us, and a special Bullying Line was set up for a period of time.

The difference from our normal calls was very great. Gone was the wish to remain anonymous: we were told the time, the place, the names of those involved, and how often the teacher had been told. We discovered that children viewed bullying quite differently from adults. There is a belief among adults that if bullies are ignored they will stop bullying; others think that bullying is an inevitable phase of childhood that will pass without their intervention. Still others think that children must learn to 'stand up for themselves', so that adult intervention to protect victims of bullies would merely inhibit a valuable social lesson. What children told us on the Bullying Line throws serious doubts on these beliefs. Bullying does not stop of itself; it does not 'go away'. It may continue for years, eroding a child's confidence and making his/her life miserable.

Adult intervention can be effective and children often need adult help. If help is offered early and with insight it may involve little effort on the part of the adult and much relief for the child. Assessment and treatment of bullies must also be seen as equally necessary as the protection of victims.

We set up a special Boarding School Line following the experience of helping a number of boys at a boarding school near London. In this instance systematic sexual and physical abuse by the proprietor and a number of teachers at the school had gone on for years. There was appalling bullying and the situation as a whole had been made difficult for the parents because of the school management's refusal to hold parent - staff meetings, and because many of the parents were military families abroad. Previous investigations by police and social services had not produced evidence clear enough to act on. With help and support this time a number of boys were able to come forward, and went through a harrowing court case which resulted in the abusers being jailed.

It was following that, and experiences in 2 or 3 other schools, that it was agreed that we would open the special Boarding School Line. We are now working with schools to look at some of the issues which have emerged. When young people themselves were asked about what they thought about the idea of the line, the comments were interesting; I think it's a good idea since if someone was abused his parents might not believe him because they don't want to.' 'You can express your problems to someone even if your parents think it's a load of rubbish as well as your friends when you say you've been abused or GBH by the friendliest teacher.'

One last issue which some of our callers tell us about is one which causes us much concern. These are the calls from young people who tell us that they themselves are abusing younger children. There have been calls from teenage boys who are sexually abusing their younger siblings, most of them indicating that they want to stop but don't know how. A 17 year old boy, for example, rang in a frightened state to say that he had raped an 8 year old whom he was baby sitting the previous evening.

Together with the National Children's Bureau and the National Children's Home we have been working to identify what is being done in this field and to review the - very limited - amount of help which is available up and down the country. This work has raised many questions - and few answers: Should there be criminal proceedings if these young abusers have themselves been abused, and what do you do about that in terms of therapy? Are the children primarily offenders or primarily children? What's the difference between a young burglar who grows out of offending behaviour, and a young sexual offender who often does not? What is normal sexual behaviour in children? There seems to be a real professional anxiety about investigation or treatment because that may label the child, with all that may entail, but a recognition that help is urgently needed.

Children and young people have told us much about their lives and about what is needed to enable them to achieve and maintain a state of well being and of mental and physical health. Sometimes what is needed to help them deal with their lives is what we can provide; a service and people who listen, who accept, who care. For some of the children and young people who call us this may be the first time someone has really listened, the first time they have felt of value. For others the opportunity to sort out feelings, thoughts and opinions with a caring but non-partisan helper enables them to help themselves, to live more positively and more happily within their homes or families, schools or relationships.

Calling ChildLine may also be a first step towards help for a youngster whose problems are more serious, or a youngster who continues to struggle with issues. There needs to be available for these young people more, not fewer, high quality services which offer support and help and therapeutic work. Sometimes we try to move a child on to face to face contact, but have found a steady reduction in services which are available. We may therefore continue to counsel children on the line when it is clear that we should not be doing so - but the alternative is to offer them nothing.

I have described to you our work at ChildLine, and have tried to tell you something of what children tell us of their lives, their experiences, their problems and their hopes.

Children tell us of the abuse which is a part of the lives of many of them, of their fears of telling about that abuse, and of their worries about the system which tries hard to help them. These voices also talk of bullying, and of what it's like to be a child in care, or a child who abuses other children.

We must, as adults, as parents, as professionals, listen to the voices of these children. If we do not, the damage to the mental health of these children today and in the future will be considerable. The promotion of mental health must start with the children of today, who will be the adults - and the parents - of tomorrow.

2 A critical review of psychiatric care in the '80s: The implications for the promotion of mental health in the next millenium

R. Olsen

Abstract

In recent years the question of psychiatry - how to define it and its objectives, how to determine its purpose, worth and effectiveness - has once more become the centre of controversy and debate and the focus for considerable adverse media attention. The anti-psychiatry critique has fostered some improbable alliances between groups of social administrators, sociologists, lawyers, doctors, politicians and the media. The criticisms vary in content and emphasis, and are often contradictory in their conclusions. Some are of the view that psychiatry is no more than an agency of social control, constituting a threat to individual freedom and rights. Contrary opinion argues that the system provides pious excuses for social transgression and lawlessness, and encourages a cult of social and personal irresponsibility. An opposing view criticises psychiatry for its over-reliance on medication - 'the pharmaceutical cosh' - in place of a proper concern with the effects of social disadvantage and psychological explanations for motivations and actions. Perhaps the most important and significant discontent relates to the loss of public confidence which has shown itself in the criticisms of service users, the concerns of relatives, a hostile media and Parliamentary mistrust, which has resulted in an expansion of regulation, control and inspection of psychiatric practice. Overall, in considering the recent past I am driven to two conclusions: first, that whilst we have isolated centres of excellence, overall our recent history is little more than the register of our continuing neglect and confusion; and second, that most of our recent history is not fit to repeat itself. The aims of this paper are twofold :a) first, to analyse the events which have led to this state of affairs, and b) second, to propose solutions to the current dilemmas for the promotion of mental health services in the next millennium.

Psychiatric care in the eighties

The most important and significant event of the eighties was the enactment of the Mental Health Act 1983. The crucial question is why was it necessary for Parliament to introduce legislation to reform the 1959 Mental Health Act, which on its introduction was heralded as a 'monumental achievement', 'a bi-partisan triumph which enjoyed the solid backing

backing of the medical profession and the public' Lindsey, 1962[1]. An examination of the forces which led to the Parliamentary reform shows that during the 23 years of the 1959 Act grave reservations were expressed, not only about the organisational, professional and therapeutic failures, but also about the cruelty and neglect which was consistently reported by Ministerial investigations and Committees during the years 1962-82.

In my view these failures arose out of five following inter-related issues:

(i) Theoretical Conflict. The range of literature which discusses the aetiology of mental disorder presents explanations which go beyond theoretical conflict and are diametrically opposed. Interpretations include the possible significance of such factors as clinical, behavioural, genetic, familial, sociological, psychological, gender, cultural, and social. Students and practitioners are left to choose their preference according to their own predilections and school or professional allegiance, too often without the requirement to demonstrate the validity by objective analysis. Rather like a supermarket.

The result persuades critics that mental health services are governed by vested opinions and dogmatic testimony, and confuses the public, the courts and Parliament as to the true nature of mental disorder or its successful management. **The Times,** in its Leading Comment (1982)[2] following the trial of the notorious Mr. Sutcliffe, who became known as the 'Yorkshire Ripper', had this to say about the state of the art of psychiatry and of the judgment which was reached: 'The judge would have been wrong to accept the Attorney General's instinct at the outset (of the trial) to accept the plea of diminished responsibility. The Attorney General was wrong even if the jury had accepted that Sutcliffe was mad. The whole course of the trial showed that the question of his insanity could not be left to the professionals. No responsible doctor could have declared an oath of absolute certainty that this secretive and crafty man was not pretending to be mad. From a common sense point of view it is pure nonsense even to ask whether Sutcliffe was sane. The poor showing of the psychiatrists in the witness box is less evidence of incompetence than the fact that in these remote areas of psychology ordinary criteria do not apply.'

(ii) Doubts about the Physicalist Ideology. The second issue which I want to address relates to the doubts about the physicalist ideology which pervades much of current clinical practice. There is little doubt of the importance of drugs in the management of mental disorder, particularly those of a short-term nature. However, overall the situation remains as described by Eysenck some 30 years ago[3]: 'When we compare the potential usefulness of drugs with our present knowledge of their effects and the clinical use made of them at the moment, we cannot but note the wide gap which separates expectancy from achievement. Empirical studies there are many, but they are frequently contradictory and bedevilled by many experimental, statistical and methodological errors. Clinical applications show frequent failures to obtain expected results and a general difficulty of predicting the reactions of individuals to the given drugs, to say nothing of the eternal problem of dosage. The present position, therefore, cannot be regarded as satisfactory either from the research or the applied point of view.'

In 1987[4] Dr. Ernesto Spinelli reported an interview with William Sargant, whom many regard as the man who pioneered physicalist psychiatry, eg ECT, Leucotomy and induced abreaction. Except in the use of drugs, his methods have become either redundant or severely curtailed. The drug approach remains the major plank of contemporary psychiatry, even though such treatments are open to a variety of criticisms about the fact that they do not cure, the unpleasant and sometimes serious side effects, the dangers of dependency, and the fact that it is not known how many of these treatments work. Spinelli asked why then does psychiatry lean so heavily on drugs as the management of choice; Sargant concluded that 'conviction has been replaced by convenience, necessitated by public and governmental disinterest in the plight of the mentally distressed.' Dr. Sargant thought that contemporary psychiatry 'is really a rather tragic mess.'

If we are to progress it is important that the standard response of psychiatrists to adverse reports on the condition of their patients is changed from 'What medication is he/she on?' to 'Why should this have occurred?'

(iii) The Myth of Community Care. The third issue to confound psychiatry is the myth of community care. What was conceived by the Piercy Committee (1954-57), and endorsed by Parliament in the Mental Health Act 1959 as 'care in the community' has, with the passage of time, become 'community care' - an entirely different concept. The original idea was inspired by the emergence of the first tranquillisers in the early 50's, and the belief that such medical treatment could in many cases by administered without recourse to hospital. This notion was firmly embraced and enlarged by Enoch Powell, when Minister for Health, in his Hospital Plan (or should I say Hospital Closure Plan) for England and Wales, issued in 1962. From then on the idea of an alternative system evolved, in which the community would become the main locus of care. However, this radical substitution has never been underwritten by central or local government policies, organisation or resources. The result is that in the field of mental disorder nothing, more than community care, reveals the yawning chasm between government policy statements and actual provision.

It is estimated that at any one time about 25% of the population will experience mental disorder or emotional distress. Some 95% of this number will be in the community. In spite of this knowledge, I know of no local authority which allocates more than 3.5% of the social services budget to direct services for the mentally disordered, and the majority give over significantly less. As a consequence, too many of those who suffer mental disorder spend their days without employment or occupation, in a state of relative poverty receiving no, or only marginal, support from the public services. The result is the loss of public and media confidence in community care as a viable alternative to hospital. It is a sad fact that a quarter of a century after the Report of the Royal Commission on the Law Relating to Mental Illness and Mental Deficiency (HMSO 1957), there is no comprehensive system of community care for the mentally disturbed. Instead, it is a principle which remains in our imagination to inspire future ideals, to support our fancy that what we are currently doing is in the best interests of all, to deaden our anxieties about the hurt that this policy may cause patients and their families, and to help us to bear the fact that in spite of the political acceptance of the necessity for the provision of comprehensive community care services, the need will in the foreseeable future remain, in the words of Barbara Castle when Secretary of State for Social Services, 'simply a statement of objectives' (DHSS 1975: iv).[5]

(iv) Continual Service Reorganisation. Before embarking upon the final issue of concern, I wish to make passing reference to the issue of the constant reorganisation, inspired by both central and local authorities, which has plagued our health and social services for the past two decades. It seems that the response to any presenting problem is to shuffle the pack of individuals who deliver the services, give them different titles, change the rules governing their functions, make them reapply to see if they can stay in the game, increase individual and collective responsibilities (preferably by Government circular), and raise consumer expectation but offer no additional resources. For many services this amounts to a perpetual merry-go-round which absorbs considerable energy and resources particularly at the highest level, creates staff anxiety and, most important, distracts staff from what should be their primary concern - the care of their patients or clients and those with whom they live. In relation to the mental health services we must ask for whose benefit these reorganisations take place, and if anyone can evidentially point to a more effective service to patients and their families, or to more successful treatment outcomes as a result of reorganisation.

(v) The Continuing Loss of Rights. My final focus of concern relates to the continuing loss of rights of individuals and their families. At the beginning of the 80's we saw the tail-end of the numerous Ministerial enquiries which spanned two decades, beginning with the investigation into patient care at Ely Hospital in 1962, and ending with the examination of practices at Rampton Hospital. In large part the Mental Health Act 1983 was devised to introduce a number of measures to protect patient rights. Not least: the re-introduction of the Mental Health Act Commission; increasing the opportunity to appeal against continued detention; a statutory right to after-care for those detained on treatment orders; the better training of Approved Social Workers; clarification of the rules of consent to treatment and the provision of independent second opinions; care within the least restrictive conditions possible; halving the duration of treatment orders before consideration for renewal; and the better management of patients concerned in criminal proceedings.

However, it is clear from the three Biennial Reports published by the Mental Health Act Commission[6] and others that whilst there are many instances of improvement, and individual centres of excellence, overall some fundamental rights are still poorly regarded and protected by services or individual professionals.

For example:

Poor crisis management in which the professions act in disunity; guardianship is not a considered option; and the person defined as 'patient' is removed to hospital no matter whether the cause is thought to lie within the person himself, the nature of his relationships, the social environment, or in disease processes.

A lack of alternative resources within the community.

The unavailability of Sect. 12 Doctors - the absence of duty rota systems and the reluctance of some psychiatrists to attend psychiatric emergencies in the community.

The failure to provide 24-hour emergency services, with a consequent reliance on the Police and use of Sect. 136.

A low level of understanding amongst some GPs of the requirements which the Act places upon them.

In some areas, the over-reliance on emergency powers, Sect. 4, for administrative and organisational convenience.

The misuse of Sect. 136 (Police Powers). The study by MIND (1987) [7] showed that in the South East at least, the use of Sect. 136 was questionable. It is clear that the purpose of the detention under Sect. 136 is for a Doctor and an ASW to carry out an investigation. Yet in this study only 8.6% of those so detained were interviewed by an ASW.

The unwillingness of nearly all to consider guardianship.

The failure to implement the statutory requirements placed on health and local authorities to provide after-care under Sect. 117 to patients discharged from treatment orders.

The mismanagement of mentally disordered offenders. The Commission, in its second Biennial Report concluded 'More work needs to be done before it can be said that the 1983 Act has come near to achieving its aims of ensuring that offenders who are mentally disordered... and who require care in hospital are not imprisoned instead.'

The use of Sect. 5(2) (the Doctor's power to detain an informal patient for 72 hours) as a short-term holding order in which the views of a second opinion or an ASW are not sought.

The inordinate delays in the Mental Health Review Tribunal hearing appeals in all but Sect. 2 cases.

The variable quality and procedures of Hospital Managers' hearings.

The absence of comprehensive treatment plans for detained patients.

The absence of users' and relatives' opinions and participation in care and treatment arrangements.

The failure of the Department to issue guidelines on the care and management of De-facto detained patients, particularly those with mental handicap or confusional states.

Where provided, the narrowness of post-discharge support plans, which ignore financial, accommodation, employment and occupation needs.

Poor quality inter-disciplinary working.

Nationally, whilst the concepts of mental health promotion and development are supported, overall they are poorly developed.

The promotion of mental health services in the next milennium

It is clear that there is a need to pursue resolution to these shortcomings if the standing of psychiatry is to be promoted in the next millennium. To my mind this will depend upon great change at both the micro and macro levels of activity. Of these, four issues stand out as deserving particular attention:

The first relates to **the position of psychiatry in society**. Mental Health workers are deeply concerned with people who are usually socially and economically disadvantaged, to represent people who are not always able to fulfil normal social expectations, to advocate on their behalf and ensure the adequacy of the systems and social institutions which affect them. In this sense mental health workers embody and express the social conscience of society. This places immense responsibility on professions which are

13

asked to implement a set of values to which society gives contradicting and only partial support. Society's ambivalence towards the mentally disadvantaged is reflected in their poor political status and the amount of government policy which remains discretionary and unfunded.

This suggests that psychiatry must seek to clarify what society in general and our institutions expect from it in terms of its knowledge base, its values, practices and its objectives.

The second task must be to establish effective central and local strategic planning. We must discover ways to overcome the idea that joint planning should be dedicated to the principle of maintaining the status quo, territorial boundaries, and to the avoidance of resource transfer.

The third duty is to systematically evaluate the wisdom of the common man - that much of what we call mental disorder is due to social disadvantage, stigma and relationship problems. The persistence of the medical model, which views all mental disorder as a disease-like entity which can be treated by medical means, is built upon a shaky foundation. It argues that mental disorder has an existence, like pneumonia, outside the value judgments of those who observe it and the cultural norms of society. My colleague Prof. Brockington, Professor of Psychiatry at Birmingham, in his inaugural lecture reached this conclusion: 'If Kraeplin were living today, he would be dismayed at the effects of his creative thinking. He would see that he had led psychiatry down the wrong path.' This is not to argue that the clinical perspective has no standing. However, neither psychiatry nor our patients are served by our failure to evidentially differentiate between those disorders which are primarily physical and those which are primarily social. We must promote an understanding and intervention which admits not only to the possibility of clinical factors, but also the significance of social facts.

The fourth and final objective which I wish to propose is one which I believe deserves particular attention. It relates back to the issues discussed earlier - the theoretical conflicts and the physicalist ideology. In part these doubts arise out of the failure of psychiatry to demonstrate that it can treat according to a set of stated objectives, and can reasonably define the likely outcome to its intervention within a predicted time scale. What we do know is that the relapse and readmission rate of around 73% appears inordinately high unless we can explain the reasons for it. We must promote a professional activity which measures, evaluates, estimates and appraises results and outcomes in some form that rests on anything beyond faith, assertion and the illustrative case. In the absence of outcome measures we have to ask what is guiding and informing the professional effort.

My current work with colleagues of St. Matthew's Hospital, Burntwood, shows that it is possible to construct and successfully apply a model of intervention which steers practice towards an approach which works by predictive forecasts and outcome measures, to the benefit not only of the patient but to staff as well.

Conclusion

The theme of this conference - the Promotion of Mental Health - is of vital concern, not only to the professionals and volunteers who work in the field, but also to the public we serve. The lessons from the 80's are clear. If the problems are to be resolved and the

14

promotion of mental health achieved, we must foster a new movement. Such a movement must first own up to its own confusion, and then determinedly address the conflicting theories of mental disorder and competing therapies given to our patients. The task is not easy. The role of psychiatry has yet to be satisfactorily defined; the knowledge base yet to be established; and skills yet to be demonstrated; at a time of deepening frustration, continuing reorganisation, and a lack of resources.

However, I remain optimistic. The effects of the past decade have not been without achievement: we have at least articulated the issues and established the need for a search for accuracy.

References

1. Lindsey, A. (1962). *Socialised Medicine in England and Wales,* p.325, Chapel Hill.
2. *The Times* Leading Comment, 'Too Many Victims', 23.5.81,p.13.
3. Eysenck, H.J. (1957). Drugs and Personality: theory and methodology. J.Ment.Sci, 103, 430, 119.
4. Spinelli, E., A double-edged legacy to psychiatric care. *The Listener,* 23.4.87, pp.14-15.
5. DHSS (1975). *Better Services for the Mentally Ill.* Cmd.6233, HMSO.
6. Mental Health Act Commission, *Biennial Reports* 1985, 1987, 1989, HMSO.
7. Rogers, A. & Faulkner, A. (1987). *A Place of Safety*, MIND Publications.

3 The promotion of mental health: Meaning and tasks

N. Sartorius

Introduction

The word promotion has many meanings and so has the word health. Put together they can be interpreted in so many different ways that they can cover almost any activity that a health service or an individual may wish to undertake. This is not only a theoretical possibility: the two words have been used to cover deplorable interventions in the name of eugenics, publicity campaigns for certain foodstuffs, naturopathy and homeopathy, courses on meditation, health education, disease control, and a variety of other topics.

I shall therefore first describe the way in which I hope these two words could be used and then suggest steps that could be taken to promote mental health and mental life.

What is Health?

The word health has its origin in the word *Hal*, an Anglosaxon word meaning the whole: health, therefore, is meant to describe the integral existence of a being. The word implies that health is indivisible, that it involves and is apparent in mental, physical and social functioning which are interdependent. Mental health and physical health cannot exist on their own: they depend on each other and are complementary. Human beings have a mental life which refers to inner experience linked to interpersonal relationships which make them human and aware, conscious and alive. Mental life is not a state of being permanently carefree and joyful, blissful and elated: it has unpleasant as well as pleasant contents and includes worries as well as optimism, regrets as well as plans. It is a characteristic feature of human existence and cannot exist on its own.

By the same token, mental and physical disorders cannot exist on their own. Mental disturbances can accompany, follow, cause or precede physical disorder and vice-versa. The words 'physical disorder' and 'mental disorder' do not mean that the mal-function is limited to an organ or function: rather, they indicate predominant signs of involvement of an organic system. Both physical and mental disorder affect the health state of the individual - a health state in which various diseases and impairments can occur.

The word 'disorder' is useful in this context because it covers the conceptual spheres of disease, illness and sickness. Other languages do not have the luxury of three different words describing the three main facets of a disorder of function - the word <u>disease</u> - indicating a medically defined disturbance of physiological functioning, usually with a structural damage to a tissue of the body, often with an identifiable cause, understandable pathogenesis, course, response to treatment and outcome; the word <u>illness</u> - referring to the feeling one has about one's body and its functioning, an opposite to feeling well; and the word <u>sickness</u> referring to the societal recognition of a disorder in the functioning of the organism, as for example contained in the term <u>sickness benefit</u>. Not everyone will use these three terms consistently in the different senses described here: the distinction between the three concepts, however, is generally recognized. What is also recognized, though less widely and less clearly, is the fact that many people who have a medical disease do not feel ill, that many of those who feel ill do not qualify for recognition as sick by those who surround them or by wider society and that many of those declared sick have no medically identifiable change of tissue, of structure or of physiological functioning.

The borders of the three terms are vague and changing from culture to culture and from one time to another. The closest to a stable definition are perhaps diseases but even there, there are difficulties. The limits of the normal and abnormal shift: the minimum blood pressure which will make someone hypertensive, the blood sugar level that defines diabetes, and many other standards, have changed over the years and will probably continue to change with the increase of our knowledge and under the impact of other factors. Recent years have also brought with them an uncertainty about the borders between disease and impairment (is stable adult diabetes in the obese an impairment or a disease?) and between communicable and non-communicable disease (if hepatitis brings about liver cancer in the offspring - should it be called a communicable disease or a first stage of non-communicable disease?)

It is therefore difficult to define health in a negative way by saying that it is equal to the absence of disease and all the more reasonable to define it as a state of balance within oneself and between oneself and the environment. Such a state can incorporate impairment: health and disease or impairment in this definition are orthogonal to each other rather than opposite. Health is always present, regardless of the presence of disease: as the skies are always present in spite of clouds on the horizon. Illness, particularly if severe, can make it difficult to be aware of health - as clouds can become so dense that the blue serenity of the skies is unimaginable.

Clouds can bring rain and continually blue skies can be boring: disease or disorder do not necessarily (nor always) mean only damage to the individual. People who have learned that they have a grave disease which may have a lethal outcome often report that the time which they live suddenly changes in quality, that every event which occurs is of different dimensions, that life is fuller, more satisfying than ever before. This in no way means that we should try to enrich human existence by inducing disease or by diminishing our efforts to eradicate it: all that it says is that a different comprehension of health and disease may render life more tolerable in the presence of unavoidable misery so often accompanying disease and impairment.

A further consequence of accepting the definition of health as a state of balance within ourselves and between ourselves and the world around us is that the state of health has to be assessed in a dynamic way, in relation to a variety of elements, both internal and external. The disappearance of a disease may therefore not necessarily mean an improvement of health in the same way as the presence of a disease does not necessarily mean that health is absent. The fact that we had to pay a high price - e.g., in terms of limitation of mobility or in terms of loss of sexual attractiveness - to get rid of a disease must be presented with just as much fervour as the diminished prevalence of the disease. Gains or losses - in terms of quality of life - must be given just as much attention as the disappearance of symptoms of a disease because one does not automatically imply the other. Other criteria of success of health care also emerge as important if health is viewed in this way: thus, for example, gain in family well-being and changes in community tolerance of the individuals affected by a particular disease - say, schizophrenia - must be chalked up high on the success side of the board even if the disease could be only partially removed and if a significant impairment remained in the individual affected by it.

Above all, however, such a comprehension of health means that responsibility for its improvement cannot be given to health services alone. Many other social sectors, from education to labour and from environmental protection agencies to religious authorities, have a role to play if progress is to be achieved.

What do we mean by Promotion?

Promotion is the second controversial word in the title of my talk. The dictionaries define it as advancing a person to higher office, as encouraging a process, actively supporting the passing of a law, as the initiation of a project, or the publication and advertising to sell a product.

In health care, however, the term 'promotion of health' is used to describe the diminution of severity or frequency of a disease, for example, through its prevention and treatment, or the increase of fitness due to physical exercise, better diet and other means, or education which will prompt people to clean their teeth more regularly and more vigorously. None of these actions - useful as they may be - seem to correspond to the meaning of the word 'promotion' as described in the dictionaries. Prevention and control of disease are perfectly clear and well understood terms and there is no need to provide them with another name; the same is true for all but one of the other uses of the word 'promotion' in relation to health.

The word promotion should, however, be used in its legitimate sense describing the process of moving health to a higher position on the scale of values of individuals, communities and societies. If we succeed in making people value their health more highly, we shall have allies in all the other tasks - in preventing disease, in adopting healthier lifestyles, in surviving disease and in helping others to live a life of better quality. Promotion of mental health in this sense - particularly while changes in value systems are recent - may not be accompanied by any immediate decrease in the prevalence of mental illness nor by changes in medical practice. The effects of promotion of mental life will often be remote; perhaps decades or generations will go by before an

19

effect can be clearly seen and measured: once established, however, the new value system will just as stubbornly reject changes as the present ones do.

Obstacles to Promotion

Defining the promotion of health as a change in value systems may not be so popular with the many who interpret it differently at present. This is comprehensible: it is not only the word that changes; we also have to change the method of work, the indicators of success and the leaders of action. Changing values is not something which doctors or psychologists can undertake on their own. Nor can governments act without the people themselves, without parents, teachers and friends who will provide children with the first elements of their future values, without the priests, the media and many others.

If society were to decide to commit itself to the promotion of mental health there would be little problem in deciding how to proceed. Governments have been engaged in the process of establishing or changing values held by individuals and communities for a long time. From all that we see in the world today and over centuries they have been effective, often in regrettable ways.

Most governments however, have not yet decided that the value of mental health and mental life needs promotion. Occasionally there are sparks of hope that they might do so but these are no more than flashes after which the darkness is even more depressing. Several years ago, the Government of Venezuela, for example, declared that a prerequisite for true democracy is that the population can understand issues about which it has to vote and that, therefore, the Government has the responsibility to do something about it. It established a Ministry of Intelligence and placed a significant budget at its disposal. A variety of activities were initiated in schools and at places of work; the media were engaged in the programme; politicians publicly gave their support to it. A serious programme of evaluation was put in operation and a special institute was created to provide technical and scientific support to the initiative. The results were surprisingly positive: there was a clear gain in intellectual performance of those involved and the attitudes of the general population to mental health, learning, and intellectual pursuits became positive. No significant side-effects of the programme were recorded. Some of the programmes failed to produce gains in terms of intellectual performance but seemed nevertheless to contribute to the acceptance of efforts to improve intellectual performance, gain knowledge and expand awareness. The programme lasted for several years, then grew weaker, mirroring the decrease of power of the officials who had put it into operation. Some activities survived; others - particularly those which required changes in work style - disappeared. In other countries and at other times there were also efforts - usually on a less ambitious scale; none of them, however, resulted in inserting the effort to increase the value of mental life into the nation's school curricula and the governments' agenda.

It is therefore necessary to start promoting health without a firm hope that governments will jump at the opportunity and provide ample, generous and long-lasting support, people and facilities: the opposite may in fact happen because most authorities watch efforts to change value systems in which they have gained importance and power with justified suspicion.

20

The path of Promotion

The steps that are likely to be necessary if we are to succeed are not difficult to imagine: they resemble those used in other silent or violent revolutions. The first will be to clearly define the goal - making certain that it is distinct from other pursuits in this field.

This step sounds easy: yet it is likely to take much energy and time. The field of mental health characterized by the multiplicity of conflicting definitions of key terms, vague and nebulous plans of action, exclusive jargon and a preference for learned explanations of reasons which made things happen, over a realistic consideration of what could be done, using current knowledge and available resources.

In the past three decades there have been major advances in the effort to create a common language which will allow mental health workers to understand each other. WHO, working with a large international network of centres developed standardized methods of assessment of mental illness and a system of diagnosis and classification accompanied by precise guidelines. It produced definitions of terms to describe psychiatric services and standards of care. A variety of conventions about ways in which treatments will be assessed have been published. This work took many years: now however there exist tools for understanding one another when talking about mental disease and it is highly probable that they will be used worldwide in the very near future.

In the field of health promotion and in matters dealing with mental health and mental life rather than with mental illness, however, there are no such tools and the task of producing them is before us.

Changing value systems is not a painless process: the promotion of one value means downgrading at least one but usually several others to a lower place. The fact that we complain that there is insufficient money for mental health services, that there is stigma attached to the mentally ill and their families and that children are not stimulated in their growth is an expression of the difference between a system of values which we hold and the system of values held by others who consider other things more important than the treatment of the mentally ill or the initiation of school mental health programmes. Bringing the value of our pursuits higher on the priority list means downgrading others which will be opposed; sometimes we shall also have to give up things which are dear to us.

Once it is clear to us what promotion of the value of mental life and of mental health is we can proceed to the second step and start to seek allies who will not only believe in the importance of promoting mental health but will also be in a position to help in effecting the change. Here emerges an important difference between mental health promotion and care for the mentally ill: while the latter requires at least elementary knowledge about treatment and rehabilitation and thus, to a large extent depends on the mental health system producing knowledge and providing continuity of mental health care, the former - promotion of mental health - is not restricted to mental health workers. In fact, the more different the people participating in this effort the better: changes of values of a society must include many professions and people from all walks of life, speaking a variety of professional jargons and class or group idioms.

Third, it will be necessary to involve those who hold specific knowledge and skills usable in the process of value change. These may be psychologists, specialists in the business of advertising, people in the media, salesmen. They will not be able to help us unless we have translated our demands into an immediately comprehensible message. These have to be simple, if at all possible suitable for presentations in visual form as well as in words. They have to convey single ideas related to recognized problems, shared by the audience. They must be relevant to other pursuits of society though not necessarily harmonious with them. They must be endorsed and supported by all those who will work on the promotion programme and they must not be at variance with scientifically demonstrable facts. Once we are convinced that they have understood what the task is and that they have the competence necessary to do it we have to find the strength to withdraw from the process which they will set into motion to arrive at the goal. Often this is extremely difficult because it seems obvious that they are doing the wrong thing, that they will never succeed, that they are vulgarizing too much, rendering our noble ideas into something as ordinary and as unlikely to help us as a hamburger. They do however succeed - often in an amazingly short time and we have to let them do it without interfering.

This does not mean that meanwhile we have to be idle: the tasks of finding new converts, of monitoring progress and possible side effects must remain on our agenda as a permanent item. Also, high on our agenda must remain all efforts to find money. Here a vicious circle is often in play - low value given to mental life also means that only a few are ready to give a little money for the effort. To break it, some play 'lottery of celebrities' - approaching many of the opinion makers in the hope of finding one or two who will put their weight into the effort; others link the effort to promote mental health to another drive which is already corresponding to an established need in society - for example, to be admired by others. Some plod along believing that they must work hard and accumulate examples which will make society come to its senses, become inclined to give preference to campaigns aiming to make people understand the beauty of being alive and comprehending the world around us over grandiose plans to build another weapon or prison.

Once we have a clear understanding of the meaning and strategies of promotion, have recruited allies, found agents of change and resources to feed the campaign, we shall have to face the most insidious and pernicious of difficulties: the need to find inner strength and conviction to continue with the same routine activities, in a repetitive manner for a long, too long, time without many visible or revolutionary successes. Treatment tasks are often clear in their nature and, although strenuous, usually bring satisfaction to the patient and the provider. Rehabilitation tasks are often more challenging but enormously rewarding when successful. Preventive chores can also lead to visible results in a reasonably distant future. Promotion of mental health - defined in terms of shifts in the value system - even when successful leads to imperceptible change, to a gradual veering from one course of action to another. When results are obtained it is difficult to be certain that this was the result of the action which we have undertaken: numerous other factors could have made the difference. The gnawing doubt that all of our efforts were in vain is present even when there is success: and all the more so when nothing happens for a very long time.

The motivation for continuing to try must therefore be sought elsewhere, not in visible achievements. It must stem from the deep conviction that the effort will eventually bring fruit and produce changes which will help the cause, perhaps long after we are gone. Also, it should stem from the sense that we are not alone in what we are doing nor in the belief that the course of action is useful and noble. Meetings like this one sometimes help to meet people who believe the same and are willing partners on this long and arduous road: often, however, we shall have to continue working alone.

Promotion of mental health is a worthy cause. It is a doable task, a necessary ingredient of action that may be undertaken to make our world progress, to help humanity survive as a society of humans rather than as an assembly of creatures striving to live a life unaware of themselves and of the links which tie them to their past, their future and those around them.

SECTION TWO
THEORETICAL ISSUES

4 The spiritual dimensions of mental health

A. Borthwick

Introduction

As mental health professionals and their clients move from the large psychiatric hospitals the role of the Chaplain in Mental Health care is coming under scrutiny. The decision by West Lambeth Health Authority to close its psychiatric hospital at Tooting Bec gave rise to the need to research the possible extension of the chaplaincy service into the community. The University of Surrey agreed that the subject was worth investigating and made their research facilities, including computer time and staff assistance, available. I am grateful to the Health Authority who funded the research.

The case for the appointment of Chaplains to Mental Health Units with a community dimension has, in the past, been proposed by Chaplains themselves, the very people who might be thought to have a vested interest in the situation. The 1985 symposium arranged by the Joint Committee for Hospital Chaplaincy was attended by Chaplains, and Browning (1986) during his research addressed his questionnaire to hospital managers, but he anticipated that managers would consult with their Chaplains.

> The questionnaire was explicitly sent and addressed to managers in order to offset any bias on behalf of Chaplains themselves - although the covering letter suggested that it was envisaged that it may well be appropriate for managers to discuss the completion of the questionnaire with one or more of their Chaplains. In the event it became clear that this happened in many instances (Browning 1986:5).

My project was an attempt to assess whether or not the appointment of a Chaplain to the mentally ill in the community is thought to be either necessary or desirable by those most likely to be affected by such an appointment, e.g., staff, clients and, of course, parochial clergy. Three hundred and twenty-two questionnaires were sent to staff in the Mental Health Unit in West Lambeth, clients attending the Elm House Day Hospital in Tooting Bec, parochial clergy in the West Lambeth catchment area and a representative sample of Chaplains to Mental Health Units in other Districts. In the event one hundred and eighty-five questionnaires were completed and returned for analysis; a response rate of 57%. This was disappointing, but sufficient in number to warrant proceeding with the analysis. Interestingly the lowest response rate was from nurses, followed by parochial clergy - 45% and 50% respectively - the nurses only needed to use the internal mailing system, the clergy kept the stamps from the addressed envelopes. The highest response rates were from clients and ancillary staff - 80% and 85% respectively.

It was the purpose of the project to elicit attitudes to the role and function of the Chaplain with special reference to community care. The questionnaire design took into account research into the role of the clergy although this was almost exclusively upon the role of parochial clergy. Examples of this research are Blizzard (1956), Caniel (1967) and Ransom, Bryman and Hining (1977). Six categories of clergy activity emerged: 'Pastor', 'Celebrant', 'Preacher', 'Counsellor', 'Leader', and 'Administrator'. Questions were devised based on a Chaplain's activities within each role category, providing a list of twenty-seven questions. These were rephrased in the form of a statement, and respondents were asked to record their attitudes to each statement on a Lickert ordinal scale ranging from Agree Strongly to Disagree Strongly across the continuum.

For example: under the role category of 'Pastor' the statement was made 'The Chaplain should visit patients in their own homes.' Under the role category of counsellor the statement was made 'The Chaplain should counsel and advise patients and their relatives.' In order to avoid a 'response set' the statements in the questionnaire were, for want of a better word, randomised. A response set may occur when questions in the same category are grouped together,. Respondents may recognise the theme and there is a possibility that this may influence subsequent answers.

The Lickert scale provided answers in a suitable form for computer analysis. The Prime computer at the University of Surrey was used and provided factor analysis through the SPSSX package.

Analysis

The computer programme asked that six factors be identified and it was expected that the factors would correspond to the same role categories that were used to create the questionnaire. In fact only five factors were found to have a value of any significance and because of the nature of the responses given within each factor they were named as follows:

The community factor

The chaplain must have a community role which involves educating the church about mental illness, being involved with staff colleagues in planning community care, linking the local church with the health service professionals and visiting clients at home.

The pastoral factor

The Chaplain should have the pastoral care of clients and their relatives as well as staff working in the community. Church services should be conducted in clients' homes, either private homes or in supported houses, and the chaplain should be readily available to counsel staff.

The church factor

The chaplain is seen as pastor to clients, relatives and staff members in the community with a status equal to, but not subordinate to, the parish clergy. The clergy are seen as a valuable link between the resources of the church and community staff who may need the support of such resources as the church is able to provide. The questionnaire did not investigate what the community staff could offer the church, particularly the parish clergy, but it would seem to offer a great deal of help to clergy who may be apprehensive about dealing with the mentally ill in their parishes.

The health service factor

The work of the Chaplain is considered valuable only as long as the Chaplain remains a health service employee and is seen as being a colleague by other staff members. This gives the Chaplain authority and a right of entry which would be denied if the Chaplain did not have an official position within the service. The Chaplain is seen as providing a valuable link between staff who may be in isolated situations in the community, in small groups cut off from management and the heart of decision making. The Chaplain should be involved in staff training and the Chaplain's work should be subject to monitoring by health service and church assessors together.

The secular factor

It was difficult to find a suitable title for this factor and this label still seems unsatisfactory. The attitude items making up this factor are indicated by negatives, e.g., 'The Chaplain should not try to convert individuals to Christianity' and 'The Chaplain should not discuss individuals with the parochial clergy without the individual's permission.' Also 'The Chaplain should not be subordinate to parochial clergy although the work will require the Chaplain to function across parochial boundaries.'

Conclusions

The questionnaire assumed that the chaplaincy already had a function in the community. Those who felt that there was no role for the Chaplain had the opportunity to express their view by responding in a negative way to the attitude items. For example, a respondent who consistently responded in the areas 'Strongly Disagree' or 'Disagree' on the Lickert scale would be indicating opposition to the concept of community chaplaincy generally. The factors derived from the computer programme indicate a model of chaplaincy envisaged by the respondents and also which areas of the Chaplain's role they would not like to see continued after hospital closure.

Two roles for the Chaplain in the community are perceived as being important: (a) the role of adviser and counsellor to clients, their relatives and to community staff, (b) the role of educator and supporter of parochial clergy and other church people. It is clear that the pastoral role is the one most respondents would welcome and would wish to see retained in a community service. This is congruent with the findings of Blizzard (1956) and Daniel (1967) who both found that the role of pastor was the one that clergy themselves viewed as being most important.

Many respondents were positive in their responses to the questionnaire and would appear to welcome a movement of the chaplaincy service into the community alongside those other departments of the institution which have moved, or are preparing to move, out of the hospital. A Chaplaincy model is envisaged which provides a pastoral, educative service integrated with the local church community but professionally linked with the clinical and support services within the NHS.

The conclusions do, however, offer little comfort to those who believe that the chaplaincy service should be the exclusive domain of the established Church of England. Only 21% of respondents thought that the Chaplain should be an ordained member of the Church of England, whilst 53% disagreed with such a proposition. This gives weight to Browning's conclusion that 'special consideration should be given to appointing an *open denomination* whole time chaplaincy.' (Browning 1986:30).

To conclude, may I express one reservation. Patients moving into the community from the hospital are a discrete group of people. There will come a time when all clients will be cared for in the community by friends, relatives, supported by Health Service community professionals. If there is a perceived role for a community Chaplain today it could be that, in the future, the role may be devolved to parochial clergy and their congregations. On the other hand community chaplaincy may evolve and become an essential support for parochial clergy, but whether this should be provided by the NHS, the Church or the Local Authority is another question.

5 Mental health and Daoism

H. Chiu

ABSTRACT

The study of well-being as such can be influenced differently by the stand point one takes. The contribution of academics on controversies as such may not be fruitful, as our role should extend to more than merely conceptual clarification and theoretical creations but rather rudimentarily, the pointing out of reality and order for people to take references for living. The meaning of mental health need not depend on dwelling on what is the definition of negative mental health versus that of positive mental health.

According to Daoism (Ma, 1987), there are four dynamic and interactive levels of Dao. The highest of which is 'Universal Change', the second is 'Ecological Interaction', the third is 'Societal Timex', the fourth is 'Mind and Body Integration'. The well-being of man depends very much on his awareness of his living with an ever expanding life space that communicates with the Four Levels.

The Western mental health classic, Jahoda (1958), delineates six criteria for positive mental health: (a) attitudes toward self, (b) growth and self-actualization, (c) integration of personality, (d) autonomy, (e) perception of reality; and (f) environmental mastery. Humanistic psychologists may start their enquiry from the stand of 'being human'. Whereas the Daoist may start with an approach by means of the 'Levels'. The argument is that one knows not enough of one's destiny without referring to the Dao. The consideration of the present paper, then is whether the humanist way will eventually meet with the Daoist's.

From reviewing the humanist quest for well-being, the author discovers some possible meeting grounds. The first is about the nature of 'self-actualization', the second is about the issue of 'perception of reality' and third, 'environmental mastery'.

It is reminded that, Maslow (1987) has pointed out, though not in detail, that self-actualizers are able to have the feel of natural order. Their moral judgment, according to Kohlberg (1984), to are of nature law order orientation. This is equivalent to an enlightenment stage of a person as profiled by Chuang Tzu (Giles, 1980). The paper will give a thorough account of how 'Self-Actualization' facilitates 'Perception of Reality'. Mainly, reality is not distorted if the perceiver has 'no mind' (Alan Watts 1978).

As Lau Tzu states (Cheung,1981): 'Attain utmost emptiness. Maintain profound tranquillity. All things are stirring about. I watch their cycle. Things flourish, and each returns to its root. Returning to the root is called tranquillity. This is what is meant by returning to one's basic nature. Returning constancy is called enlightening. Not to understand constancy is blindly to do unfortunate things.'

The paper goes on with its line of reasoning that from the Daoist point of view, 'Environmental Mastery' appears a term reflecting the egocentricity of the human species, the anxiety to survive without the awareness that man is only part of nature in the universe. Man and human creation are all governed by natural law.

Of course, such natural law depends on the comprehension of the human mind, resilience comes into play on the constant reformation of the understanding of the power and functioning of the greater order. Non - viligant holding on to world constructs will easily result in stagnation of the mind which contradicts the First Level of Dao that 'Universal Changes' always take place and the mind is in the 'changes' as well, correspondingly. Of course human beings are not helpless, the emphasis is as we are not that omnipotent as we think we are.

Introduction

As a phenomenon in relation to the psychological functioning of mankind, 'mental health' has caught the attention of psychologists, psychiatrists as well as those in helping professions for several decades. A careful review of literature on mental health of the last four decades reveals that several elements have repeatedly been advocated by different authors, such as correct attitudes toward the self, interpersonal competence, environmental mastery, integrated personality, growth and development, cognitive skills, efficient contact with reality, autonomy, problem solving, and so on. (Jahoda, 1953; Allport, 1955; Frank 1953; Maslow & Mittelman, 1951; Anderson & Creswell, 1976; Alder, 1982; Lewis & Lewis, 1984; Warr, 1987)

The approaches to study of the phenomenon by the above quoted authors tends to be value laden as men tend to ask for the 'right', the 'best' answer to the ways human beings exist. It may be the case that different studies might have focused on different aspects of the total and each claims to be contributive. Therefore, it is rare to find any work in the existing literature which tries to present a clear picture of what mental health is and at the same time locates well what has been done by others under a well defined structure. This therefore is an aim of the present paper.

Apart from theory building, in its way, this paper also tries to highlight the contribution of an Eastern Philosophy, Daoism, on mental health as an answer to human existence.

Before entering the theme of the discussion, a very fundamental but philosophical question about mental health must be answered. Why do human beings need to be mentally healthy? The question reflects the orientation of mankind in striving for betterment. As Freud has discerned, human beings are motivated by the pleasure principal.

Happiness has been considered by many philosophers to be the highest good, ultimate motivation for human action. It means satisfaction with life (Diener, 1984), success (Tartarkiewicz, 1976) and the predominance of positive affect over negative affect (Bradburn, 1969). In addition to these values, the ideal life makes an individual feel himself as meaningful, fulfilled, elated and ecstatic. (Tsang, 1986).

These feelings, though they may appear subjective and individual, do not happen to come out of the blue, but essentially arise from the exchange between an individual the environment. In this sense, mental health is therefore related to the pattern of cognition, emotion, attitudes and behaviour by which an individual interacts with the environment.

These merit inquiry into the characteristics of the individual.

Self-awareness

One the characteristics we first find interesting is self-awareness. One cannot choose wisely for a life unless he dares to listen to himself, his own self, at each moment in life. A mentally healthy person should be able consciously to aware of his or her desires, abilities and limitations, responsibilities and rights, acts and their purpose with the minimum of distortions. A mentally healthy individual should be capable of perceiving and recognizing his or her self realistically and objectively. This process is extremely important as it provides an efficient contact with reality, both internal and external.

If one is able to identify one's characteristics, potentialities, needs and values correctly without distortion, one is said to have a clear sense of identity. Based on this, one relates with the world. One's object relation is therefore more realistic. One who is not sure of his identity shies away from interpersonal intimacy; but the surer he becomes of himself, the more he seeks it in the forms of friendship, combat, leadership, level and inspiration. (Erickson, 1950).

The Daoist approach to the issue of identity (self-actualization) is of crucial importance to mental health. It focuses on one's nature. An identity schema like 'I am a Psychologist' is a cultural or socialization product which may not be able to reflect the real self of the person; in brief, it is the natural manisfestation of the self which is independent of cultural or societal context. The self, in this state is acultural and amoral.

The self in its most original form can be contacted by means of meditation. There are various denominations of Daoist practice of meditation. However, when in the proper mode, thesecan bring people to experience the ever unfolding inertia of life which is independent of the history of the practicer, with potentials awaiting to be actualized.

Reality testing

In order to interact effectively with the environment, one necessary condition at first is to get a clear understanding of the environment so as to enable the individual to locate the situation that he or she is in. What the mentally healthy person sees should correspond to what is actually there. However, the sense of correct perception lies in the process itself as reality is always subject to interpretation of different individuals. Therefore, our attention should be placed on the way by which the individual perceives the world.

Sometimes, perception is influenced by emotions or subjective needs. 'The mentally healthy person will test reality for its degree of correspondence to his wishes or fears. One lacking in mental health will assume such correspondence without testing' (Jahoda, 1958).

Saul & Warner (1982:11) assure that 'the less developed a person's sense of reality and the more powerful the force of his feelings, the greater is his confusion in perceiving whether these sensations come from within or without, that is, the stronger is the tendency to project these inner feelings and fantasies upon the outside world from which they now seem to originate... fantasies can cause all forms of mental and emotional disorder, as well as asocial and antisocial behaviour.'

As a cognitive process, perceptions are limited by human cognition itself. People may construe their situation wrongly because it is a characteristic of human cognition to be parsimonious. For the sake of being parsimonious, people may hold on to world designs that may not correspond to their actual experience or that may not coincide with the present situation. Examples of the former could come in form of any cultural heritage, beliefs, teachings, ideologies or stereotypes. Examples of the latter could come as inappropriate constructs people use in making sense of their world (Kelly, 1955 : 831).

Efficient contact with reality therefore needs to be considered in conjunction with the time perspective that an individual views things from. The humanistic movement in psychology advocated the Here-and-Now perspective stressing that the reality of life is that we can only live in the present moment. Wisdom of the past may not be appropriate for the present. It is argued that the past is mute and only the interpretations we make of it today give it meaning (Bugental, 1971). Undoubtedly, focusing on the existing environment surrounding us is of great significance in enabling an effective interaction as it is only in the ever-flowing present that one can realize the potentials which finally determine the future.

So far we have come to the situation that mentally healthy individuals are able to perceive themselves and reality realistically: the question then is how does that sense of well-being come into being?

The criteria for well-being : competence

Human beings need resources to survive. An individual's ability to identify, acquire and create an adequate supply of potentially available resources can well determine the effectiveness in interacting with the environment. This idea first caught the attention of Rae-Grant, et al. in 1966 and Adler further clarified and incorporated it into the concept of competence (1982:42).

On the operationalization of competence and its relation with mental health, a more precise idea could be referred to Warr, (1987). He states that affective well-being can be understood by three levels of specificity : Context-free, Job-related and Facet-specific. This means that the individual is able to remain mentally healthy over the tides of life and in the demands, be it specific or general, of his occupation.

The process involves firstly a recognition or identification of resources, then understanding the implication or ways of acquiring the resources, and finally developing access to resources and influencing these controlling the resources. A competent individual must be able to take a line of relatively greater advantage, avoiding actions which are self-defeating, ineffectual, or act to close off the possibility of creating or acquiring resources.

This is not to imply that our mentally healthy subject will not encounter problems or difficulties. Problems he encounters are real problems in contrast to those who in their failing to perceive and accept reality, make life difficult for themselves. He is elastic, receptive and there is an absence of rigidity in the approach to handling tasks. People who are able to apply the right strategies for the right time are resilient. It is also a characteristic of the mentally healthy (Emory, 1988). They have a sense of control and time will tell that they has chosen the correct path. They believe in their ability in handling tasks. In novel situations, they have the creativity to work a way out. In light

34

of forthcoming events, their path will not sway.

This sense of inner satisfaction and hopeful aspect, according to Binite (1984), 'is not related to wealth, position in life, or prestige. It is a feeling of inner strength based on an internal knowledge that one has chosen the correct path, that one is achieving it, and one has the psychological and physical energy to maintain this state, There is the further knowledge that nothing can change this feeling..... The inner satisfaction we have described implies the righteousness of the cause and the belief that time will show one to be right. Without this, the internal feeling of happiness and satisfaction will soon give way to doubts, later dissatisfaction, and loss of inner security.' However, according to Daoism, this state still needs further advancement. As Zen Buddhism regards it, such a state is compatible to Hinayana, the Lesser Vehicle.

Emotional dimension of well-being

One may wonder what kind of emotion reflects a healthy mental state. Does mental health simply imply an individual experiences happiness, joy or any other kind of positive feeling? This appears to be the case when researchers try to study the relation between mental health and affective well-being (Alder, 1984; Worchel & Goethals, 1985). Undoubtedly, positive feeling is generally valued as 'good' to human beings. Nonetheless, whether an emotional state is healthy or not cannot be decided soley by looking at the valence (positive or negative) of the emotion an individual experiences. The question cannot be answered without referring to the context in which the affect arises.

Bearing the context-dependent nature of emotion in mind, a mentally healthy person, as others do, experiences both positive and negative affect. The essence lies in whether the affect arises from a reasonable perception of an individual over the situation he is in. This points to a 'healthy' cognitive state of the individual overlooking the tides of life. With transparent perception upon self and reality, one would recognize favourable and unfavourable circumstances as being natural phenomena in life to live with equally. It is to let go one's nature with spontaneous affection but at the same time not to be carried away by strong emotions, be they positive or negative.

One of the teachings of Daoism is to see thing as they are without lingering and exaggeration. Another is not to take sides when things are at least dual. The sense of well-being we find in mentally healthy people is not happiness in vacuum but is built upon the trust of self : competence. It is a sense of control and inner satisfaction, with a feeling of betterment for the future.

The Daoist perspective

The above discussion may reflect the close resemblance between humanistic psychology and Daoism on the grounds of personal adjustment. The well adjusted subject we have profiled so far is compatible to the state of 'Lesser Vehicle' in Buddhism. In the Daoist perspective, this is a narrow sense of mental health or state of human potential.

In deeper self-awareness, one is able to experience the inertia of life striving for higher goals which is beyond individual adjustment. One is able to feel from within, the passion for mankind, for creation and for future generation. The temporal dimension of awareness is expanded to the future. The spatial dimension of awareness is expanded beyond the immediate. Not only is it necessary to see clearly the essence of self but also its relative nature in relation to other creations. The self then is not an isolated phenomenon but a member of networks of interactions. One is unable to get a whole picture of the self without referring to the greater order behind.

Ecologists may find the above discussion interesting yet familiar. However, the lesson they give is that no one and no species is the master of the world. Creations, both living and non-living, are independent in their existence (Brewer, 1988:822-824). As an analogy, the ways an ecological system sets up in equilibrium represent some natural laws over and above each and every member/element of the system. Looking at the specific property of each member alone cannot reveal the natural law behind. It can only be discovered by studying the whole system.

By this, the Daoist puts forward a unique way of perception. It concerns the point of origin of perception. The destiny of the self cannot be comprehended from the point of origin of the self alone but should also take into account the existence of a greater order behind. As Mittelman (1991) writes:- 'Being open to the world, at least in the case of human beings, is for me not simply or even primarily a matter of acquiring information and using it creatively and efficiently. A non-egocentric interest in or receptiveness to the world, which includes an attitude of respect for living things and other parts of the world, is also an important aspect of openness.'

The passion for creation can then be comprehended, as it is from the greater order which the individual emerges. Here, Westerners use the term 'mother nature' to coin the relationship. It is therefore possible for a person to be capable of enlarging their concern for others and the world outside. Then, a rich, differentiated and ever-growing life will be one of the characteristics of a mentally healthy person. Coan (1983:20) described it as the relatedness to others for the sake of that person. Adler used the term Germeinschatsgefuhl as a sense of community with our fellow humans and with the whole of mankind.

This respect confirms the expectation held by some psychologists regarding mentally healthy persons as socially productive, constructive and useful (Verma, 1988; Srivasdtava, Rai & Rai, 1987).

The four dynamic and interactive levels of Dao

The significance of this paper then is to introduce to readers the Daoist perspective on mental health. It is because the Daoist way has systematically delineated how mental health can be achieved starting from self awareness to the awareness of greater order (natural law). The following discussion starts from lower to higher levels of awareness..

Mind and body interaction

In order not to do harm to life, one ought to do something with oneself as the starting point. The first step is to achieve individual freedom. To do so, one has to live independent of both the good and bad wills of relativistic cultures. The idea is similar to the Existentialist's 'Beyond Good and Evil'. Thus, one then is able to live according to one's natural affinity.

When one is able to be in touch with oneself direct (void of the distortions of 'Good and Evil'), one is able to appreciate how thoughts and feelings interact with bodily functions. This is what Daoism means by the unification of mind and body (Ma, 1987:68; Giles, 1980 : 48). 'It is simply one application of the Unifying Principle Yin-Yang of the Philosophy and Science of the Far East' (Ohsawa, 1981).

Societal timex

Fromas early as what has been described by Huang Dai (The Yellow Emperor) in his Book of Internal Medicine, the following ideas have been explicit. The study and promotion of mental health should not be separated from social environment. This is because cultures vary with times and places and therefore, ways of living vary. Healthy cultures and interpersonal relations contribute to mental health. To improve mental health, plans are set taking into consideration the ways of living at that time. Our contemporary cross cultural and indigenous approaches to sciences carry the same wisdom. For the individual level of concern, one should be able to transcend what his society gives and have it hinders him, and live according to his nature. By the same analogy, mental health providers of a society/community should therefore consider possible factors/resources according to the call of human nature. As Eisenberg 1981 writes:

> we are equally blind to the effects of the 'cultural field' (akin to the gravitational field) on biobehavioral phenomenon because we think and act within a cultural 'coordinate systems'. We only become aware of the field forces of our cultural system when we extend our vision to the study of other times, other places and other modes of social organization.

Ecological interaction

The Daoist idea of 'Ecology' is a rubric that includes from as micro as any habitat, to an open system, to planet Earth. Man's destiny cannot be understood in isolation from the ecology of planet Earth. Of course, Man's wisdom qualifies him not only to learn, and adjust but also to predict and control Earth for his benefit. However, the other side of the coin also carries truth. Once the ecological equilibrium of Earth suffers irreversible upset, all creations on planet Earth suffer. This is the old saying of 'Man and Heaven Interaction' (Ma, 1987:61).

Ecological interactions amongst living and non-living things on Earth are not time and space limited. Man's action not only exerts effect on his history but also that of natural history. In this sense, man should not only learn, adjust, predict and control the resourcing of ecological Earth, but also learn, adjust, predict and control his own behaviour. Man should therefore manage himself and creations from a consideration beyond his own egocentric reference in time, space and entity. That is why we see, in Kohlberg's (1984) highest stage of moral development, man begin to reason in terms of natural law.

Universal changes

From what we have discussed alongside with the earlier levels of dynamic and interactive levels of Dao, we are able to get a glimpse of the importance of an open mind and a loving attitude towards existence. Human wisdom has discovered that there is a greater order to live by. Scientists may call it natural law. Of course, such natural law depends on the comprehension of human mind.

A lucid consciousness comes into play on the constant expansion and integration of the understanding of the power and function of the 'greater order'. Non-viligant holding on to world constructs will easily result in stagnation of the mind which will easily lead to the stagnation of life and thus existence. Such cognition contradicts the First Level of Dao that 'Universal Changes' always take place and the mind is in the 'Changes' as well, correspondingly.

Concluding remarks : What does a mentally healthy person look like?

By now, it is important to profile what does a mentally healthy person look like so that readers can get a feel of issues related to self awareness and reality testing; we understand that the mentally healthy person is open to himself and has an ever expanding human consciousness that extends from the here and now to the future and beyond. Central to this phenomenon is the ever expanding human consciousness which Mittelman, 1991 names as 'openness'.

From this ever expanding human consciousness, he is able to be in touch with the pulse of life to live for the betterment of himself, man and creation. He has a kind of inner satisfaction built on the trust of his competence to lead realistically a life of satisfying quality.

References

Anderson, C. L., & Creswell, H. W. (1976). *School health practice.* St. Louis : Moxby Co.

Adler P. T. (1982). An analysis of the concept of competence in individuals and social systems. *Community Mental Health Journal,* 18(2), 34-45.

Bradburn, N. M. (1969). *The structure of psychological well-being.* Chicago : Aldine.

Binite, A. (1984). Mental Health and the Third World : Mental Health in African societies. In R. C. Nann, et al. (Eds.), *Mental Health cultural values and social development,* 61-77. London : D Reidel Publishing Co.

Brewer R. (1988). *The science of ecology.* New York : Saunders College Publishing.

Bugenthal J. F. T. (1976). The Humanistic ethic. In W. Kathkovsky, & L. Gorlow (Eds.), *The psychology of adjustment,* 36-47. New York : McGraw-Hill Inc.

Cheng, M. J. (1981). *Lau-Tzu : My words are very easy to understand* North Atlantic Books, California: Richmond, Ch.16.

Diener, E. (1984). Subjective well-being. *Psychological Bulletin,* 95(3), 542-575.

Eisenberg, L. (1981). The social context of health : Effects of time, place and person. In Stuart H. Fine, Robert Krell, and Tsung-yo Lin (Eds.), *Todays priorities in mental health : Children and families - needs, rights, and action,* 35. London : D Reidel Publishing Company

Emory, C. (1988 August). Resilient children, psychological wellness, and primary prevention. *American Journal of Community Psychology*; 16 (4) 591-607.

Erickson, E. H. (1950). Growth and crises of the 'Healthy Personality'. In M. J. E. Senn, (Ed.), *Symposium on the healthy personality*, 135-142. Josiah Macy Fr. Foundation.

Giles, H. A. (1980). *Chuang Tzu, Taoist philosopher and Chinese mystic.* London : Unwin Paperbacks.

Hall, C. S., & Lindzey, G. (1970). *Theories of personality.* (2nd Ed.) New York : John Wiley & Sons Inc.

Jahoda, M. (1953). The meaning of psychological health. *Social Casework,* 34 349-354.

Jahoda, M. (1958). *Current concepts of positive mental health.* New York : Basic Books.

Kelly, G. A. (1955). *The psychology of personal constructs.* New York : Norton.

Kolhberg, L. (1984). *The psychology of moral development : The nature and validity of moral stages.* New York : Harper & Row.

Lewis, J. A., & Lewis, M. D. (1984). Preventive Program in Action. *The Personnel and Guidance Journal,* 62, 550-553.

Ma, Y. T. (1987). *Chinese mental hygiene.* Sing Tao: Sze Chun Science and Technology Publisher.

Maslow, A. H., & Mittelman, B. (1951). *Principles of abnormal psychology.* New York: Harper & Bros.

Mittelman, W. (1991). *Maslow's study of self-actualization : A reinterpretation.*

Ohsawa, G. (1981). *MacroBiotics: The way of healing.* Library of Congress Catalog: California.

Rae-Grant, Q. A. F., Gladwin, T., & Bower, E. M. (1966). Mental health, social competence, and the war on poverty. *American Journal of Orthopsychiatry,* 36, 652-644.

Saul, L. J., & Warner, S. L. (1982). *The Psychotic Personality.* New York : Van Nostand Reinhold Co. Inc.

Srivastava, S. S., Rai, D. H., & Rai, V. K. (1987). A study of mental health of post-graduate students. *Indian Psychological Review,* 32 (3), 30-33.

Tatarkiewicz, W. (1976). *Analysis of happiness.* Hague: Martinus Nijhoff.

Tsang, A. K. T. (1986). Mental health and the quest of well-being, Inkhoo, T P *Mental Health in Hong Kong,* 36039. H K : Mental Health Association of Hong Kong.

Clinical Psychology, 15, 6-11.

Warr, P. (1987). *Work, unemployment, and mental health.* Oxford : Oxford University Press.

Watts, A. (1978). *The way of zen.* Middlesex : Penguin Books.

Worchel, S., & Goethals, G. R. (1985). *Adjustment : Pathways to personal growth.* New York : Prentice-Hall.

6 An evolutionary approach to the conceptualisation of mental health

P. Gilbert

Introduction

When Woody Allen was asked why he had been in psychoanalysis for nearly thirty years he is reported to have replied 'because I am sane, but it's a mad world out there'. Most of us might have difficulty with this idea since we usually assume that mental health precludes such needs. But perhaps, in a way, this attests to our problems of defining what we mean by mental health. Certainly the boundaries between mental health and mental illness have never been clearly defined (Kendell, 1988) while concepts such as illness, disease, impairment, dysfunction and health and wellness remain open to debate (Sartorius, this volume). Add to this questions about various models of epistemology of causation (Tudor, this volume) and cross-cultural relevance of definitions - and we see the measure of the problem. Certainly, although mental illness and mental health are often viewed as a bipolar dimensional construct this view is misleading (Trent, this volume.

Another issue concerns the distinction between the prevention of mental illness versus the promotion of mental health. In the former case concern may be centred on identifying populations at risk, and preventing relapse in those who have experienced an episode of mental illness (e.g., via the use of drugs or various psychosocial therapies). In this case treatment automatically involves concern with, and prevention of, relapse. Mental health promotion however may involve completely new and different strategies with different goals and different measures of outcome. For example outcome might be measured as the reduction of rates of incidence (new cases of mental illness episodes). Or alternatively mental health promotion might be concerned with the measurement of increasing the potential of a population in the domains of self-confidence, self-understanding, relating and other skills development, ability for self-help and so forth. Thus although mental health promotion may well involve efforts to reduce various forms of risk of illness, it is also much more than this. Health education may be part of health promotion but cannot

41

be subsumed under it. There is now clear evidence that people often know what they should do to improve their health but don't do it, for various reasons.

Researchers who have been concerned with mental health suggested that mental health is related to a number of factors, including personality traits such as sociability (e.g., Argyle, 1987). Other suggestions are that mental health is:

1. Related to states of happiness and well being.
2. Related to control over personal goals.
3. Related to a sense of social cohesion and meaning.
3. Related to the absence of symptoms plus social adjustment.
4. Related to the ability to love and work (Freud's definition).

From an evolutionary approach the linkage of states of well being to mental health is questionable. This is because evolutionists prefer to speak in terms of adaptiveness and function rather than happiness and well being. Indeed at times anxiety and dysphoria may be highly adaptive responses to situations, and in some cases the absence of anxiety and dysphoria can be signs of mental ill health. Importantly then, mental health must include a recognition that the ability to act defensively to threats, to anticipate dangers and either overcome or avoid them, must also be characteristic of a healthy mind. So maybe Woody Allen has a point. Such concerns indicate that mental health cannot be defined purely by recourse to positive affect and well being.

Targets for health for all: World Health Organisation, 1985

Mental health concepts should make some attempt to be socially contextualised. This was recognised by the World Health Organisation in their publication, Targets for Health for All.

> Without peace and social justice, without enough food and water, without education and decent housing, and without providing each and all of us with a useful role in society and an adequate income, there can be no health for the people, no growth and no social development. (p. 13)

The concept of personal control must also be contextualised. What gives me a feeling of control, well being and happiness may be detrimental to another. The extreme might be the torturer but other less extreme forms can be those whose sense of well being come from the power to persecute, dominate or control others. From an evolutionary perspective dominance behaviour might have adaptive properties but is hardly a source of well being to the dominated. The social environments, especially the rank relationships, are a major source of poor health (Henry and Stephens, 1977, Gilbert, 1989, 1992). We cannot side-step this issue by arguing that those who wish to dominate others are mentally ill.

These are just some of the problems that accompany any definition of mental health. Nevertheless if we focus on states of well being for a moment then evidence suggests that social relationships are a major contributor to such states (Argyle, 1987). Cutting through a lot of the data it seems that two central aspects are involved here. The first is that individuals who feel their lives are (involuntarily) controlled by others tend to be less happy than those who do not feel this way. Second, freedom from others' control by itself is not enough, rather individuals need to feel valued in their significant relationships, and their social roles (as the World Health Organisation notes also) and not marginalised.

In evolution theory a concept that helps with understanding what we mean by being valued is that of social investment (Trivers, 1985). That is, to feel valued we need signals from others that our efforts and self-presentations are attractive to them and that they will invest time, energy and other resources in us. This is true of all relationships both intimate relationships and social and public (Gilbert, 1989). Thus the issue of control and the issue of value go hand in hand.

In this talk I would like to suggest, as have many others, that social behaviour is a useful way to approach the question of mental health. Furthermore that humans have evolved two primary social orientations that guide interpersonal relating tactics. The first relates to a dimension of power, individualistic control and coercion. The second relates to tactics to elicit from, and give investment to, others. Time does not allow me to explore the mechanism of evolution, except to say that nowadays we see evolution as driven by reproductive success (e.g., Trivers, 1985). However, in primates reproductive success tracks social success and social success depends on the enactment of various roles (Gilbert, 1989, 1992). There are three basic types of social relationships that have evolved and are observable in many species.

1. Attachment between parent and offspring.
2. Formation of alliances.
3. Ranking behaviour.

Our emotions provide the urgency necessary to pursue certain biosocial goals (e.g., to rise in a rank or seek out friends and allies). To a considerable degree our affects are influenced by these types of social relationships. Thus we tend to feel good when we feel cared for, feel a sense of belonging within a group, have access to friends, gain respect and prestige and find a mate. Whereas negative emotions are associated with not being cared for, feeling alienated from others - an outsider, losing or failing to obtain respect and not finding a mate (Nesse, 1990). Affect systems then are set up to help track particular social relationship outcomes.

Types of relationships

Our next question is therefore what are the types and forms of social relationship that are associated with social success. Now there is no commonly agreed classification of the types or numbers of social goals that humans are adapted to pursue. However, in my review of the literature we can outline four basic forms of biosocial goals which are by no means comprehensive but merely a start. These are care eliciting and care giving, which evolved from attachment; cooperating, which evolved from alliance formation and ingroup-outgroup; and competing, which evolved from dominance and ranking (Gilbert, 1989, 1992). In what follows I wish to outline how each of these biosocial goals are influenced by the internal evaluative schema of self and others and by the signals of harm or investment from others.

One further point should be made here. Each of the above biosocial goals can be expressed in different social contexts. These vary on the dimension of intimate, personal, social and public (Gilbert, 1989). Thus intimate care eliciting might include efforts for love and affection while public care eliciting might arise as one nation asking help to deal with a famine.

43

	SELF AS	OTHER AS
CARE ELICITING	Needing inputs from other(s): care, protection, safety, reassurance.	Source of: care, nurturance, protection, safety, reassurance.
CARE GIVING	Source of: care, nurturance, protection, safety, reassurance.	Needing inputs from other(s): care , protection, safety, reassurance.
COOPERATION	Of value to other, sharing, appreciating, contributing, affiliative.	Valuing, contribution sharing, appreciating, affiliative.
COMPETITION	Contestant, inferior-superior	Contestant, inferior-superior

Core social mentalities

Table 1

Care eliciting and care giving

Each goal can be pursued if the individual is both motivated to pursue it and understands the nature of the relationship that is sought. Thus in the care eliciting situation the self targets behaviours towards another who is seen to be capable of providing what the self needs. In the care giving situation the individual is motivated to help and provide the other with that which is necessary for growth and the alleviation of some distress state. The latter may involve the affects of sympathy, empathy and affection. For both self and other a sense of well being may arise from the successful enactment of these various roles. Thus the child feels secure and content on receiving parental care and the parent feels happy at seeing his/her offspring react positively to their input. This in essence forms the basic dynamic of attachment behaviour between parent and offspring.

The crucial concept that comes out of this is that of investment - that is the child elicits the investment of the parent in terms of time, energy, attention and other resources. While on the other side the parent is prepared to give this investment often via the affects of love and affection for the child. When the parental investment is not forthcoming (e.g., neglect, or harm) the child suffers in various ways. In addition to suffering negative affective states he/she may develop internal working models of relationships which suggest to him/her that other people's investment in them is precarious. It is the conditions by which the child experiences the investment of others that lay down the styles of attachment behaviour, e.g., of anxious, avoidant, self-reliant, and secure (Bowlby, 1980, 1988; Sroufe and Flesson, 1986). These in turn will have long terms effects on subsequent relational style and therefore mental health.

Although we often concentrate our attention on the receiver of care, the giver of care has sometimes been overlooked. However, in adult life it seems that many humans gain a sense of well being and purpose in life from giving to others. Indeed today most of us here have chosen careers that involve a desire to be of value to others, to invest time, energy and other resources in trying to improve the quality of other people's lives. Many individuals state that helping others is a source of personal meaning and purpose.

Cooperation

Cooperation probably evolved from both kin and reciprocal altruism (Trivers, 1985; Gilbert, 1989). In humans this reciprocation often involves reciprocation of signals of value and investment. Heard and Lake (1986) capture this aspect well when they suggest that:

> The goal of companionable relating is reached whenever an individual construes from the emotive messages sent by companions, that they are taking interest in and showing appreciation of his contribution and the way he his making it; and at the same time, realises that the interest he is taking in the contribution of his companions is also appreciated. (p. 431).

The evolutionary benefits of cooperation over individualistic action have been great. It has been the bedrock for the evolution of much that we take as being human - of language, and culture. We have become knowledge accumulators, building models of the world piece by piece, from the minds of others now long dead. Thus society does not exist at the level of the gene, but has to be created a new with each generation. If we no longer value an idea or aspect of knowledge it drops away. The lost of the use of knowledge of herbs and plants in hunter-gatherer societies is a case in point. If we were nothing but individualistic competitors then none of these things would be possible. Rather it is the power of the group and its adaptive significance that has given rise to cooperation - a system based on mutual gain on the one hand and the desires to belong and be valued by others on the other. We cooperate when we experience that our contribution is valued and is positively reinforcing to others. We are in William James terms appreciated. Thus we aspire to enact roles within our groups and between ourselves that elicit others' value. And the World Health Organisation recognises this aspect to health. An evolution approach informs us of why this is so important. Nothing may disturb us more than to find that our efforts are marginalised and devalued ridiculed or not taken into account. Thus, be it in individual relationships (intimate) or even at the level of different cultures (public), cooperation will break down when one party perceives the other as devaluing of their contribution. The main way we track our value is via the attention, resources and investment, that others bestow to us.

I would like to talk about this dynamic in terms of seeing oneself has having value to others. I would make a claim that the perception that we are of value to others is a central part of states of well being and is particularly important to mental health both at an individual level and at a group level. Further that various motive systems have evolved which help us track how much we are valued by others. Thus in 1984 I argued that one source of depression arose from experiences that one has no value to others, that one is a burden perhaps, that the world could get by easily without one, and so forth.

A sense of being of value to others (arising from both care giving and cooperating) sits centrally in our psychology for good reason. This is because we are a group living animal

45

and our security depends on our position within, and attachment to, our groups and relationships. Thus if you value me you will not persecute or attack me; if you value me you will not abandon or reject me; if you value me I will be chosen to fulfil various roles. If you do not value me then none of these things can be taken for granted and life becomes more fearful. Signals of being of value then also help to reassure us and to feel safe. Whether it be in the socially anxious experience of being boring and uninteresting to others, or the depressive who feels they are inferior and unable to offer anything that is recognised to be valuable, or whether it be in the benefits of community service for the petty criminal who learns, perhaps for the first time, that they can do something that others value - all these experiences attest to the central importance an experience of value to others has.

In my view the evolution of cooperation as an adaptive behaviour has also given rise to the emotive-evaluative system that underwrites moral behaviour. When we act morally we inhibit our own exploitative behaviour and bestow rights on the other. We recognise that harmony and safety in relationships are created by a bestowing of rights and resources to each other and guilt arise when we transgress our moral codes. Furthermore, moral behaviour acts as a form of security and allows for the emergence of difference. Thus moral behaviour involves the recognition to be different without attacking. In this sense racism, sexism, ageism etc., are forms of failures of moral awareness and behaviour, usually the result of individuals trying to rank themselves (put themselves one up) by such differences.

Competition and power

The above have been concerned with the sending and receiving of signals of value. However the fourth biosocial goal is of course competing and ranking. While to some degree individualistic competition is sacrificed for the group, groups themselves often behave exploitatively to others. Thus the access to resources that provide for well being, happiness and health in one group may come at the expense of another group. Certain aspects of power and control may be good for men but less good for women who may feel marginalised and whose values are de-valued. The West may have the high standards it has partly because of an ability to exploit other societies and parts of the world. We cooperate, yes, but only with those we identify to be like us - who share similar goals and values. Hence there is much to cooperation which also relates to self-interest.

Competitive behaviour then remains one of the most central problems for humans, is often the source of suffering, and has a very early origin traceable back to the reptiles and beyond. Does this mean that we should stop competing or allowing hierarchies to form? The answer must be no. Try as we may, we will find it inordinately difficult to live without the emergence of hierarchy. Indeed, avoiding ways of ranking people to fulfil at least certain of society's roles seems inconceivable and questions of leadership are unavoidable. How we rank ourselves, however, is open to debate. Is it on the basis of knowledge, wisdom, ability etc., and are leadership roles voluntarily bestowed or obtained via coercion? And how do people protect their roles and ranks once obtained? Even at the point of birth we find ourselves in ranked relationships (parents and siblings) where others are able to limit as well as support our activities. As Price discusses (this volume) power is often involved in mental health issues.

However, even here evolution may have provided for us a path that allows us to minimise the trauma of ranks. This is by making a distinction between authoritative power and authoritarian power. The distinction is between rank sought, achieved and maintained via strength power threat etc., and rank that is bestowed for socially prescribed roles or talent.

SELF		OTHER
	Inferior - Superior	
	Controller - Controller	
	RANKING SYSTEMS	
	(TACTICS)	
POWER AGGRESSION		ATTRACTIVENESS
Cohesion		Talent
Threat		Role competence
Authoritarian		Democratic-authoritative
		To be valued
		To be chosen

IF SELF IS CONSTRUED AS
LOSING/INFERIOR
Shame
Envy
Hostile Resentment
Revenge
Depresstion
Social Anxiety
Defeated
Controlled by Others
Involuntary Subordinate
Internal Attack

Mentally competetive ranking

Table 2

Thus with authoritarian power the strongest become the more dominant and their reign is maintained by their ability to threaten others, induce submission behaviour and inhibit activities. It is the submissive behaviours of others that seem to relax the dominant. Power depends on threat. Those that follow this evolutionary rule have attitudes that seem to emphasise the power of punishment and down putting - it is the kick ass mentality - noted particularly in criminal groups, street gangs and armies of various kinds. Be it nations or individuals, in an intimate or public domain, some feel secure and happy via the submissive, appeasing and compliant behaviours they receive from others. Even religions that are supposed to preach love and compassion rarely avoid an undercurrent of threat of punishment for non compliance. Hence again we see the problem of concentrating on individual states of well being without concern with how these are achieved.

The alternative to authoritarian ranking has arisen from cooperative behaviour and a recognition that a bestowing of value on another is the key to success. It has also, in my view, been a spur to intelligence - for competing for value allows individuals to be selected with particular characteristics. Others voluntarily accept the difference in rank because it is helpful to them to do so, that is those of higher rank must show that they can benefit those of lower rank rather than just impose their own will.

Thus ranking in humans has to some degree moved from a desire to intimidate to a desire to impress - that is we try to gain rank via being seen as attractive to others, which technically; has been called social attention holding power (SAHP; Gilbert, 1989, 1992). It is an interesting question, whether those who are particularly rank sensitive and needing to receive constant signals of SAHP, who are either aggressively seeking dominance or are fearfully submissive, may have had low or less than optimal signals of investment and affection early in life, or inconsistent signals.

We should note that, however rank is achieved, there are various consequences to losing it or feeling inferior. And this brings us back to our sense of value. Thus societies that produce major social inequalities and rank differences can be expected to activate the more primitive responses of envy, greed, resentment and so forth, many of which bubble forth in mental health problems and crime.

Mental health promotion

We are beginning to recognise that mental health is not the absence of illness but rather something far more positive. Equally it is something that must be worked for. It relates not just to the absence of threat but to the presence of a set of relationships that are valuing. This is not the same as a need for control over personal goals, as some psychologists tell us, since as I have pointed out, one person's control can be another person's tyranny.

Thus be it in our parent child relationships in our marriages and families, in our work relationships or even in our inter-national relationships if we follow the path of authoritarian power some of us will suffer. Mental health promotion then can be focused as much on the creators of stress for others (e.g., bullies, and authoritarian solutions) as it is on the those who suffer as a result of being recipients of neglect and put-down from others.

It follows therefore that mental health can involve various domains.

1. Self awareness training

a) Internal experience: The ability to recognise and cope with various aspects of self (e.g., emotions and fantasies) that can the source of confusion and conflict is important. This leads us into educational concerns as outlined by Sunderland (this volume). Shame (feeling inferior or different) about one's internal experience is often a serious source of suffering. Shame prone individuals may either be submissive and inhibited or lash out under threat (Gilbert, 1992). Lack of awareness of the nature of internal experience and the sense of weakness and difference that certain experiences may invoke can be overcome with clear educational endeavours and opportunities to share experiences in non-authoritarian social groups.

b) Cognitive factors: Evaluations that increase risk of negative affective states, such as chronic self-blaming, self-criticism, inferiority beliefs, together with unrealistic expectations of roles (e.g., of mothering) can be targeted with educational interventions. It would be a fairly simple task to outline various attributional styles and basic negative self-other attitudes that increase risk. Indeed in America there have been efforts to identify children with self-blaming and pessimistic styles and offer retraining (Seligman, 1989). The long term effects of this are unknown.

c) Behavioural interventions: Behavioural interventions could focus on the acquisition of skills, opportunities to master difficult or feared situations, and the increased awareness of the dangers of avoidance as a defensive strategy. Such interventions may be fairly circumscribed or more adventurous. For example, outward-bound courses have, under some conditions, been found to have significant effects on developing self-esteem and affiliative relationships. Gilbert (1989) suggested that these provide contexts for social learning that are similar to hunter-gatherer societies and hence may be particularly powerful.

In each of these cases there is a shift from a devaluing (harsh, critical, punishing or inhibiting) relationship to a valuing (accepting, understanding, exploring and growth promoting) relationship. This shift may be internal, that is we learn not to self-devalue, self-criticise and/or at least recognise the function of our self-criticism (Driscoll, 1989). Further, we may learn how to value others, an often neglected element in mental health training. Moral and cooperative behaviour, for example, depends on the recognition and tolerance of difference (Gilbert, 1989).

2. Power and conflict resolution

a) Marriage: No relationship that lasts for any length of time can avoid conflict. This is another vast area where education has an important role to play in both preventing mental illness and maximising health possibilities. Spouse criticism is one of the major predictors of relapse in depression, for example, (Hooley and Teasdale, 1989). Thus as Price (this volume) points out, poor conflict resolution is perhaps the single most common cause of distress and mental illness. Many people simply have not had the opportunity to develop skills for dealing with conflict that do not result in one person being put down. Perhaps they may come from homes where rows and aggressive interactions are rife. The preparation for marriage and the establishment of long term stable relationships (that are vital to child development) are not easy. But recognition of the destructive switch to an authoritarian relationship at points of conflict may do much to head off at least some, avoidable difficulties. To get one's own way by devaluing and putting the other down is a poor solution to conflict. It is thus a source of concern then, that be it in schools, religious groups or families, there appears to be little in the way of preparation for conflict resolution. Instead there is an idealised and unrealistic expectations that love will overcome all (Beck, 1989).

b) Child rearing: Increasing evidence points to the role of the early environment as both sources of mental illness and subsequent health (Rohner, 1986; Bowlby, 1988). A high percentage of those who become vulnerable to non-psychotic illness grow up in families lacking warmth, with various distortions in the child-parent roles. Sexual and physical abuse are obvious examples. However, it is well to remind ourselves that not so long ago authoritarian relationships were actively promoted as the correct way to bring up children (Miller, 1983). Fear of authority was confused with respect, and still is, in various forms of relationships (e.g., some religions and families). Clear evidence now shows that authoritative relationships give rise to high self-esteem children whereas authoritarian relationships give rise to low self-esteem and poor affiliative behaviour (Rohner, 1986). In spite of great strides in our understanding of the importance of child-parent relationships, of attachment (Bowlby, 1988) and the importance of mirroring and giving a child a sense of value (Kohut, 1977), still this knowledge is yet to filter through to the population at large in anything like a systematic and consistent way. Attitudes to child rearing require major efforts in health promotion.

   c) Society: Cultural values on relationships are portrayed and displayed in various ways. As the extended family fragments and traditions loosen, perhaps the mass media become an important source of social values. Some film producers actively argue for their right to explore any form of violence they feel appropriate and to place on celluloid styles of relationships that are projections of their emotional problems. More often opportunities to make money by titillating the excitement of aggressive conflict is at issue. Casting an eye around my local video shop it is difficult not to be impressed by the preoccupation with violence and aggressive means of resolving conflict and entertaining. Authority figures are often presented as aggressive, manipulative and untrustworthy. Even if this is a reflection of reality questions must be asked as to what values are being mirrored here, and their effects. Thus the mass media tend to portray agonistic solutions to conflict (e.g., the need for revenge - the Rambo character, the avoidance of being seen as weak or of giving in, sulking and withdrawing). If one observes (say) soap operas about police work, the heros nearly always are portrayed as having an agonistic relationship with their immediate superiors in the organisation. It is their ability to get around authoritarian pressure that marks them as heroic.

   Cultural values and the role of the mass media are of course contentious issues but ones which we cannot turn a blind eye to It is not simply that we are amusing ourselves to death as Postman (1985) claims but also that mass communications have the effect of shaping values, especially those of relationship.

   In regard to poverty it is not absolute poverty that causes the greatest harm, otherwise mental health would correlate highly to GNP. Rather it is comparative poverty, that is the sense of inferiority that goes with poverty. Further, comparative poverty focuses people to become aware of what activities they cannot participate in and that they are marginalised, have no voice and social power. It is thus comparative deprivation that carries the greatest risk. People come to believe that no-one cares about them, they are regarded as having no contribution to make, and so forth. Anyone who doubts that cultural valuing plays such a large role in mental health need only look at the vast rise of suicide, depression and alcoholism that has resulted form the breakdown of cultural systems (e.g., the Australian aborigines and American Indians).

   d) Reconciliation: Related to power and conflict resolution is the issue of reconciliation, another area where our society is deficient in preparing individuals for the tension of living. Negative attitudes to reconciliation often include a concern of being seen as weak, giving in, getting ones own way as manly, and unresolved resentment or confusions with the need to submit to maintain the peace. Do we teach people how to disagree without being disagreeable (with a special focus on nonverbal communication)? Do we teach that conflict of interests and desires are part of life and that one-up, one-down solutions may appear satisfactory to the victor but in fact are not, and will set up the next source of conflict?

Overview

These are only some of the potential areas where efforts to actively promote and teach certain types of social behaviour may well have pay offs in the long term. In this presentation I have tried to show how we should begin our analysis with a broad canvas that has as its scope and understanding of human nature (Gilbert, 1989). No programme will get far if it runs counter to basic human dispositions and human needs. Cooperative behaviour may well be at the heart of sociability (Argyle, 1991, although he fails to distinguish care eliciting and care giving relationships from sharing and truly cooperative relationships). More important is the need for valuing from our fellow human begins, to feel we have some worth and can make some contribution. We can learn to value others also. We can learn to disagree without being disagreeable, to recognise that the punishers and autocratic types need as much consideration as their victims. We can learn to be honest about our feelings, to expose our negative and destructive attitudes to re-education.

We can, in effect, move towards an appreciation that human beings are social animals and their forms of adaptation reside in the complex matrix of relationships in which they reside. Mental health promotion is perhaps one of the greatest challenges in the coming decades, for it will require of us radical changes in our patterns of living and education practices if we are to be successful over the long term. From our study in social psychology and work with human suffering our knowledge of the role of valuing is clear. This knowledge needs to become more widely available. Mental health will be advanced when we appreciate the crucial role care giving and cooperation has had on human evolution. A focus on human evolution is not a collusion with our irrational side, rather it is to promote a rationality that is also compassionate.

References

Argyle, M. (1987). *The psychology of happiness.* London: Methuen & Co.

Argyle, M. (1991). *Cooperation: The basis of sociability.* Routledge.

Beck, A. T. (1990). *Love is never enough.* London: Harper and Row.

Bowlby, J. (1980). *Attachment and loss, Vol. 3. Loss: Sadness and depression.* London: Hogarth Press.

Bowlby, J. (1988). Developmental psychiatry comes of age. *American Journal of Psychiatry,* 145, 1-10.

Driscoll, R. (1989). Self-condemnation: A conceptual framework for assessment and treatment. *Psychotherapy,* 26, 104-111.

Gilbert, P. (1984). *Depression: From psychology to brain state.* Hove: Lawrence Erlbaum Associates Ltd.

Gilbert, P. (1989). *Human nature and suffering.* Hove: Lawrence Erlbaum Associates Ltd.

Gilbert, P. (1992). *Depression: Types concepts and theories: An evolutionary synthesis on the themes of power and belonging.* Hove: Lawrence Erlbaum Associates Ltd.

Heard, D. H. & Lake, B. (1986). The attachment dynamic in adult life. *British Journal of Psychiatry.* 149, 430-438.

Henry, J. P. & Stephens. P. M. (1977). *Stress, health and the social environment: A sociobiologic approach to medicine.* New York: Springer Verlag.

Hooley, T. M. & Teasdale, J. D. (1989). Predictors of relapse in unipolar depressives: Expressed emotion, marital distress and perceived criticism. *Journal of Abnormal Psychology*, 98, 229-235.

Kendell, R. E. (1988). What is a case? Food for thought for epidemiologists. *Archives of General Psychiatry*, 45, 374-376.

Kohut, H. (1977). *The restoration of the self.* New York: International Universities Press.

Miller, A. (1983). *For your own good: The roots of violence in child-rearing.* London: Virago.

Nesse, R. M. (1990). Evolutionary explanations of emotions. *Human Nature,* 1, 261-289.

Postman, N. (1985). *Amusing oursleves to death.* London Methuen

Rohner, R. P. (1986). *The warmth dimension: Foundations of parental acceptance-rejection theory.* Beverly Hills: Sage.

Seligman, M. E. P. (1989). Explanatory style: Predicting depression, achievement and health. In M. D. Yapko (Ed.), *Brief approaches to treating anxiety and depression.* New York: Brunner/Mazel.

Sroufe, A. L. & Fleeson, J. (1986). Attachment and the construction of relationships. In W. W. Hartup, & Z. Rubin (Eds.), *Relationships and development.* Hillsdale, N. J: Lawrence Erlbaum Associates.

Trivers, R. (1985). *Social evolution.* California: Benjamin/Cummings.

World Health Organisation. (1985). *Targets for health for all.* Geneva: World Health Organisation.

7 Imaginative assessment of personal health needs

H. Graham

Abstract

Within the field of mental health there is broad acceptance of the notion that health is contingent upon the fulfilment of personal needs. The existence of these needs is generally not doubted and statements of need often form the basis of policies and practices. Accordingly there is widespread commitment to the principle that community health provision should be based on a realistic assessment of the health needs of the individuals within that community. Moreover, conceptualizing mental health in terms of needs is viewed as progressive and enlightened, inasmuch that it prioritizes the promotion of psychological well-being. While acknowledging the importance of need fulfilment to health in the widest sense, this paper challenges assumptions about the nature of needs, and the means of their assessment, arguing that the implied objectivity and validity of the latter is spurious, and potentially antagonistic to effective health promotion. It offers an 'imaginative' approach to needs assessment which is fully consistent with the promotion of mental health, having been used for this purpose within psychotherapy since its origins in Ancient Greek civilisation, and more recently within the wider field of psychological healing.

Introduction

The term *health* originates in the German *heilen*, meaning whole. This is closely related to the Old English words *hael* (whole) and *haelen* (heal), from which the English term *hale* (as in the phrase 'hale and hearty') and the Welsh *hoil* derive. These terms are very similar to the German *heilig* and the Old English *halig* which mean holy. Etymologically speaking, therefore, to be healthy is to be whole or holy, which clearly embraces both spiritual and physical features rather than merely the latter.

This holistic concept was central to the thinking of the Ancient Greeks, in which all

53

Western medicine is rooted. Health was viewed as an index of the status of the soul, psyche, or life force, which was conceived as the overall dynamic balance or harmony of opposing traits, and thus essentially as a spiritual rather than a physical issue. Accordingly it was deemed necessary for a person to be attuned to and in harmony with both spiritual and physical realities in order to be healthy, or whole. All illness was viewed as symptomatic of *psychopathology* -literally dis-ease or sickness of the soul, and treatment was directed to *psychotherapy*, the cure of the soul, through restoration of its balance or harmony.

Such a view remained central to the healing arts until the seventeenth century when Descartes introduced to Western thinking a separation of mind and matter. This resulted in a materialistic medicine concerned solely with the physical body; a psychological medicine addressed to mental issues; and the loss of the soul, as a medical concern, in the chasm which opened up between them. Such a division is quite aberrant when viewed against the history of Western medicine, which, since its origins in the principles established by Hippocrates, had recognized the importance of the soul-mind-body complex and the necessity of working through the mind.

With the reinstatement of a holistic concept as a central principle in medicine, there is now, some 2000 years after Hippocrates, a growing movement towards healing these divisions. What is termed a biopsychosocial approach to health is increasingly being promoted within materialistic or bio-medicine by proponents who describe it as a programme of prevention and treatment which provides for both the full utilization of medical science and the full development of the human healing system, combining the high technology and symptom-suppressing methods of bio-medical medicine with those concerned with an understanding of the psychological and social origins of illness. Arguably, as such, it still fails to accommodate spiritual factors, but it is clearly a movement towards a more adequate definition of health.

The holistic concept within psychological medicine

A more fully holistic concept of health was restored within psychological medicine some thirty years ago by Abraham Maslow, who was for many years Professor of Psychology at Brandeis University. He was concerned to promote the study of the whole or healthy person, and thus to shift the emphasis within psychological medicine from what he considered to be a negative focus on mental illness to a more wholesome concern with mental health.

Maslow considered self-denial as a major cause of illness and distress inasmuch that he viewed health as synonymous with self-fulfilment, or the satisfaction of all personal needs; and illness as an indication that these needs are not being met. He conceived of a hierarchy of needs, basic to which are physical needs for water, food, air, light, warmth and sleep. These generally have to be met before psychological and emotional needs for contact, safety, love, attachment, identity, self esteem, relationships, sexual fulfilment, intellectual and other achievements, respect and prestige are fulfilled. Thus a person suffering from starvation, chronic thirst, lack of air or exhaustion is unlikely to be too concerned about his popularity or prospects for promotion. Similarly, spiritual needs for meaning and purpose in life are usually addressed as and when psychological and emotional needs are met. However, studies (reported by Siegel 1990) suggest that those people who are truly healthy not only have a clear hierarchy of needs, but, unlike most people, pursue all of them simultaneously, thereby functioning in a holistic manner.

Needs and illness

Clearly ill health is likely to occur when physical needs are unmet. Without the basics of food, water, hygiene and sleep a person will fail to thrive and is likely to succumb to illness.

Failure to meet psychological needs may also result in illness which may manifest at the psychological level as neuroses, or at the physical level in so-called psychosomatic disorders.

According to the psychotherapist Frederick Perls the neurotic is essentially a person who does not recognise their psychological and emotional needs and therefore cannot satisfy them, thus remaining in a state of psychological disequilibrium which may justifiably be described as 'unbalanced'. Being unable to meet their needs they cannot be self-reliant and tend to manipulate the environment for support in a number of ways, which may include illness. Psychosomatic illness may therefore be regarded as a way of obliging others to meet one's needs and take over one's responsibilities, often with dire consequences for their well-being.

In a culture where feelings are regarded as being of little importance, emotional needs are frequently ignored, and illness can provide a way of meeting needs that a person is otherwise unable to fulfil. These needs may be for space or time for oneself, freedom from duties and responsibilities, or relationships. Illness is a socially acceptable way of not fulfilling various functions and roles, and makes it easier to say 'no' to unwelcome duties and tasks. It may also give a person permission to do things that they have always wanted to but have never had time for; or it may be an excuse for failure. It is often the only way in which a person can ask for help or love; or express unhappiness. Illness therefore gives a person permission to allow themself and others to do things that they would not or could not do if well, and to do so without guilt and the need to explain or justify.

The extent to which illness is used as a means of self-justification is generally given little attention. However, in a work-oriented culture with an emphasis on productivity there are no 'well-days' that can be taken off from work or study in order to relax, or avoid stress and potential breakdown. The only way for many people to take time off is to be, or pretend to be, sick. Frequently the guilt and anxiety generated by the latter produces actual illness, so at best this strategy ensures that a person derives little benefit from the break in normal routine, and at worst proves totally counterproductive. For the full-time caretaker who does not go out to work, staying at home provides no respite whatever, and so 'well days' are often impossible. The only way for them to do so may be to breakdown, mentally or physically.

Illness usually functions as a message to change, or provides a person with something they are not otherwise getting from their lives. As such it can be a temporary and useful interlude, but it may be a trap for those who find that it is the only way in which they can gain attention, love, relief from stress, or avoid unpleasant activities. For such persons

55

permanent 'disability' may be more attractive than health. However, the benefits of illness, whether mental or physical, may not be consciously recognised, much less acknowledged, by the sufferer. Nevertheless, closer scrutiny invariably reveals that it is an outer manifestation of some inner turmoil, which may be spiritual in origin.

The psychiatrist R.D.Laing observed that much mental illness is often not a sign of disintegration but of an attempt at reintegration into the larger whole, or scheme of things; an attempt to discover a meaning or purpose in life which is often misunderstood, misrepresented and thwarted. Viktor Frankl, Carl Jung and Roberto Assagioli are among many noted psychiatrists who also view much mental illness as a failure to find meaning in life, and thus to acknowledge or satisfy spiritual needs. Jung perceived spiritual needs as being of particular importance, claiming not to have seen one patient over thirty-five years of age whose problem, in the final analysis, was other than that of not having found a spiritual outlook on life, or meaning within it.

Within the field of psychological medicine there is thus widespread acknowledgement that failure to meet physical, psychological or spiritual needs may result in physical or mental illness, and in a great deal of pain, discomfort and distress, not only for the individual concerned but also for those around them, much of which could be avoided if their needs could be met in other ways. The conceptualization of mental health in terms of need is therefore widely regarded as a progressive and enlightened framework, and there is widespread commitment to the principle that community health provision should be based on a realistic assessment of the personal needs of those who are ill and those who care for them.

Identifying needs

However, this apparently straightforward objective is fraught with difficulties, some of which are highlighted in a report published by the Health Education Council (undated): *Action research with informal carers of elderly people: Patterns and processes in carer's lives*. This indicates that carers often may have needs which for some reason they do not articulate. The authors suggest that this may be because they do not expect these to be met, being variously unaware of what is available to them; feeling that what is available may not apply to them; or believing that their requests will be declined. Thus although able to respond to questions concerning specific services and facilities, they tend to indicate only what they need most urgently, or in relation to what they know is available. Thus the most commonly expressed needs are for aids and services such as transport, relief and respite care, and financial assistance .

Although one of the specific objectives of this study was to allow carers to express *their* needs within the caring situation it was found that few did so. Thus while nearly 40% of the respondents said that they would like someone to talk to, less than 4% of them asked for emotional support. This suggests that carers place a lower priority on their needs than upon those of the person in their care. Indeed, the question of how carers care for themselves is addressed by the report, and, to a great extent answered.

The difficulty carers have in holding a sense of their own value was seen sometimes to lead to a refusal to accept help potentially available. In fact almost all the carers we talked to seemed to hold a relatively poor idea of their own worth, consistently putting themselves and their own needs last. These were not ideas that were openly discussed but these sorts of attitudes tended to emerge in discussion. In these circumstances it is unlikely that carers will feel able to do much to take care of themselves, since they are generally going to feel the needs of the elderly person must always come first.

As the report indicates:

> Carers' work needs to be acknowledged, their value recognized, their worries and feelings heard. They deserve and need attention for themselves, and all interviewed carers made it clear how important -if rare - such acknowledgment of their value is for them.

> The need to express feelings is of particular importance. Wonham (personal communication 1991) indicates that in a course for carers run by The Mental Health Foundation of the Mid-Staffordshire NHS Trust in Cannock (1989) the need of the carers to talk about their feelings of anger, sadness, loss, frustration and grievance was such that it occupied seven and a half hours of the twelve hours available.

However, as professional attention is focussed on the dependent person, carers' needs usually receive little attention. Not surprisingly therefore, over 50% of the Health Education Council sample indicated that their role as carers had adversely affected their health, and for those caring for heavily dependent people this figure rose to 74%.

Given these findings the authors conclude that it behoves professionals to articulate the needs which carers do not express. They suggest that professionals can assess these needs in two ways: from measurable indicators, such as the number of relief breaks taken by the carers of heavily dependent people; and from the professionals' interpretation of need, based upon 'indicators that cannot be directly measured like the feelings and conflicts carers express' (p.59).

Stated thus the assessment of need appears to be largely a matter of empirical study or close observation by the relevant professionals, who are assumed to be able to recognise and respond to needs which individuals display, and infer needs which are neither expressed nor displayed, mainly or solely through their observation of these individuals. Unfortunately in practice the matter is not so simple.

Discriminating needs from wants

As the study shows, even people who are aware of their needs may not articulate them. However, many people are unable to express or act upon their needs because they do not know what they are. Frequently they mistake wants for needs, and fail to recognise that they are not necessarily the same. This is partly a semantic difficulty, the two words frequently being used interchangeably. However, the term *need* is endowed with a rather more complex meaning structure than *want*, conveying an element of necessity as opposed to desire, and therefore having a more powerful impact.

A want *may* indicate a need: Wanting a dishwasher may indicate a person's need for more time free of domestic chores; and wanting a holiday may indicate a need to get away from it all and relax. Frequently, however, when a person gets what they want they find it doesn't satisy their needs. Sociologist Ann Oakley has pointed out that labour-saving devices such as washing machines and dishwashers actually increase the amount of housework. Similarly, a holiday will confer no benefit whatever if the person takes their worries, anxieties and concerns away with them and fails to relax. More typically, wants obscure needs, or are a rationalization of them. Thus a person may insist that they don't want a holiday or a home-help even though they know that they need a break from looking after a dependent relative, or a respite from duties and responsibilities, because they feel guilty about admitting to these needs.

Sometimes wants bear little or no relation to needs. Most of the commodities advertised in popular magazines can easily be lived without, as can the contents of the increasing number of unsolicited home shopping guides which are distributed to almost every household. Medical journals and advertising encourage the belief in both doctors and their patients that certain drugs are a necessity and these claims are invariably unchallenged. Thus patients frequently insist that they *need* the drugs and medications they want their doctor to prescribe, and not uncommonly doctors insist that their patients *need* medications that they do not want.

Indeed everyone is conditioned to believe they need what other people want them to. Other people's wants are imposed upon us throughout life. Parents tell children that they *need* to eat their meals because they do not want to throw the food away; that they *need* exercise because they want them out of the house for a few hours on a Saturday afternoon; that they *need* a good education because they don't want to support them financially for the rest of their days. Males are told that they *need* successful jobs and sex to be fulfilled, and females are told that they *need* marriage and a family. These messages are merely reinforced and exploited through advertising and the mass media. It is therefore less than surprising that many people find it difficult to distinguish their needs from other people's wants, much less articulate them, or to perceive how much of their time and energy are taken up with the latter.

Assessment of needs

As a result judgements about needs tend to be made by policy makers and professional observers rather than the individuals whose needs are being assessed. Unfortunately the professionals charged with the task of assessing the needs of those persons unable or unwilling to do so are frequently in no better position than the individuals themselves because they too invariably make assumptions about a person's needs on the basis of what they and society want for them, rather than what is appropriate. In practice, therefore, as Woodhead (1991) observes, the word 'need' conceals a complex of latent assumptions and judgments which tend to indicate rather more about the cultural location and personal values of the user than about the person to whom this term is applied. Nevertheless, many health and social workers are in little doubt about the existence and nature of these needs, statements of which in many cases form the foundation of the policies and practices they implement. However, as Woodhead indicates, framing professional judgements in terms of needs serves to direct attention away from the particular value position from which they are made, and projected onto others they acquire a spurious objectivity. Therefore, it is tempting to accept them on face value as authoritative statements of fact. Thus framed, prescriptions of needs may serve important functions for those who make them, notably the greater authority that comes from projecting their decision-making criteria onto others, but as a consequence they often fail to identify what is in the best interests of the other. Thus it may be deemed appropriate to admit a mildly incontinent elderly person to a community home rather than to provide them with a downstairs lavatory, which in addition to being more convenient enables them to retain their much needed independence and autonomy; or to continue to supply dependency producing anxiolytic drugs rather than the counselling and support that a person requires. Such prescriptions are common in a materialistic society whose focus tends to be upon physical and material factors, and thus on services and facilities, rather than psychological, emotional and spiritual issues. While they may be functional for the professional making them, they are frequently much less so for the the person concerned because they fail to meet their real needs. Thus, while ostensibly addressing their problems and difficulties, frequently they actually compound them, and create additional stressors which may result in greater distress and disability. How then are health promotion stategies to avoid inadvertent promotion of illness and invalidity?

Creber (1987, p.104) concludes his report on the problems faced by the sufferers of psychiatric illness and of those caring for them, with the plea for 'more attention, more resources and more *imaginative* facilities to be provided for people in their situation' (italics added).

What is being argued here is that this should include rather more *imaginative* assessment of their health needs.

Imaginative assessment of health needs

One might be prompted to direct an observer to use their imagination in assessing the needs of those persons who will not or cannot articulate their needs. However, for a number of reasons it is preferable to direct them to use the imagination of those persons whose needs are to be assessed.

As previously indicated, the problem for many people is not that they will not articulate their needs, but rather, that they cannot because they are unaware or unconscious of them. Throughout the history of medicine healers have recognised the processes of the imagination, or imagery, as affording an invaluable means of accessing and revealing the dynamics of the mind, especially those aspects of which we are normally unconscious, and its relationship with the body. They recognised that a person's imagery yielded clues to factors, such as fears, anxieties, emotional and social issues or conflicts, which had given rise or contributed to illness, and which needed to be addressed or 'treated' in order to effect improvement in their condition. Traditional healers throughout the world can therefore be regarded as adepts of 'imaginative medicine' who diagnosed and treated disease by way of the imagination.

The processes involved in this approach are now recognised and are becoming more fully understood, although much more research is needed to fully explicate them. Nevertheless, it is now clear that imagery serves a number of functions, both cognitive and emotional.

Cognitively, imagery provides an alternative means of representing issues and in this mode novel and significant features of which one was formerly unaware or unconscious may become apparent. It therefore provides a different perspective or way of looking at issues which is fundamental to effective problem solving and creative functioning.

Within the different representational mode afforded by imagery an individual may also access features such as physical feelings and emotions which may not gain expression in other ways and which may be highly significant in revealing aspects of the self. Imagination is therefore a rich source of information about the individual, and the richness and variety of the imagery that can be generated and used is complemented by a great range and diversity of methods by which these can be accessed and explored.

However, with the divorce of mind and body during the 17th century these methods were lost to physical medicine, although they could still be discerned within psychological medicine.

Sigmund Freud recognised the value of dreams -a rich source of imagery -describing them as 'the royal road to the unconscious'; and Jung also made extensive use of dreams, everyday fantasy and reverie in his psychotherapy.

During the 1930s Happich explored the therapeutic uses of guided fantasy. This is a process, rather like a waking dream, in which a person, guided by another, creates an experience which in part if not in its entirety, has not been represented previously in his or her model or cognitive map. Guided imagery is therefore most appropriately employed when a person's cognitive representation is too impoverished to offer an adequate number of choices for coping in a given area. It thus serves as a therapeutic tool in two ways: by presenting a person with an experience which is the basis for representation in his model where previously there has been none, or inadequate representation; and by providing the therapist with an experience which can be used to challenge the person's presently impoverished model. As such, guided imagery is highly appropriate for the task of helping a person to identify needs of which they are wholly or partly unaware.

A similar technique was used by Desoille (1945), who claimed that by journeying through the landscapes of their imagination people could relate to their own symbolism and discover within it ways of dealing with the problems of life.

Walter Frederking (1948) also directed his patients in physical relaxation and imagework, enabling them to confront directly the contents of their personal unconscious and relate them to their problems. He claimed that this meeting with generally unrecognised aspects of the self effects deep transformation and healing.

Friedrich Mauz (1948) claimed that through imagework the suppressed emotions of psychotic patients could be uncovered, thereby facilitating meaningful conversation with them, and arousing positive feelings and meanings within the person which enables them to connect with feelings and the world around them. He claimed that the creative power which flows from these feelings and symbols aids in closing the breach within the patient's personality, thereby effecting healing.

Frederick Perls also recognized that more of the reality hidden within the imagery of dreams and everyday fantasy can be explored and understood if individuals invest themselves within it, becoming aware of their physical feelings, perceptions and responses as they do so. He made extensive use of guided fantasy and other imagery, encouraging people to imagine symbols or situations and explore them as fully as possible, because in so doing they project unconscious and otherwise unexpressed aspects of themselves into the material. Perls drew attention to the many different ways by which imagery can be accessed and explored, including verbalised fantasy, creative writing, artwork, movement, mime, dance, psychodrama, and even puppetry.

Common to all these approaches is the active provocation of the unconscious by way of the imagination, the person being directed to make its creative possibilities available for problem solving and healing. The individual therefore takes an active part in the process, which has the advantage of being quicker and more immediate, and without transference of their problems onto others. Furthermore these methods can be used most effectively with relatively inarticulate, non-verbal subjects such as young children, the mentally ill, the mentally and physically handicapped. They can also be used to broach subjects which are normally difficult to talk about such as death, dying and bereavement, guilt and blame. Another advantage, according to Kretschmer (1969), is that to be effective these approaches do not necessarily require medical or psychological training, only simple human relationship.

Recognition of these factors has led to imaginative methods being widely used and researched within areas of health care other than psychotherapy; in helping people to cope with chronic pain, severe orthopaedic trauma, rheumatoid arthritis, diabetes, burn injury, alcoholism, stress-related disorders and childbirth (Achterberg & Lawlis 1978); cancer therapy (Simonton et al., 1978; Fiore 1974; Meares 1981; Bradley & McCann 1981, Donovan 1980; Harley 1989, Siegel 1986); in working with the terminally ill and bereaved (Kubler-Ross,1977; 1982); and with children and adolescents (Oaklander 1978), including those with learning difficulties (Singer 1973) and those with serious and terminal illnesses (Cleary, 1988; Gillespie 1989).

As a result, imaginative methods are increasingly being included in the training of social and health care workers, nurses, radiographers, and counsellors; and employed in a wide variety of settings.

What is being argued for here is a movement away from purportedly 'realistic' attempts to assess personal health needs in favour of an altogether more fantastic approach through the inclusion of such methods within all mental health promotion programmes, and relevant education and training packages. Failure to do so could prove to be costly, not only through the inadvertent promotion of illness and invalidity, but also in the broader economic sense of cost-effectiveness, because as the novelist Patricia Wentworth has observed, people don't get tired of what they need.

References

Achterberg, J. & Lawlis, G.F. (1978). *Imagery of cancer*. Champaign, Illinois: Institute for Personality and Ability Testing.

Bell, R., Gibbons, S., & Pinches, I.(undated). *Action research with carers of elderly people: Patterns and processes in carer's lives*. Report on Phase 2. Health Education Council Health promotion Service, Cambridge.

Bradley, B.& McCann,T. (1981).Autonomic responses to stress: the effects of progressive relaxation; the relaxation response and the expectancy of relief. *Biofeedback and Self-Regulation*, 6, 235-251.

Cleary,B. (1988). Rachel's story.In *Caduceus*,No.4,p.5.

Creber,A.(1987). The response of carers. In Bernard, M.(Ed.), *Developing services for elderly mentally infirm people: Responses to the Rising Tide initiative*.Published jointly by the Beth Johnson Foundation (Stoke-on-Trent) and the Dept. of Adult & Continuing Education, University of Keele, Staffs.

Desoille,R. (1945). *The waking dream in psychotherapy: An essay on the regulatory function of the collective unconscious. (LeReveille en psychotherapie)*. Paris: Universitaire.

Donovan, M.(1980). Relaxation with guided imagery: A useful technique. *Cancer Nursing,* 3,27-32.

Fiore, N.(1974). Fighting Cancer: One patient's perspective. *New England Journal of Medicine,* 300,284.

Frederking, W. (1948). *Deep Relaxation and Symbolism.* Psyche, 2.

Harley, G.(1989). Mind over body in cancer care. *Sunday Times* 30 April.

Gillespie, J. (1989).*Brave Heart.* London:Century Hutchinson.

Kretschmer, W. (1969). Meditative techniques in psychotherapy. In C.T. Tart, (Ed.). *Altered states of consciousness.* London: John Wiley & Sons, (pp.219-231).

Kubler-Ross, E.(1977).*On death and dying.* London: Tavistock.

Kubler-Ross, E.(1982). *Working it through.* Cother, New York: MacMillan.

Mauz, F. (1948). The psychotic man in psychotherapy. *Archiv.feur psychiatrie.*

Oaklander, V.(1978). *Windows to our children.* Utah: Real Peoples Press.

Siegel,B.S. (1986). *Love, medicine, and miracles.* London: Rider.

Siegel,B.S. (1990). *Peace, love and healing..* London:Rider.

Singer, J. (1973). *The child's world of make believe.* New York:Academic Press.

Simonton,O.C.,Matthews-Simonton, S. & Creighton,J. *Getting Well Again.* New York: Bantam.

Woodhead, M.(1991). Psychology and the cultural construction of 'children's needs'. In M. Woodhead, P. Light, & P. Carr, (Eds.), *Growing up in a changing society.* London: Routledge.

8   The role of health education in promoting mental health

J. Harris

Introduction

I would like to define what is meant by health education and describe developments in health education practice which have contributed to the promotion of mental health. Then, like a good social scientist, I would like to consider the definition of mental health and underline some of the health education methods that can be used to promote positive mental health, focusing particularly on a skills based approach which has been developed in the South East Thames Region, by Dr. Bob Wycherly, a District Psychologist in Hastings.

'One impression of health education is that it is about telling people what to do, giving out leaflets, letting off balloons at health fairs and sitting on exercise bicycles having your photograph taken. In fact that kind of promotional information activity is one of many approaches which may be used. Education for health is not only concerned with enabling the general public to gain the knowledge and the skills, motivation and confidence to live healthy lives. It is also concerned with educating those who come into contact with the public to communicate sensitively and effectively; with helping key decision makers in organisations to introduce health policies; and with fostering a climate of public opinion which makes it possible for local and national policy makers to take other broad public health measures (such as legislation) which protect or enhance the health of the people.' [1]

Over the past decade four developments have occurred in the practice of health education or health promotion, which have contributed to the promotion of positive mental health. The results of these developments have been largely ad hoc and unrecognised.

During this period, there has been a significant rise in the use of personal and social skills teaching materials so that about 30% of all schools organise classroom activities based upon this material. Much of this material is aimed at promoting self esteem and confidence and is concerned with increasing children's awareness of self image and social development, through such transitional periods as puberty. The second development has been the increasing emphasis on the training role of health education officers. In many routine training programmes organised by health promotion departments, such courses as assertiveness, relaxation, communication skills, presentation skills etc., have been organised, and the approach adopted has been mainly that of problem solving and client centred experiential learning. By starting with people and their experiences and developing their skills for health education purposes, the link has been made that these topics and training methods would constitute an appropriate approach to promoting positive mental health.

The introduction of community development methods based on empowerment theories has led to the involvement of health education officers in self-help groups and community support projects such as tranquilliser groups and mother and toddler groups, and much of this work has impinged upon mental health issues.

Finally, organisation development has occurred and this has been involved with the formulation and the implementation of health promoting policies such as smoking policies, stress management and alcohol abuse. The implementation of these policies has involved Health Authorities and other agencies such as Local Authorities in establishing counselling and other services to deal with the underlying mental health issues which have emerged as a result of these policies.

Many of these developments have occurred under the heading of other disease specific or client based programmes such as the prevention of heart disease or health promotion for parenthood programmes, so there has been little overt recognition of the ability of combining these various activities into a coherent positive mental health programme or strategy. Where this possibility has been discussed, one of the largest impediments to progress has been the difficulty in conceptualising mental health and how to promote it. I am sure that this is going to be a reoccurring point made by many of the presenters during the conference. Interestingly, when the South East Thames Regional Health Authority formed a multi disciplinary group to develop this area of work, the group had no problems in devising a programme of activity, which they did within an hour or two. The main problem was conceptualising and developing a definition of mental health. In the place of a definition a set of important characteristics was agreed, which could be used to inform subsequent discussion on this issue. There was general agreement that mental health was not simply the absence of mental illness. Rather, because of the difficulty of determining the interface between mental health and mental ill health, the most useful notion was that of a spectrum or cluster of mental states. The value of this way of considering mental health was that it did not imply a static or fixed phenomenon, but the individual could be in different states of mental health according to life events or different stages of life. The idea of different mental stages is also valuable to avoid labelling and stigmatising individuals.

The next set of overlapping characteristics was that of strength of mind or emotional stability and psychological integration. This was seen to be the ability to address and come to terms with major life events, albeit with the above concomitant but temporary changes in mental health. However, the stress, anxiety and depression which could be caused by long term environmental conditions and antecedents including the social and cultural environment were acknowledged, such as racism, sexism and isolation due to old age, ill health, loss of family support etc. The final set of characteristics was derived from a Canadian document and was the development and use of mental abilities to gain knowledge, forge conceptional links and form attitudes and values. The use of these mental abilities was demonstrated in making sense of social reality and attaining individual and collective goals with the associate feeling of achievement and well-being. Obviously it has to be acknowledged that this attempt to define mental health is laden with the values of the individuals or the group and of society in general. However, it does acknowledge the possibility of genetic and biological factors, as well as social and environmental stress as being important in influencing mental health state.

Strategies for Mental Health Promotion

From this definition, one can go on to develop strategies for mental health promotion, which were outlined by Dr Bob Wycherly in a conference organised by South East Thames on mental health in June 1987.[2]

Broadly speaking there are four major strategies for mental health promotion. First of all, we can try to increase people's skills in managing life events so that they are more able to plan their lives successfully.

Secondly, we can assist them in obtaining sufficient resources to buffer them against adversity - good housing, adequate income, and so on.

Thirdly, we can try to provide environments which are conducive to mental health which do not create unnecessary or undesirable stress. So, for example, in the health service we would be looking at things like waiting lists, how we handle patients when they come into hospital, the information people are given, and so on - the process people go through.

Finally we can try to create a climate of public opinion which does not stigmatise mental illness by demystifying explanations of its nature and causation.

The possible range of promotional health activities is enormous, and can be divided into individual, group, organisational, community and societal levels of intervention. At the individual level there is an exhaustive list: living skills; individual political action; knowing your rights; having confidence; adequate social support; and so on.

In the group field comes: encouraging good child-rearing; social services family units; ante-natal classes; tenants associations; self help groups; and so on - an enormous range of possible ways of promoting mental health.

Organisational issues include consideration within organisations of adequate systems of communication and support; stress management counselling; reasonable size working groups; democratic processes in organisations; staff welfare and supervision.

The community facilities include: leisure; health; well-people clinics, sheltered housing, meals on wheels; and so on - an enormous range again of possible interventions.

Finally, at societal level, there are: legislation on rights; policies on health; housing; education; and so on. You can see where the policy aspect comes into health promotion.

Focussing now on the skills approach

The 'skills approach' aims to enhance people's skills in managing life events successfully and it does not imply that the person is in any way ill or defective or deficient. The 'skills approach' is doing things better rather than being labelled as deficient. It can operate at the individual, group and organisational levels.

Skills can be divided into three main areas: physical skills; cognitive skills (things like thinking, reasoning, learning); and social skills. Physical skills are things like knitting jumpers, wallpapering rooms, running half-marathons, bricklaying, and so on. Cognitive skills are reading, writing, arithmetic, music, and decision-making. Social skills include body language, starting conversations, being rewarding to other people, maintaining friendships, and so on.

Living skills come from all three categories. I will illustrate how the issue of living skills has been approached by quite a wide variety of people in different situations. Firstly, there is social skills training. This approach arose mainly out of behavioural psychology and research work on social processes. It covers a very wide field, including things like body language, initiating, maintaining and closing conversations, greeting people, introducing yourself, monitoring your own social behaviour, appearance, assertiveness, and so on.

Secondly, there are counselling skills. People who work in counselling situations are typically taught skills such as asking open-ended questions - questions which cannot just be answered yes or no, reflecting back things that have been said to them, giving prompts to keep people talking, summarising what has been said, asking for clarification, using self-disclosure, in order to facilitate the person talking about themself, and so on. There is a group of skills around the counselling area which are to do with living skills.

Thirdly, there is management training. In recent years, management in commercial organisations has been the subject of a great deal of skills training. That comprises: partly cognitive skills, for example, planning and decision making; partly personal, for example, time management again; and partly interpersonal, for example, teaching people different styles of negotiating - negotiating to win, for example - versus negotiation for compromise. There is a lot of literature on styles of negotiating in management.

These useful skills have now begun to emerge into non-business life. There is a number of books published for schools and colleges on teaching children decision making, for example.

The fourth area is the growth movement of the sixties, the preoccupation with eastern religions and mysticism. Quite a number of skills from then have carried on, such as yoga and meditation. They are another group of skills which have proved to be useful in, for example, coping with stress.

Fifthly, there is a self-help area, and self-help groups teach their members skills which they will find useful in their particular areas of concern. For example, trade unions teach their officers negotiating skills or a women's support group may teach skills such as how to be assertive or physical self-defence. So again there is a number of self-help areas which give rise to skills.

The final few are really to do with more complicated programmes of skill training on relationship enhancement, such as demonstrating empathy, expressing feelings etc.

The Living Skills Pack

The 'Living Skills' Pack was produced in the South East Thames RHA and draws upon many of these approaches.

It was decided that the material should be first of all for use in groups, and secondly, it should be promotional rather than preventive. As it is promotional we have completely avoided all ideas of mental illness.

There were a number of requirements for the pack, which is aimed at health educators. We wanted it to teach living skills to a variety of adult groups and to be adaptable to groups with a variety of aims. We wanted the material to suit groups who wanted to do different things, not just aimed at, say stress management. We wanted it to be for groups to be able to develop their own kind of programme.

The skills we actually included were: Caring for Yourself; Assertion and Fighting; Rational Thinking; Stress Management; Relationships; and Planning and Organising.

We based the pack on a theoretical model called a transactional stress model. It is developed by Cox and Mackay and basically argues that the environment makes continuous demands on people. To meet those demands people have certain resources which might be external, like money or power, or internal, like self-esteem or intelligence, or skills like assertiveness or the ability to make relationships.

The person might perceive his capabilities or the demands on him either accurately or inaccurately. Perceived demand is how he sees it rather than how it is. The crucial stage of the model is the idea of appraisal, where that person continuously tries to balance in his mind the demand on him and the resources to meet the demand. Now if he decides that his resources are well above the level he needs to meet the demand then he will not really suffer any stress. He will just get on with doing whatever is necessary to deal with the situation. If he assesses that the demand is greater than his capability, his resources, he will begin to get stressed because he cannot really see any way of dealing appropriately with the situation. In this model, stress results from the imbalance between demand and resources.

The rest of the model is really to do with how people respond emotionally, behaviourally and psychologically to the stresses, the things they do and the feedback from the things they do to the early part of the model. It suggests that when you have appraised the situation you do something, then you assess the effect of what you have done; you re-appraise and do something else - it is a continuous interaction. All this is dealt with in the 'Living Skills' pack.

The pack consists of a handbook which gives the group leader or the members of the democratic group background information on stress, and the model that the pack is based on. It gives lots of advice on how to run groups and various discussion topics, a resource list and references. The handbook is a 'resource' for people who are involved in running the groups.

There follows a set of practical units which cover the main areas: Caring for Yourself; Assertion and Fighting; and so on, as mentioned earlier. They are separate modules which can be mixed in different orders so that groups can use any or all of them, in any order. Groups can, therefore, set up a programme which actually meets their needs, rather than having a set programme.

Each unit is separated into workshops which each deal with a particular topic. Every workshop is separated into exercises, each of which has a different name and deals with particular themes within that topic.

The first workshop in each of the units is an evaluation one. It enables the participants to make an assessment of their skills at the outset and to set themselves certain goals for working on during the group. The last workshop again allows them to reevaluate their skills, see where they have got to and see where they have got with their goals.

Conclusion

As far as I know this was the first of these skills training packs for adults, and subsequent to this a second one has been produced on stress at work. There are a number of similar packs for children and young people. One of the skills in health promotion is to be able to critically appraise which of these types of resources are most appropriate for different circumstances and also at what stage of the life cycle such interventions are most effective.

Within the field of health education there is widespread support and appreciation of the value of the personal and social skill development in primary and secondary schools as providing a sound psychological underpinning to the prevention of such behaviour patterns as glue sniffing, drug abuse, smoking and alcohol abuse etc. In adult life a key stage for healthy education intervention is before pregnancy. There is an increasing recognition that along with the physical and cognitive skills that are taught in ante-natal classes there is a need for social skills teaching to improve parental craft, particularly with regard to positive child rearing practices so as both to enhance child management and to use encouragement and praise as a more effective way of shaping behaviour so as to engender confidence and high-self-esteem, thereby promoting positive mental health into adulthood.

References

1. HEA - *A briefing paper on Health Authorities and Health Education*. August 1991.
2. SETRHA - *Life Matters, A Conference report*. SETRHA 1987.

9 The changing language of mental health

J. Henden

Abstract

In this paper, the author takes a detailed look at the constantly changing language of mental health. Three stages in this process are considered. The overriding concern is that we use a language of mental health, rather than one of mental illness. The many ways in which language has changed is discussed and numerous examples are given. For example, 'the mentally ill' have become 'people with mental health problems'. The proposition is put forward that those in the vanguard of the mental health movement are mainly behind this change. Also it is suggested that the language used indicates one's philosophical position within the mental health field. The contrary point of view is considered: that some clients actually prefer to be called by medical labels for a number of reasons. The author affirms that issues such as being positive; normalising mental ill-health; and boosting the self concept of clients are most important considerations.

Introduction

I quote from an extract of a Somerset Coroner's report in 1904: '...They had, of course, the important fact bearing upon the point, namely that her sister had been sent to Cotford *Asylum*, which showed that there was *insanity* in the family. ...She...appeared very worried about the *lunacy proceedings* which were being taken in connection with her sister's affairs. Verdict: the deceased committed suicide...whilst of *unsound mind*.'[1](author's italics).

Words such as those I emphasised in this quotation were a fundamental part of the 19th Century Moral model which prevailed at the time. As the mental institutions increasingly came under the medical profession's influence, there occurred a shift in terminology which became the specialist language of the Medical model.

Recent changes in health care spurred on and/or initiated by the Community mental health movement seem to be as fundamental a change as that from the earliest 19th Century Moral model.

Psychologists, occupational and art therapists in community units are often inclined nowadays to call themselves 'therapists' or 'mental health practitioners' and nursing staff are tending to opt for 'key worker' or 'primary therapist' rather than 'psychiatric nurse'. The sister/charge nurse is now called the 'ward manager' in many Districts.

Patients are now 'clients/residents/users/consumers/receivers/customers', or to slip into Arthur Daley parlance - 'punters!' We are hearing now not of 'patients with a psychiatric disorder' but of 'clients with a mental health problem (or mental health difficulty)'. It is not as acceptable nowadays to say 'I have diagnosed him as schizophrenic' but rather 'currently, he appears to be experiencing some psychotic features/symptoms' (or similar).

Mental Illness Units have become Mental Health Units and some universities have renamed their Department of Psychiatry, the Department of Mental Health.

What is behind all this name changing and where is it leading us?

I believe it is a sincere attempt by those in the vanguard of the community mental health movement to emphasise the positive in all they do, or are involved with. The various approaches to mental ill-health they embrace are about regarding people as having potential for growth; as opposed to reducing them to a set of symptoms thus marginalising them within society as 'psychiatric patients'.

We can easily respond to individuals in terms of their negative labels and assume a certain set of negative characteristics.

A former service user, writing in the Spring '91 issue of *Asylum magazine* writes: 'Once you've been given the identity 'mental patient', it's difficult to convince people to employ you. I have been given stupendous references by professionals, but they were flawed, simply by any mention of mental illness... The fact that you're given sickness invalidity benefit or income support tends to reinforce a negative stereotype with which you've been stuck with, and which tends to perpetuate any lack of self-esteem you have of yourself as a non-class person.' [2]

Had a more positive language been used by professionals in describing the user and the mental health difficulties he had experienced, and if '*in-validity*' benefit was known by another name, giving some hope, then employers might take a different view. In talking of our clients as having 'a mental health problem', instead of 'a mental illness', we are surely emphasising the positive and thus assisting clients with their self-concept.

There are many mental health workers who are now totally committed to re-humanising all aspect of their work. In addition to the self-concept just mentioned, other considerations such as civil liberties and normalisation are uppermost in the minds of many, when treating people and their problems. As the user movement, with governmental encouragement through the NHS Act gathers momentum, we will need to listen more closely to what those who actually receive services, think and feel. As a professional and manager, I have developed my own views [3] based on over 20 years working within mental health services in a number of roles and especially from observing staff-client interaction, and listening closely to users' opinions.

Negatively labelling our users as a way of pigeon-holing their illnesses or them, may be convenient and self-satisfying for us professionals and managers, but it does not do the user any good. It has been suggested it is a 'mentalist' [4] approach, often stigmatising people - sometimes for life. One user, who has experienced 'Milliganesque mood swings' (and I am sure Spike Milligan, who has been an avid campaigner within the mental health movement will not mind me using his name in this context) said, 'Being labelled manic-depressive is not good for one's self-esteem. Manic depressives are conditioned to believe that theirs is a terminal illness. An eminent professor of psychiatry upset me recently by asking me if I had gone this long before 'between episodes', implying that a further episode is inevitable.' [5]

One thing is certain, all of us will from time to time have fluctuations in mood, to varying degrees, and this is quite normal, but it is not certain that once someone has experienced the extreme form just described, they will continue to have such experiences for ever.

In returning to the negative stereotyping effect of medical model language, I will consider 'auditory hallucinations'. Hearing voices has long been seen by clinical psychiatry as a symptom of schizophrenia, severe depression and multiple personality disorders. Some mental health researchers are now questioning whether this is necessarily the case, and anyway, what proportion of the population at large would admit (confidentially of course!) to having heard voices at one time or another?

It has been suggested that 'hearers' is a term of preference, rather than 'the auditorily hallucinated' and I am sure many delegates to the first British Conference for Voice Hearers in Manchester two years ago were heartened to 'hear' they were among noted company - Joan of Arc, Carl Gustav Jung and Evelyn Waugh.

It is not only the language of the medical model we should guard against, as we can sometimes slip into an institution-oriented language of our own making, finding ourselves describing our clients as 'manipulative', 'attention-seeking', 'inadequate' or 'a management problem'. The effect can be the same - a distancing of therapist from service user, where the professional relates negatively to the label rather than to the person and their difficulties.

The language of mental health and the health press

How can one expect the mass media to report on mental health matters positively if our own health press shows a reluctance to move away from the same old language? Across the broad range of journals I scanned in preparation for this paper, terms like 'mental illness', 'psychiatric hospitals', 'in-patients' and 'out-patients' were all too common when referring to our services and their users. There seemed a general unwillingness to use any other term than 'patient'.

The MIND journal *Openmind*, has for many years been using a more enlightened terminology, and examples from an issue earlier this year are as follows: '53% were in employment when they first began to experience mental health problems'. [7] The author could have said: '53% were in employment when they first became mentally ill'. Later on in the same article, the author continued, 'If we can influence the development of their ('firms') employment practices in favour of mental health services users, then part of the battle will have been won'. [8] Again the author could have said, 'If we can influence the

71

development of their employment practices in favour of the psychiatrically ill, then part of the battle will have been won'.

I would suggest to you that a potential employer reading the *Openmind* version of both these quotations would be more favourably inclined towards service users than those reading the changed versions.

The Department of Health journal, *Health Trends* published some articles recently about the Worcester Development Project. In one of these articles [9] the author suggested it be more appropriate to refer to 'replacement services' rather than the more emotionally charged 'hospital closure' when describing our hospital run-down programmes. Since I have taken up their suggestions, I have found when talking to lay people about my work in this regard I no longer get asked the question, 'where will all the poor patients go?' (which one invariably got when using the term hospital closure). Instead it is 'what sort of service are you going to provide instead? A much more positive response.

Should we not change our language?

It has been suggested[10] that language, which is a means of understanding and communicating, should be used accurately, and therefore we should mean what we say. Should we talk of the National Health Service when we really mean the National Illness Service? Should we, it is suggested, talk of 'mental health' when we really mean 'mental illness?'. Proponents of this view say that to speak of mental health is a distortion and can not only affect our understanding of the term but also how we identify and conceptualise issues connected with it. How we make policy decisions concerning mental health and health promotion could also be affected, it is suggested. I can understand this concern, but believe users' views about themselves, about their current mental health problems and their future aspirations are more important considerations. A compromise solution could be to use the term 'ill-health' rather than 'health' when referring to illness.

Another view is that we should not change the language of mental health until attitudes have changed, although a change in attitude would require a new language. (And this is not just the attitudes of the general public, but as one service receiver has point out, the sometimes elitist and authoritarian attitudes amongst doctors and nurses). If we did change the language first, (and I quote): 'the new terms would simply become new euphemisms which would take on the old derogatory meanings'.[11] I ask, would this necessarily be the case if language and attitudes changed simultaneously?

Another reason for not changing our terminology has been put forward by frequent sufferers who argue that medical diagnostic labels accurately describe the pain people undergo, and imply the need for help, cure and care. Their concern is that by revising the language, it side-steps the issues and tries to minimise the suffering involved.[12] It follows that some supporters of this view do not mind being labelled 'schizophrenic' or 'manic-depressive' if it produces an appropriate treatment reaction from professionals. However, they would seem generally not to want their friends or family to label them in this way, but to relate to them as the *people* they are, warts and all!

Which way should we go?

Although I believe it is important not to try to diminish in any way the depth of people's

72

suffering, I think we need to support those who are now insisting on a non-medical description of their distress. Illness labels are a powerful way of persuading victims to blame themselves, e.g. 'It's not your life circumstances, it's your metabolism'. A community mental health language can shift our attention in a very positive way - away from the negative labelling process with its accompanying mystification, stigma and discrimination.

Reductionism considered

The use of medical labels can be part of a reductionist approach to human distress and suffering: 'nothing but the product of biological, psychological and social conditions', or 'nothing but the product of hereditary and environmental influences'.[13] 'The schizophrenic' then becomes nothing but a collection of auditory and visual hallucinations, and one who withdraws from society; and the 'manic-depressive' one of life's perpetual see-saws that one meets.

Whatever and whenever the problem, suffering or difficulty, is it not better all round to consider the problem as being merely on a continuum of experience thereby emphasising the normality of it? There is plenty of scope for positively reframing our descriptions of clients, and their difficulties or problems. If I was referred 'a 23 year old male, deluded psychotic', this is more likely to conjure up a negative picture as opposed to 'a 23 year old man, who is currently hearing voices and believes there is a network organised against him'. Describing people's experiences as they relate to mental ill-health in a positive way can be both liberating for users, and lead to greater optimism amongst therapists. Rather than 'the illness' becoming something one is stuck with, 'a current set of symptoms' becomes something one can take a view on, consider ways of alleviating, or knowing what course of action to take should they reappear in the future. The process can occur as just one part of a person's life -it does not have to *become* their life - as encouraged by medical labelling.

Those with physical disabilities do not escape reductionists' views - and I am not suggesting that there are any parallels to be drawn here with mental health problems, as physical disabilities more often tend to be permanent and continuous, whereas mental health problems tend to be temporary although sometimes recurrent. I remember hearing of an occasion when a man with a severe walking difficulty climbed onto a crowded bus and made his way slowly down the aisle to look for a seat. The father of two boys who was sat someway away from them bellowed out to the nearer of the two, 'Let the 'poor cripple' have your seat'.' The man reported how he became quite depressed for a few weeks following the incident, as he neither considered himself poor nor crippled.

In other areaS, the terminology we use is being updated. The mentally subnormal became the mentally handicapped and have now become people with learning difficulties. I could cite a number of other examples.

Can we agree on a new terminology?

One textbook on community care and social policy as it relates to mental health, illustrates the problem: 'We are all trying to turn patients into people who can live ordinary lives. ...If the word patient will no longer do, somebody had better invent a new

73

one.' Of course, we have invented a new one,[14] but they are legion, namely: user/client/resident/consumer/receiver/etc. It may not matter that we cannot agree which is the most desirable term and anyway are not some more appropriate for particular types of service receivers?

Also, are not such terms as 'mental health difficulties' and mental ill health' all more desirable than 'mental illness' for the images they create amongst the public, providers and users alike?

The new language and health promotion

I believe we have much work ahead of us in promoting mental health in any substantial way amongst the nation as a whole. We have really only just begun. Up until the 1960's, our predecessors were largely concerned with tertiary prevention. A lot of energy has been put into secondary prevention over the past one or two decades, and it is only recently that primary prevention and health promotion have started edging their way towards the top of the agenda.

I believe we are better now at discussing with users what factors led to their current mental health problem; what action they could take in the future to avoid a recurrence; and where to go should the problem recur. I also believe that users who have long standing difficulties are now more likely to be encouraged by professionals to develop healthier life styles within their various constraints than they were hitherto (another paper could be presented on this subject alone!).

On the so-called normal and healthy end of the continuum, there is the larger public. It is difficult to estimate the enormous cost of resources needed to promote mental health effectively within schools, further education and the workplace, or anywhere else where it may be appropriate to engage in health promotion.

It is my considered view that it will be many years before everyday mental health problems become anywhere near being accepted alongside physical health problems; and clients with mental health difficulties are really only ordinary people with ordinary (although sometimes extreme) experiences.

In order for our promotional efforts in this regard to be successful, I believe it is vital to use an everyday, positive language of mental health.

Acknowledgements

I am grateful to Mr. Rob Wondrak for reading through the text, and for the improvements he recommended.

I am also grateful to Mrs Jacquie Culverwell and Mrs Ro' Harris for their patience in typing out to my specific instructions.

References

1. Summary of Coroner's Report affixed in *Female Medical Casebook Vol. 6* 1904: Museum collection, Tone Vale Hospital, Taunton, Somerset.
2. Hutchinson, P. Benefits - Who benefits? *Asylum* 1991 Vol 5 No. 2 (Spring) 4.
3. Henden, J. Mind your language. *Openmind* 1990/91 48 (Dec/Jan): 10-11.

4. Lawson, M. The Language of Mentalism. *Openmind* 1990/91 48 (Dec/Jan): 11.
5. Cookson, S. My label's manic-depressive, what's yours? *Asylum* 1991 ibid: 5.
6. Aziz, C. Heard but not seen. *Asylum* 1991 ibid: 13 -14.
7. Kessler, E. People first. *Openmind* 1991 50 (April/May): 6.
8. Kessler E. ibid.
9. Khoosal, D. and Jones P. Worcester Development Project - Where do we go when hospitals close? *Health Trends* 1990/91: Vol. 22 No. 4. : 137 - 141.
10. Rakussen, J. Emotional Education. *Openmind* 1990: 46 (Aug/Sept) 10.
11. Wallcraft, J. Psychiatric labelling. *Openmind* 1986: 23 (Oct/Nov) 14.
12. Narod, N. Letters. *Openmind* 1991: 49 (Feb/March) 9.
13. Frankl, V.E. *The Unheard Cry for Meaning*. Hodder & Stoughton, 1978.
14. Jones, K. *Experience in Mental Health - Community Care and Social Policy*. Sage publications, 1988: 6.

10 Can social problem-solving training help people with learning difficulties

K. Loumidis

Abstract

Social Problem-Solving Training is a cognitive-behavioural approach for improving social competence and psychological adjustment based on the pioneering work of Goldfried and D'Zurilla (1971) and Spivack, Platt and Shure (1978). This approach has been successfully applied in a variety of clinical and community settings, with both adults and children of normal intelligence. The ultimate goal of training is to equip people with the necessary Problem-Solving skills to manage their everyday problems.

Many people with learning difficulties have poor or defective Social Problem-Solving skills, which prevent them from taking advantage of the current philosophy of self advocacy, normalisation and providing care in the community. Since there is evidence showing that training can be beneficial to those with a learning difficulty, it is important to teach strategies and processes to be applied in a wide range of potential everyday problems, even in the absence of carers. In this way, Social Problem-Solving Training could be regarded as a means of promoting mental health in the community for this population.

This paper presents (i) social problem-solving training as an approach to promote mental health, (ii) the difficulties that people with learning difficulties face in dealing with everyday problems, (iii) a review of the limited literature on using social problem-solving training with people who have a moderate learning difficulty, (iv) a critique of the methodology while proposing guidelines for more rigorous research, and (v) an argument for a more extensive use of this cognitive-behavioural technique to care for adults with moderate learning difficulties.

Social problem-solving and Mental Health Promotion

Mental Health is a quality of life, conceived differently according to one's belief system, cultural context, or theoretical orientation. The term Mental Health has often been used to connote lack of mental illness. However, professionals in this area have increasingly started to conceive mental health as a distinct concept, quite different from mental illness.

77

While avoiding defining mental health as the absence of mental illness, one could attempt to indicate some of the components of psychological health. Adopting some ideas from Jahoda's (1958) model of mental health, one can expect psychologically healthy individuals to be able to:

a. take decisions according to their own standards and goals and consequently act upon them;

b. perceive the world accurately with as few distortions as possible;

c. hold positive attitudes towards themselves, as well as being sufficiently motivated to control their lives; and

d. master in an adequate manner their own physical, personal and social environment.

Consequently, when problems in everyday living challenge one's psychological well-being, competent individuals can actively problem-solve if problem resolution is possible, or change their way of thinking about the problem if problem resolution is not possible (e.g. terminal illness, bereavement). The process by which people attempt to identify, discover, or invent ways of dealing with everyday problems, has been called *Social Problem-Solving* (D'Zurilla, 1971) or *Interpersonal Problem-Solving* (Spivack and Shure, 1976). It is at the same time a social-learning process, a self-management technique and a general coping strategy (D'Zurilla 1971, 1986) and is relevant to a wide range of everyday problems (i.e., personal, interpersonal, psychological, community). According to D'Zurilla's model, this cognitive-behavioural-affective process has a motivational component called problem orientation and a set of four specific problem-solving skills. These goal directed tasks aim at: (a) defining and formulating the problem, (b) generating alternative solutions, (c) evaluating the solutions and making appropriate decisions, and finally (d) implementing and verifying the solutions.

The relationship between social problem-solving skills and mental health becomes apparent when considering the following findings:

Firstly, there is evidence suggesting that these skills are positively related to social adjustment (Spivack and Shure, 1976) and inversely related to psychological distress (Nezu, 1985).

Secondly, lack of or inefficient use of, those skills has been observed in people with psychological and social adjustment problems, psychiatric patients (Platt and Spivack, 1974), and depressed students (Nezu and Roman, 1988).

Thirdly, a relationship between social problem-solving skills and positive mental health is supported from applied studies demonstrating the therapeutic effect of *Social Problem-Solving Training* or *Therapy* (see D'Zurilla, 1988). This approach has been successfully applied in a variety of clinical and non-clinical settings, with both adults (D'Zurilla and Nezu, 1982) and children (Denham and Almeida, 1987). Training aims at equipping people who may have difficulties in coping with everyday problems, with the necessary skills to deal with problems challenging their psychological or mental health. One of the distinct features of this approach is that it teaches the *process* of dealing with everyday problems rather than the *content* of solutions to specific problems which is the objective of Social Skills Training.

In these terms Social Problem-Solving Training is regarded as an effective and direct means of promoting and enhancing mental health, while preventing maladjustment and psychological distress.

Social problem-solving and learning difficulties: What are the problems?

Social Problem-Solving becomes particularly relevant in the care of people with learning difficulties for the following reasons:

Firstly, people with learning difficulties by definition have impairments in adaptive behaviour (Grossman, 1983). Training could focus on deficits in adaptive behaviour and promote positive mental health.

Secondly, there is evidence suggesting that people with learning difficulties are deficient in social problem-solving skills as compared to people without learning difficulties (Smith and Greenberg, 1979). In addition, the types and variety of problem-solving strategies utilised by children with learning difficulties (IQ=48-81) are at a lower level than children matched for chronological age, but at a similar level to children matched for mental age (Smith, 1986). Furthermore, children with learning difficulties (IQ:$\underline{M}$=59) generate significantly fewer solutions to hypothetical problems, and more irrelevant responses as compared to children without learning difficulties (Herman and Shantz, 1984). These poor social problem-solving skills may then account for problems in community adjustment of people with learning difficulties (Foxx, Kyle, Faw and Bittle, 1989). Furthermore, people with learning difficulties may have specific difficulties in successfully dealing with problems (Ashman and Conway, 1989; Bouffard, 1990). Such difficulties as proposed by Ashman and Conway (1989) are:

a. difficulties in comprehending the requirements of the problem;
b. difficulties in isolating any relevant factors while disregarding irrelevant information;
c. the lack of problem solving strategies;
d. dealing with problems in a random, trial-and-error manner, rather than using systematic, planned approaches; and,
e. motivational, attentional and memory difficulties.

Inappropriate problem solutions could be attributed to the following sources (Bouffard, 1990):

a. deficiencies in the content of and accessibility to the knowledge base;
b. lack of spontaneous use of strategies;
c. insufficient metacognitive knowledge and understanding;
d. lack of executive control; and,
e. inadequate motivation and practice.

However, there is evidence to suggest that once trained in specific areas, people with learning difficulties can overcome some of these problems. Systematic training can help them enrich their background knowledge, overcome self-regulatory deficits (Brown and Campione, 1986), set standards and regulate their behaviour independently (Litrownik, Cleary, Lecklitner & Franzini, 1978), apply self-monitoring strategies independently (Borkowski and Varnhagen, 1984) and enhance in that way their ability to deal more effectively with everyday problems.

Thirdly, people with learning difficulties, especially those with a long history of institutional life, may have deficient social problem-solving skills due to insufficient motivation or low self-efficacy (Balla and Zigler, 1979). People who have lived for a long period of their lives in residential care have learned to accept rather than challenge any problems they encounter. In the past, institutions tended to put an emphasis on external control by the staff on the residents rather than on the promotion of independent decision making. Residents may then be enveloped in a 'cloak of competence' (Edgerton, 1967), disguising some of their real difficulties.

Finally, the problem of emotional disturbance in people with learning difficulties may be prevalent, but is often overlooked or attributed to intellectual impairment. This confusion has been labelled diagnostic overshadowing (Reiss, Levitan, and Szyszko, 1982). Since social problem-solving skills are inversely related to psychopathology, training could be an effective way to promote mental health for this sensitive population.

Training people with learning difficulties in social problem-solving

Training people with learning difficulties in selected components of social problem-solving was attempted in the 1970's, to improve situational problem-solving and planning (Ross and Ross, 1973) and selection of the best alternative (Ross and Ross, 1978).

An early attempt to apply a social problem-solving programme for elementary school children with mild-moderate learning difficulties (IQ=50-75) was made by Healey (1977). Despite the fact that social problem-solving skills and behavioural adjustment were found to be positively related, changes in social problem-solving skills were not statistically significant, possibly due to the short duration of the programme (15 sessions).

However the efficacy of social problem-solving training with people having learning difficulties living in the community was confirmed by Castles and Glass (1986). In their study they examined the effects of social-skills training, social problem-solving and a combination of both with 33 adults (IQ=44-81, M=62.5). They argued that mildly handicapped people improved in terms of interpersonal Problem-Solving skills even without training, while the moderately handicapped group required training to demonstrate improvements in skills. However the group that received training in social problem-solving only, failed to improve on the role-play measure of social-skills, or on the two maladaptive subscales of the Adaptive Behaviour Scale (ABS: Nihira, Foster, Shellhaas, and Leland, 1974). In addition, the treatment gains failed to generalise to role-play situations they were not trained in, the other two factor scales of the ABS, and the locus of control or measures of self-efficacy. This was attributed to the short duration of the training programme (15 sessions x 60 min) and the fact that strategies for generalisation were not built in the programme.

In a residential setting, Bramston and Spence (1985) compared the effects of social skills and social problem-solving training (4 x 30 min x 4 weeks) with a group of 48 adults (Binet IQ:M=40.06; WAIS IQ:M=55.20). The group receiving social problem-solving training generated significantly more alternative solutions but failed to produce detectable changes in staff ratings of general social competence. Bramston and Spence attributed the relatively weak effect of both training programmes to environmental variables and recommended the use of 'booster' sessions for further studies, an increase in the length of sessions and a combination of both cognitive and overt behavioural skills training in future programmes.

Social behaviour in work settings was also improved by a social problem-solving approach to social skills training (Park and Gaylord-Ross, 1989). Three developmentally disabled youths (IQ=58,65,45) participated in a study evaluating social problem-solving training and a combination of other methods (role-play training) measured by a multiple baseline design. While role-play training failed to generalise to new situations (illustrated), the 'rule governed' problem-solving training (30 min/session) led to substantial generalisation and maintenance of social behaviours in natural work settings.

Helping 9 mothers with learning difficulties (IQ=58-74) to deal with child-raising problems, was the purpose of training in effective decision-making and problem-solving (Tymchuk, Andron and Rahbar, 1988). Both identification of problems and the use of decision-making components were significantly improved after group training (6weeks x 90min) and maintained for a month. Still, there was no assessment of the mothers' daily decision-making.

Furthermore, social problem-solving training has also been used to enhance dating-skills (Mueser, Valenti-Hein and Yarnold, 1987), public transportation skills (Welch, Nietupski and Hamre-Nietupski, 1985), or employment related social skills (Foss, Auty and Irvin, 1989).

Finally, interpersonal problem-solving training was used for children in a special education class (Vaughn, Ridley and Cox, 1983). Training in this study also included components on cue sensitivity and empathy (8 weeks, 40 sessions). Significant improvements in problem-solving behaviour were reported for the trained group (n=15, IQ:$\underline{M}$=58) as compared to the control group (n=15, IQ:$\underline{M}$=61). However, the long range effects of the programme were not evaluated, nor was generalisation of skill acquisition to other settings.

Critical points and proposed guidelines

In reviewing some of the literature on social problem-solving for people with learning difficulties, and on the basis of clinical experience, some critical points emerge forming guidelines for more rigorous research.

Increase in duration and 'booster sessions': From selected studies, it becomes evident that the duration of social problem-solving training for people with learning difficulties has been as brief as 4-weeks, producing in many cases weak and non-lasting effects. Most of the studies recommend an increase in the amount of training sessions with the potential use of booster sessions to attain the maximum effect. Furthermore, metanalytic evidence from a review of 50 social problem-solving studies with children reported that interventions lasting for 40 or more sessions led to better acquired skills (Denham and Almeida, 1987). Booster sessions should be encouraged to promote maintenance and generalisation of problem-solving skills. Since training will eventually build people's confidence and raise their expectations in dealing with everyday problems, extra sessions may be required for encouragement, support and corrective feedback, during the practice of the acquired skills.

Emphasis on comprehension: It is essential to ensure that the participants in social problem-solving interventions are at a sufficient level of comprehension to benefit from training. In many cases, people with learning difficulty may seem to understand some of the questions asked, but responses could be influenced by a bias towards answers in the affirmative (Sigelman, Budd, Spanhel and Scoenrock, 1981). Hence, questions should be reworded occasionally, requiring both yes and no responses. This could be detected before or during the introductory sessions of group formation and cohesiveness. Subsequently, the language and concepts used at any stage of assessment and training should be adjusted to the level and needs of the participants. Manuals and assessment materials should at best be examined by a speech therapist, or at least contain open ended questions to indicate that the concepts are understood. Failure to control for these issues may result in unfairly attributing weak training effects to the participants 'disabilities'.

Additional measures of clinical outcome: To establish the therapeutic effects on general mental health solely on the basis of existing measures of social problem-solving is insufficient.

Firstly, in many studies, improvements in social problem-solving skills were claimed due to a statistical increase in the number of alternative solutions to hypothetical problems. This was derived from one of the fundamental principles of the social problem-solving theory proposing a positive correlation between quantity and quality of solutions (D'Zurilla and Nezu, 1980; Spivack and Shure, 1982). However, an increase in the number of alternative solutions is not necessarily an index of ability to evaluate the alternative solutions or, decide which is the best and finally implement and verify it. So training people to produce more alternative solutions only, may not make them better in dealing with daily problems.

Secondly, more emphasis should be placed on the qualitative aspects of the responses. For example, problem-solving responses could be evaluated in terms of social acceptability, personal/psychological gratification, as well as effectiveness in resolving the problem.

Thirdly, to ensure that social problem-solving training is not a simple cognitive exercise, but a powerful therapeutic technique, one has to demonstrate improvements in mental or psychological health after training. Although a variety of other factors may contribute to therapeutic success and a causal relationship would be difficult to claim, it is essential to evaluate the effects of training on the basis of independent measures of adjustment. However, selecting measures of psychological disturbance that would be sensitive enough to detect changes in moods or behaviour for people with learning difficulties, could be a difficult task. This is due to the fact that in learning difficulties research, most measures of behavioural adjustment or psychopathology are staff measures designed for the quite severely disabled group, tapping quite different forms of disturbance (such as stereotyped behaviour, self injurious behaviour etc). An earlier attempt to apply a modified version of the General Health Questionnaire (GHQ-28: Goldberg, 1978) as a measure of general psychological distress with a sample of residents having learning difficulties, was shown to be unsuccessful (Loumidis, 1990). However, some of the well established measures of adaptive behaviour (e.g., ABS: Nihira et al., 1974), have some items tapping psychological distress (e.g., poor reaction to frustration).

Generalisation: It is necessary at least for ethical reasons, to ensure that the skills for which time, effort and resources were spent are maintained and will generalise to real life. Previous studies have often failed to report any generalisation of social problem-solving skills, or have reported poor generalisation over time. To promote generalisation, training programmes should contain specific tasks designed to gradually increase the conceptual distance between the training task and those of everyday life. Considering the degree of similarity/dissimilarity between these two situations is essential (Ashman and Conway, 1989).

Some of the previous studies measured generalisation by introducing novel situations of the same conceptual category. However, generalisation could be assessed over time (before and after training), across social roles, and across different types of problems which are personally and socially relevant. Emphasis should also be placed on the variables affecting maintenance and generalisation, something which needs careful consideration.

Why is it important to carry on?

Social Problem-Solving Training is not a miracle treatment that can produce dramatic results overnight. On many occasions, organismic or environmental variables may constrain the therapeutic effect. In other cases, some prerequisite skills may be absent, while some of the participants may simply not want to participate. Nevertheless, is important to be optimistic for the following reasons:

At an academic level, people have become increasingly aware of the fact that behavioural approaches to the care of people with learning difficulties cannot account for the powerful mediation of thought on behaviour, or the emotional and motivational components. Moreover, people are seen as passive recipients rather than active reconstructors of their environment. As an alternative, a variety of cognitive-behavioural treatments have successfully been adapted to the needs of people with learning difficulties (Short and Evans, 1990; Sugden, 1989; Lindsay and Kasprowicz, 1987; Shapiro, 1986; Whitman et al., 1984). Cognitive approaches give the power to the person in need, aiming at independence and dignity.

At a conceptual level, social problem-solving training is compatible with the current philosophy of self advocacy (Williams and Schoultz, 1981) encouraging people with learning difficulties to speak for themselves, and express their needs. Social problem-solving training can help them select the best alternative and make an appropriate decision to meet their own needs. This may help people with learning difficulties lead as normal a life as possible in line with the principle of normalisation (Wolfensberger, 1972).

At a practical level, the mode of service delivery is currently moving towards deinstitutionalisation and care in the community (DHSS, 1989; DoH, 1989). However, it is of vital importance to ensure that deinstitutionalised people will have the skills to deal with everyday problems as they arise, in the absence of carers. Assessing residents of long stay hospitals in social problem-solving situations, can then become part of a screening procedure to identify those residents who are competent enough to move into the community, protecting in that way the less able. Alternatively, training in social problem-solving can be used in a preparatory manner for those who may have difficulties in dealing with everyday problems. Even the people that already live independently but have difficulties at a psychological level due to ineffective social problem-solving could benefit from training.

Conclusion

The application of social problem-solving training in the care of people with learning difficulties is still at an early stage of understanding. There are many problems and even more constraints to consider at an everyday level. However, more research is needed and more enthusiasm is required in any attempt to promote the mental health of people with learning difficulties.

Acknowledgments

This research report was made possible by a Ph.D. scholarship to K.S. Loumidis from the University of Keele. I am grateful to Dr. N.A. Beasley and Dr. A. B. Hill for their critical comments on earlier drafts, and to Mr. W. Coles for his support at the Clinical Psychology Department, Stallington Hospital.

References

Ashman, A.F., & Conway, N.F. (1989). *Cognitive strategies in special education: Process based instruction*. Routledge.

Balla, D., & Zigler, E. (1979). Personality development in retarded persons. In N.R. Ellis (Ed.), *Handbook of mental deficiency (2nd. ed.)* Hillsdale, N.J.: Erlbaum.

Borkowski, J. G., & Varnhagen, C. K. (1984). Transfer of learning strategies: Contrast of self-instructional and traditional training formats with EMR children. *American Journal of Mental Deficiency*, 88, 369-379.

Bouffard, M. (1990). Movement problem solutions by educable mentally handicapped individuals. *Adapted Physical Activity Quarterly*, 7, 183-197.

Bramston, P. & Spence, S.H. (1985). Behavioural versus cognitive social-skills training with intellectually-handicapped adults. *Behavioural Research Therapy*, 23, 239-246.

Brown, A.L., & Campione, J.C. (1986). Training to transfer: Guidelines for promoting flexible use of trained skills. In M.G. Wade (Ed.), *Motor skills of the mentally handicapped: Issues in research and training* (pp. 257-271). New York: North Holland.

Castles, E.E. & Glass, C.R. (1986): Training in social and interpersonal problem-solving skills for mildly and moderately mentally retarded adults. *American Journal on Mental Retardation*, 91 (1), 35-42.

Denham, S.A., & Almeida, M.C. (1987). Childrens' social problem-solving skills, behavioural adjustment & interventions. A metanalysis. *Journal of Applied Developmental Psychology*, 8, 391-409.

Department of Health, (1989): *Caring for people*, HMSO.

Department of Health and Social Security, (1989). *Working for patients*, HMSO.

D'Zurilla, T.J., & Goldfried, M.B. (1971). Problem-solving and behaviour modification. *Journal of Abnormal Psychology*, 78, 107-120.

D'Zurilla, T.J., & Nezu, A. (1980). A study of the generation of alternatives process in social problem-solving. *Cognitive Therapy and Research*, 4, 67-72.

D'Zurilla, T.J., & Nezu, A. (1982). Social problem-solving in adults. In Kendall, P.C. (Ed.), *Advances in cognitive behavioural research and therapy*, Vol.1, (pp 200-274). Academic Press.

D'Zurilla, T.J. (1986). *Problem-solving therapy: A social competence approach to clinical intervention*. New York: Springer Publishing.,

D'Zurilla, T.J. (1988). Problem-solving therapies. In K.S. Dobson (Ed.), *Handbook of cognitive-behavioural therapies* (pp 85-135). New York: Guilford.

Edgerton, T. (1967). *The cloak of competence: Stigma in the lives of mentally retarded*. U.C.L.A.

Foss, G., Auty, W.P., & Irvin, L.K. (1989). A comparative evaluation of modelling, problem-solving, and behaviour rehearsal for teaching employment-related interpersonal skills to secondary students with mental retardation. *Education and Training in Mental Retardation*, 24, 1, 17-27.

Foxx, R.M., Kyle, M.S., Faw, G.D. & Bittle, R.G. (1989). Problem-solving skills training: Social validation and generalisation. *Behavioural Residential Treatment*, 4,(4) 269-287.

Goldberg, D.P. (1978). *The Manual of the General Health Questionnaire*, Institute of Psychiatry, London: N.E.F.L.

Grossman, H.J., (1983). *Manual on the terminology and classification in mental retardation (3rd rev.)* Washington D.C.: American Association on Mental Deficiency.

Healey, K.N. (1977). *An investigation of the relationships between certain social cognitive abilities and social behaviour, and the efficacy of training in social cognitive skills for elementary Retarded Educable children*. Unpublished doctoral dissertation. Bryn Mawr College.

Herman, M.S., & Shantz, C.U. (1984). Social problem-solving and mother child interactions of educable mentally retarded children. *Journal of Applied Developmental Psychology*, 4, 217-226.

Jahoda, M. (1958). *Current concepts of positive mental health*. New York: Basic Books.

Lindsay, W., & Kasprowicz, M., (1987). Challenging negative cognitions: Developing confidence in adults by means of cognitive behaviour therapy. *Mental Handicap*, 15,

85

159-162.

Litrownik, A.J., Cleary, C.P., Lecklitner, G. L., & Franzini, L. R. (1978). Self regulation in retarded persons: Acquisition of standards for performance. *American Journal of Mental Deficiency*, 83, 86-89.

Loumidis, K.S. (1990). *The relationship between social problem-solving skills, intellectual performance and general psychological distress in a sample of institutionalised adults with a learning difficulty.* Unpublished Masters Thesis, University of Keele, Staffordshire, U.K.

Mueser, K.T., Valenti-Hein, D., & Yarnold, P. R. (1987). Dating skills groups for the developmentally disabled: Social skills and problem-solving versus relaxation training. *Behaviour Modification*, 11, 2, 200-228.

Nezu, A.M. (1985). Differences in psychological distress between effective and ineffective problem-solving. *Journal of Consulting Psychology*, 32, 135-138.

Nezu, A.M., & Roman, G.F. (1988). Stressful life events, problem-solving and depressive symptoms among university students. A prospective analysis. *Journal of Consulting Psychology*, 35, 134-138.

Nihira, K., Foster, R., Shellhaas, M., & Leland. H. (1974). *Adaptive Behaviour Scale*: American Association on Mental Retardation. Washington, DC.

Park, H. & Gaylord-Ross, R. (1989). A problem-solving approach to social skills training in employment settings with mentally retarded youth. Special issue: Supported employment. *Journal of Applied Behaviour Analysis*, 22, 4, 375-380.

Platt, J.J., & Spivack, G., (1974). Means of solving real life problems: I. Psychiatric patients versus controls, and cross cultural comparisons of normal females. *Journal of Community Psychology*, 2, 45-48.

Reiss, S., Levitan, G.W., & Szyszko, J. (1982). Emotional disturbance and mental retardation: Diagnostic overshadowing. *American Journal of Mental Deficiency*, 86, 567-574.

Ross, D. M., & Ross, S. A. (1973). Cognitive training for the EMR child: Situational problem-solving and planning. *American Journal of Mental Deficiency*, 78, 20-26.

Ross, D. M., & Ross, S. A. (1978). Cognitive training for EMR children: Choosing the best alternative. *American Journal of Mental Deficiency*, 82, 598-601.

Shapiro, E. S. (1986). Behaviour modification, self control, and cognitive procedures in R. P. Barret (Ed.), *Severe behaviour disorders in the mentally retarded* (pp 61-97). Academic Press.

Short, E.S., & Evans, S.W. (1990). Individual differences in cognitive and social problem-solving as a function of intelligence. *International Review of Research in Mental Retardation*, 16, 89-123.

Sigelman, C.K., Budd, E.C., Spanhel, C.L. & Scoenrock, C.L. (1981). Asking questions of retarded persons: A comparison of yes-no and either-or formats. *Applied Research in Mental Retardation*, 2, 347-358.

Smith, D.C. (1986). Interpersonal problem-solving skills of retarded and nonretarded children. *Applied Research in Mental Retardation*, 7, 431-442.

Smith, I.L., & Greenberg, S. (1979). Hierarchical assessment of social competence.

American Journal on Mental Retardation, 83, 551-555.

Spivack, G. & Sure, M.B. (1976). *Social adjustment of young children*. San Francisco: Jossey-Bass.

Spivack, G., Platt, J.J., & Shure, M.B., (1978): *The problem-solving approach to adjustment*. San Francisco: Jossey-Bass.

Spivack, G. & Sure, M.B. (1982). The cognition of social adjustment: Interpersonal cognitive problem-solving thinking. In B.B. Lahey & A.B. Kazdin (Eds.): *Advances in clinical child psychology Vol. 5* (pp.323-372). New York: Plenum.

Sugden, D. (1989). *Cognitive approaches in special education*. Falmer Press.

Tymchuk, A.J., Andron, L. & Rahbar, B. (1988). Effective decision making / problem-solving with mothers who have mental retardation. *American Journal on Mental Retardation*, 92, 6, 510-516.

Vaughn, S.R., Ridley, C.A. & Cox, J. (1983). Evaluating the efficacy of an interpersonal skills training program with children who are mentally retarded, *Education and Training in Mental Retardation*, October, 191-196.

Welch, J., Nietupski, J. & Hamre-Nietupski, S. (1985). Teaching public transportation problem-solving skills to young adults with moderate handicaps. *Education and Training in Mental Retardation*, December, 287-295.

Whitman, T., Burgio, L., & Johnston, M.B. (1984). Cognitive behavioural interventions with mentally retarded children. In A.W. Meyers, & W.E. Craighead, (Eds.), *Cognitive Behavioural Therapy with Children*, (pp. 193-227). Plenum Press.

Williams, P. and Schoultz, B. (1981). *We can speak for ourselves*. Souvenir Press.

Wolfensberger, W. (1972) *Normalisation*. National Institute on Mental Retardation.

11 Accentuate the positive, eliminate the negative: The role of boosting and putting-down signals in mental health

J. Price

Abstract

Human beings exchange a bewildering variety of signals, so their study requires a classification based on a pre-existing model. An approach from evolutionary biology suggests a division into signals which affect the self-esteem of the recipient and those which do not. Those which affect self-esteem I shall call thymoleptic signals. Thymoleptic signals are of two types: anathetic signals which have a boosting effect on self-esteem, and catathetic signals which have a putting-down effect on self-esteem. Mental health is positively correlated with self-esteem, which probably evolved out of an animal precursor, resource-holding potential (RHP), which is a measure of fighting capacity. At some stage in evolution, interpersonal signals appeared which had the capacity to raise or lower RHP in a 'ritual' manner. Early in vertebrate evolution these took the form, respectively, of the threat and submissive components of ritual agonistic behaviour, but in human development they have become greatly elaborated, especially the boosting signals, which have lost their original connotation of submission. Human self-esteem is largely determined by the boosting and putting-down signals received from family and group members, and its genetic base-line setting has probably been set at a level at which it needs a net input of boosting signals in order to reach a range which is consistent with normal functioning. In this way the individual is dependent on the approval of his social group. Thymoleptic signals deserve close study. People vary very much in their general tendency to emit them. Extroverts probably emit both kinds more than introverts. High self-esteem people probably emit more boosting signals and less putting-down signals than low self-esteem people. Neuroticism is associated with a sensitivity to putting-down signals; narcissism with a requirement for boosting signals. But a lot of the variation associated with the emission and receipt of thymoleptic signals is not measured in current personality tests. The promotion of mental health requires sufficient anathesis (boosting signals) to maintain self-esteem, and the avoidance of excessive amounts of catathesis (putting-down signals).

'Great tranquillity of heart is his who cares for neither praise nor blame'

THOMAS à KEMPIS

'A man who does not love praise is not a full man'

HENRY BEECHER

Introduction

The signals that we as human beings exchange with each other are infinitely complex, and we are hard pressed to know how to classify them, let alone how to study them. Navigating on these troubled waters, it helps to have two fixed points to take one's bearings from. The fixed points I have chosen for the present analysis are clinical psychiatry and evolutionary biology. The needs of our patients and potential patients tell us what is important; evolutionary biology tells us what is likely to have evolved to create and to satisfy these needs. Even with these fixed points, navigation is extremely difficult and there are no good maps; we are dealing with matters that are too important for experimental studies, and too elusive even for descriptive techniques to have clarified the issues. We are still at a level at which individual clinical cases and anecdote are sometimes our only data, and where fiction is often more informative than science. What follows is tentative, speculative and lacking an adequate data base; however, if we do not try to chart these seas, we are neglecting a region which is important for the maintenance of good mental health.

A perspective from mental health

Looking at human interaction from the mental health point of view, we can propose at least one classification. We know that some of the signals we receive from other people leave us feeling better, while other signals leave us feeling worse. Those that make us feel better tend to raise our self-evaluation, in other words they increase our self-confidence or self-esteem; while those that make us feel worse lower our self-evaluation. This is just another way of saying that feeling good consists at least in part of a satisfactory evaluation of ourselves. There has been a lot of research into self-esteem (reviewed by Robson, 1988; see also Editorial, 1989). The causes of self-esteem are complex and various, and the signals we get from other people are only one causative variable, but since the time of George Herbert Mead it has been accepted that, at least in part, or at least in some cases, people feel their self-worth to be what they see mirrored in the eyes of other people. This mirroring, which starts in childhood and continues into old age, consists of interpersonal signals that raise or lower our self-evaluation.

Self-esteem is important for the promotion of good mental health because low self-esteem is associated with a large number of forms of psychopathology, including depressive states, anxiety neurosis, delinquency, racial prejudice, wife battering and child abuse. Although in these cases one cannot argue directly from association to cause, it seems likely that if we could raise the mean self-esteem of the population by, say, one standard deviation, we could reduce the incidence of these forms of psychopathology.

90

Some aspects of self-esteem are puzzling. One is the enormous variation in self-esteem which exists in the population, first pointed out by Maslow (1937). Another is the very fact of people making an overall, global evaluation of themselves, rather than evaluating themselves independently in different areas of functioning (Editorial, 1989).

A perspective from evolutionary biology

These difficulties can be seen in perspective if we take an approach based on evolutionary biology, seeing behaviour as evolved by natural selection. This enables us to look at other species and also to benefit from the theoretical work of behavioural ecologists (e.g., Maynard Smith, 1982; Parker, 1984). This view leads us to the conclusion that for at least three hundred million years we have been controlling each other's self-esteem by means of signals, since the time of our common ancestor with present day reptiles. The study of reptiles simplifies the study of signalling because their social life is very much more simple than ours (Carpenter, 1978). They have no affiliative behaviour, no parental behaviour and no pair bonding. Apart from mating, their entire social behaviour is concerned with the evaluation of self-esteem and the manipulation of the self-esteem of conspecifics; or, rather, the reptilian equivalent of self-esteem, which has been called resource-holding potential (RHP) (see Gilbert, 1989, for review). Moreover, reptiles communicate almost entirely by visual signals, being deaf and little concerned with smell, so that the signals can be plainly seen.

Most work on reptile signalling has been done on lizards, e.g. the Rainbow lizard, *Agama agama* (Harris, 1964). Male lizards give four main types of signal. Two of these are addressed to the world in general, and they convey the message 'I am strong' or 'I am weak'. These general messages take the form of skin colour, such as blue for strength and green for weakness, and also gait which may be swaggering or furtive, and posture which may be upright or crouched. The other two messages are the result of an evaluation of themselves and a potential rival, and they convey the messages 'I am stronger than you' and 'I am weaker than you'. The form of these messages varies between species. The 'stronger' message may take the form of butting with the head, as in the case of the marine iguanas of the Galapagos Islands, or of hitting sideways with the tail, as in the case of many lizards. The 'weaker' messages often take the form of a change of colour, or of running away. The reptiles behave as though the receipt of these 'stronger' messages makes them less self-confident (lower RHP), whereas the receipt of the 'weaker' messages make them more self-confident. The mutual self-evaluation is an interesting process, since the animals have no direct way of comparing their own messages with those of a rival; but, in whatever form it exists, their brains must contain some analogue of self-esteem, and this entity must have the capacity to be raised or lowered by the signals of conspecifics.

The effect of putting-down signals on reptiles is illustrated by the following account of *Anolis carolinensis* (Greenberg & Crews, 1983, pp. 488-9):

> Body colours of A. *carolinensis*, while rapidly reversible in agonistic situations, remain relatively stable in hierarchical situations. Under these conditions, dominant animals are generally green while subordinates are typically brown. In one series of observations, 30 isolated adult males were scored as to body

color and three behavioral traits associated with behavioral dominance: posture, perching site selection, and activity levels. When pairs matched along these dimensions were placed in neutral habitats, aggressive interactions occurred within 30 minutes and differences between body color appeared or increased. Over a period of several days, the colour of one individual remained relatively stable (green) while the other became darker (more brown). In concert with this, the darker individual was often less active, usually adopted a lower body posture, and invariably selected lower perching sites than the lighter lizard.

When a dominant-subordinate pair of male *A. carolinensis* is broken up, the subordinate animal's color often becomes lighter again. In certain cases, however, color change is not reversible and may reflect pathological processes that attend status change. In such animals, color becomes progressively darker and the animals eventually die.

The exchange of catathetic or putting-down signals has been called agonistic behaviour, or ritual agonistic behaviour. It has been intensively studied by ethologists and has been found in practically all species of terrestrial vertebrate, including human beings (Eibl-Eibesfeldt, 1975). It seems likely, therefore, that it has been continuously present in our ancestors for something in the region of three hundred million years, and in dealing with these signals we are dealing with something which is phylogenetically very old, and deeply rooted in those aspects of our genome that determine behaviour. However, these very primitive signals have become enormously elaborated in human signalling, and they have been overlaid with many other forms of signalling which subserve those forms of affiliative behaviour which have evolved in our lineage since our common ancestor with the reptiles; in particular, parent/child behaviour, pair-bonding and alliance formation. These new forms of signalling have not replaced the old, they have been grafted onto them (MacLean, 1985). If it were not for the evolutionary perspective, it is most unlikely that it would be possible to distinguish these 'agonistic' signals from the general 'noise' of human communication.

Putting-down (catathetic) signals

We emit these signals when two conditions are fulfilled. One is that we are in the agonic mode (Chance, 1988) which means either that we have been attacked by someone or we are not getting our own way (and therefore suffering from frustration or frustrative non-reward). The other condition is that we identify the source of our frustration and make a favourable self/other comparison; only then can we emit a 'stronger' signal. It is an indication of the difficulty of studying these signals in human beings that they do not have a technical name. They are recognised by people in everyday life and are usually described by the term 'putting down'. Thinking that signals of such ancient lineage deserve a proper terminology, I have called them catathetic signals, derived from the Greek words for 'put' and 'down' (Price, 1988). Perhaps this coining of new words is a weakness, derived from my life as a medical practitioner, in which it is well known that all one has to do is to translate the patient's symptoms into Latin and collect a fee. But at least a 'neologism' allows us to give a precise definition, and in the case of catathetic signals this is the effect on the recipient, who feels put down and experiences a fall in self-esteem. All interpersonal signals which lower self-esteem are catathetic signals, and all catathetic signals lower self-esteem. Now, it is a fact about signals that they require two definitions, one for the receiver and one for the sender. In the case of catathetic signals, I have already given the sender's definition above; namely, that they are signals of favourable relative self-evaluation, or 'I am stronger than you' signals. Of course, there may be signals which do not match both sender and receiver, and these are of great interest and importance for mental health, as I hope to show.

Catathetic signals in humans

If we substitute hitting for biting, the non-verbal catathetic signals emitted by humans are not unlike those of monkeys. Threat (particularly the threat stare), attack and chasing are similar in form. Non-verbal vocalisations are more different, taking the form, in man, of wordless shouting, roaring, growling, hissing and spitting. Human catathetic gestures are more varied, and are influenced by culture; e.g., putting out the tongue (which in Tibet is a signal of submission), wagging the finger or raising the clenched fist.

It is with language, of course, that the greatest development of catathetic signals has come. The basic message is 'I am stronger than you'. Animals, having no language, have to express this message in metaphorical or symbolic form, conveying a message such as 'I am like a child to your parent' or 'I am like a female to your male' or 'I am like a small person to your big person'; but human beings can actually say it. However, they seldom do so.

In acute agonic interactions (fights or rows) people normally choose a form of signal which causes mental pain to the recipient, in the way that hitting causes physical pain, so that the commonest forms of catathetic signals are adverse comments on the person or family of the recipient, such as criticism, insults and other forms of verbal abuse. Such fights occurring between the members of a marital pair have been studied by Raush et al. (1974) and the methods used are ritualised, stereotyped and constant over successive rows by the same couple; interestingly, there was no difference in the agonistic signals emitted by the husbands and the wives (although there might have been if the rows had been allowed to escalate to physical violence).

In chronic agonic interactions, the methods are rather different, and take more subtle forms such as teasing, sarcasm, silence, failure to pay attention to the other or to take them seriously, and omission of expected boosting signals.

Some generalisations about catathetic signals

Having said that catathetic signals are defined by the fact that they lower self-esteem in the recipient, it is necessary to qualify that definition. They only lower self-esteem if they are not reciprocated measure for measure. This was plain to Aristotle; in his *Art of Rhetoric* Aristotle points out that insults (catathetic signals) cause pain, and that if the signals are from a high-ranking person the pain leads to depression, but if they are from a low-ranking person, the pain leads to aggression. What he is describing is the self-other evaluation which is characteristic of the agonistic encounter. When a catathetic signal is received, the relationship switches to the agonic mode (if it is not already agonic) and the agonic modalities are recruited, including the evaluation of relative RHP. If the evaluation is unfavourable, an anathetic (submissive signal) is emitted, and there is a corresponding lowering of RHP. If, however, the evaluation is favourable, a catathetic (aggressive) response is made, and whether or not there is an eventual loss of RHP depends on who wins the fight. Unfortunately (or, possibly, fortunately) in human beings an evaluation of unfavourable relative RHP is not the only factor which prevents a catathetic signal being reciprocated; higher level information such as moral attitudes may also be inhibitory; but whatever the cause of the inhibition, it seems likely that the non-reciprocation of a catathetic signal leads to loss of self-esteem, and even the powerful but moral non-retaliator has to 'swallow his pride'.

The concept of catathetic signals draws together a number of signals which may superficially seem to have little in common. Particularly, aggressive acts such as punching are made equivalent to putting-down words, or even to hostile silence. There is a lot of folklore about the relative painfulness of words and blows. There is the schoolboy jingle:

Sticks and stones may break my bones, but words can never hurt me.

This is in direct opposition to the teaching of the Bible:

The blow of a whip raises a welt, but a blow of the tongue crushes bones. (Ecclesiastes 28, 17).

Giacomo Leopardi (1834) sided with the Bible:

Men are ready to suffer anything from others, or from heaven itself, provided that, when it comes to words, they are untouched (Pensieri, Vol. 1, trans. W.F.Weaver).

The potential interchangability of blows and insults was demonstrated in a chimpanzee who was trained to use sign language by Fouts. Eibl-Eibesfeldt (1975) describes the interaction as follows:

Once, while learning the sign *monkey* she was observed exchanging threats with a mature male rhesus monkey. Fouts interfered and showed her monkeys in other cages. Upon being asked Lucy correctly named siamangs and squirrel monkeys with the monkey sign. The rhesus monkey, however, was described in answer to each of Fouts' several questions as *dirty monkey*. Since then she has been observed to use the *dirty* sign as an adjective to describe experimenters who refused to grant her requests. Prior to this time the sign was used to describe soiled items and faeces only. This seems to be the genesis of an insult. p138.

In the above example, Lucy did not actually make the 'dirty' sign to the rhesus monkey, so that we cannot say for certain that the sign was interchangable with the non-verbal threats; but she showed that she could have done by going one stage further in using sign language to disparage her opponent to a third party (the experimenter). She must be the first non-human primate in the whole of history to use this typically human method of displacing aggression.

If she had made such a catathetic signal to another sign-language-speaking chimpanzee, would the latter have had the capacity to receive it as a catathetic signal, to realise that he was being called a 'shit' and to be hurt by it and to suffer loss of RHP? Or would he have received it as a nurturing signal, like 'Excuse me, but I think you've forgotten to wipe your bottom?' My guess would be that, however sophisticated catathetic signals might be, they are still received and processed in the deeper levels of the brain where the blows and head-butts were received by our human\reptile common ancestor, and where they had the effect of lowering RHP and thus causing the sort of depressive state described above in the lizard *A carolinensis*.

Anathetic (boosting) signals. In animals anathetic signals are submissive signals. The message is, 'You are greater than me'. In humans, on the other hand, anathetic signals have lost their connotation of relative strength, and may be expressed in all directions of the social hierarchy, up, down and across (between equals). Paradoxically, anathetic signals between equals often take the form of submissive signals, such as the verbal 'your excellency' in Italian, and the written 'your obedient servant' in English. They have become enormously elaborated with the use of language.

Anathetic signals include paying attention, listening, taking a person seriously, laughing with them, choosing them, helping, obeying, praising, paying, flattering, conferring honours, etc.

Unfortunately, due to the complexity of human communication, anathetic signals are not always a blessing. Gregory Bateson and his successors at the Mental Research Institute in Palo Alto (Bateson, 1972; Sluzki and Beavin, 1965; Watzlawick et al., 1967) distinguished between the command (or definition) element of a communication and the informational content. Thus if I say to you 'Pass the hammer' I am not only giving you information about what I want, but I am defining myself as someone who tells you to pass the hammer, and defining you as the sort of person who gets told to pass the hammer, and our relationship as one in which I tell you to pass the hammer. In this case the definition does not exclude the possibility that we are reciprocal about the hammer, and that you might just as easily tell me to pass the hammer. But many definition statements do in fact define the relationship as asymmetrical. Some forms of praise are only given by superiors to inferiors. Therefore if A thinks he is equal to B, and B gives him this form of asymmetrical praise, A feels boosted by the informational content of the signal, but put down by the definitional component.

In case this should seem an esoteric argument, I should mention that I have recently seen two cases of serious depression due to the catathetic definitional components of what appeared on the face of it to be anathetic signals. In one case, a mother-in-law came and offered to help the patient soon after she had a baby; the offer was boosting but it contained the unspoken message, 'I have a right to come ito your house, unasked, any time I like'; paradoxically, the offer of help made the patient so depressed that she could not look after her own baby and the mother-in-law then moved in and took up residence in the patient's house. In the other case, a manager taking on a new clerk gave her to understand she was of equal rank to the existing clerk, but told the existing clerk that the newcomer was to be her assistant; when the existing clerk gave a very friendly offer to the new clerk to check over her work after she had done it, the new clerk became depressed and went off sick.

Clinical aspects. This mention of patients reminds me that after a too brief and superficial treatment of the theoretical aspects of thymoleptic signals, I should turn to the implications of the matter for treatment. I shall take the typical case of a wife who is depressed because she feels put down by her husband, bearing in mind that in many cases the person putting the patient down is not the husband but the mother, or the father, or the mother-in-law, or someone else; and for every patient who gets clinically depressed by being put down, there must be ten more who suffer without becoming ill, and in whom the experience may lead to divorce or the breakdown of a relationship. We can look at the problem either from the point of view of the person doing the putting-down, or from that of the person being put down, bearing in mind that we are dealing with a system which has emergent properties transcending those of either member on their own, and remembering that it is now considered to be good clinical practice to treat both partners in the marriage when a wife presents with depression (Leff & Vaughn, 1985). But first of all I must deal with a theoretical objection which has been raised in dealing with dyadic, two-person situations.

Problems of a dyadic model

The complexity of human interaction is such that I will limit myself to a dyadic model. I realise that such an approach has been criticised, for example by Ricci and Selvini-Palazzoli (1984), who point out that the two person 'game' can never be truly independent of other players. They rightly say that complexity increases exponentially as the number of the group increases, and they list no less than nineteen family configurations which can be adopted by a threesome of father, mother and child on the single dimension of control. They point out that three is qualitatively different from two, in that, in a threesome, two can gang up together against the third, a proceedure impossible in a dyad. Moreover, with three people, one of them can compare the other two and decide which he will support, also impossible in a dyad. And with four people, two can discuss the relative merits of the other two, impossible in a triad.

In my view, the very complexity of N-person interaction is an argument for basing my analysis on the dyad. This is an unashamed reductionist, 'bottom up' approach which should be considered complementary to the holistic 'top-down' approach. Taking a dyadic approach, the influence of other players is reflected in the error variance. If the error variance is too large, then the dyadic approach is no good. But I think a lot of marital interaction, for instance, can usefully be studied without taking into account the very real influence of children, parents, in-laws and others. Restricting ourselves to dyadic interaction we can ignore the boosting which takes the form of prestige and comes from group approval, and also the putting down which was well summed up by Milton in *Paradise Lost*:

On all sides, from innumerable tongues
A dismal universal hiss, the sound
Of public scorn.

Even restricting ourselves to the dyad, the situation is complex enough.

The sender of catathetic signals

Our object is to understand why the husband puts his wife down, and to try to get him to change this behaviour. I will deal with the causes under the following headings:

1. Authoritarian personality. This kind of person has difficulty in tolerating symmetrical relationships, but feels the need to be one-up (Maslow, 1943; Adorno et al.,

1950). If they cannot be one-up, some authoritarian personalities are happy to take a one-down role, others try to leave the field.

Authoritarian personality may be due to:

a) role model (father dominated mother)
b) rejection of role model (mother dominated father). Typical statement: 'My mother led my father a dog's life and I would go to any lengths to avoid following in his footsteps.'
c) mother allowed son to dominate her during his childhood
d) severe sibling rivalry
e) bullying at school
f) hierarchical experience during adolescence - the boy learns that in order to be happy and/or safe it is not enough to be equal, he must be on top.

2. Culture. Many men in our culture grow up with the idea that a man should be master in his marriage, and that the wife should be obedient. However, many women in our culture grow up with the idea that marriage partners should be equal. When two such marry, they start off with incompatible definitions of the marital relationship, and it is not surprising if they start fighting and putting each other down, each trying to establish his/her own definition. Typical husbands' complaints about depressed wives are 'She is not sufficiently biddable' and 'She does not take correction.'

3. Conflict. Even when a marriage is happy, and a balance of power agreed, serious conflict may drive the partners to get their own way by catathetic means.

4. Ignorance. Some excellent work by McLean and his colleagues in Vancouver, B.C., which deserves to be repeated and extended, involved getting married couples to wear tape recorders for long periods (McLean et al., 1973; McLean, 1976). It was found that a high proportion of the signals exchanged between spouses were catathetic, but of even greater interest, many of the messages which were received as putting down were intended by the sender to be boosting; e.g., 'You would feel much better if you didn't cry all the time.' In general, advice was intended to boost, but usually had the effect of making the recipient feel put down. A recent book by an American sociolinguist (Tannen, 1990) points out that just by using a typically male style of talking, a man may inadvertently put his wife down. For instance, the male response to a problem tends to be a suggestion as to how to solve it, but the female response is one of sympathy and sharing of similar problems. When a wife presents a problem to her husband, she tends to get a suggestion for solution, which not only trivialises her problem in her view, but also puts the husband in the one-up position of the expert dealing with a client who has a problem, and so forces the wife into a one-down position.

5. Anxiety about what the wife would do if she were less depressed. Putting down is a form of coercive control in a relationship, and control is usually exercised to achieve some end. Sometimes the husband has fantasies of the wife's behaviour if he eases up on his control of her. If she became less depressed she might spend more, go out more, demand more sex from him than he could supply or even have an extramarital affair, fill the house with her friends and so destroy his peace, boss him around and restrict his movements, perhaps demanding to know where he is all the time, and so on. In order to prevent these outcomes, he puts her down in subtle (or not so subtle) ways, often quite unconsciously (remember we are dealing with a system three hundred million years old and deeply embedded in the lower parts of the brain).

In order to combat this, the wife can be taught to indicate to the husband that if she had more energy, initiative etc., she would not be likely to do these things he is afraid of, but rather would be more effective in pursuing goals with which he was in sympathy.

The receiver of catathetic signals

Turning to the wife who is being put down, if the misunderstandings mentioned above have been sorted out, and if conflict cannot be resolved by rational negotiation, then it must be recognised that she is in a fight. There are three main options for her. She can fight better and win. She can accept that she has lost and put a good face on it. Or she can get out of the situation. In two of my recent cases a subordinate wife has turned the tables on the husband and become dominant. In both cases the husband became depressed. It is possible, but very difficult, for a depressed subordinate to gain equality with the former tyrant and so to regain self-esteem and normal mood without diminishing the self-esteem of the other. Some examples are given by Rippere and Williams (1985).

Sometimes the depressed subordinate wife is holding on like grim death to something the husband objects to. One such patient was holding on to the idea of having another baby, and refusing to dispose of the baby equipment; another would not give up visiting her mother every week (the mother was even more dominant than the husband, so this poor lady was in 'no man's land' between two powerful and hostile forces). Before the depression can be dealt with, these 'transgressions' must be given up, otherwise the husband just counters any therapeutic gain with an increase in catathesis, maintaining homeostasis of his one-upness over her (Price, in press).

The discontinuing of anathesis (praise)

There has not been space to discuss the use of anathetic signals in therapy. One of the aims of cognitive therapy is to train patients to put themselves in the sort of situation in which they are likely to receive anathetic signals.

Attempts to boost the patient do not always work. This is partly because depressed patients feel undeserving of praise, and, as Benjamin Franklin said, 'Praise to the undeserving is severe satire.' The same view was expressed by Walter Savage Landor: 'An ingenuous mind feels in unmerited praise the bitterest reproof.' Thomas Jefferson put it as follows: 'Unmerited abuse wounds, while unmerited praise has not the power to heal.' And, more recently, Pearl Buck: 'Praise out of season, or tactlessly bestowed, can freeze the heart as much as blame.' In a survey by *She Magazine*, two thirds of the female respondents said they 'would not believe a compliment if they were given one.' This is a subject on which little experimental (or even observational) work has been done, presumably because of ethical difficulties. But it is a matter of great importance for therapy.

Conclusion

Many people find it difficult to maintain symmetrical relationships, especially when they feel strongly about something and cannot get their own way. The usual recourse in these circumstances is some form of fighting, or exchange of putting-down signals, which may result in one member becoming subordinate. This pattern of behaviour is deeply embedded in the human genome, and since many existing vertebrate species are unable to sustain symmetrical relationships, it is quite likely that the human capacity to do so is of relatively recent evolutionary origin. Marriage is an institution which in historical terms has been asymmetrical, but which now is often expected to be symmetrical, and culture is giving mixed messages to prospective marriage partners, often of male dominance to the groom and of symmetry to the bride. Marriage is like a business, with many executive decisions to be taken; and yet what investor would buy shares in a business with two equal managing directors? Were electors prepared to vote for a political party with two equal leaders? Even with an agreed objective of symmetry between the marriage partners, the maintenance of symmetry is not easy, but when the attempt is based on incompatible objectives, it is only the lucky or the very loving who get by.

This is a problem for society. If we want equal marriage, we should try to prepare men for it as well as women, and that means counteracting influences from the East and from Latin-American culture, including films like *The Godfather*.

More needs to be spent on Marriage Guidance. It is a scandal that one has a dozen supermarkets to choose from to buy one's food, but only one, or at the most two, organisations to go to for relationship counselling. In particular, more needs to be done about prophylactic marriage guidance. With the divorce rate running at fifty percent and probably half of those who stay married doing so unhappily, it should become axiomatic that all marriages need guidance, in the way that a car needs servicing. Let us by all means aim at symmetrical marriage, for that is the highest aim, but let us realise that symmetrical marriage is like a high performance engine, and its need for both routine and remedial attention is very great.

We should aim to create social conditions in which people want to have symmetrical relationships, to boost each other up and to avoid putting each other down. Unfortunately, many people now find themselves with attitudes like Thomas Garrison Speidel, into whose mouth, in his novel *The Eighth Day*, Thornton Wilder put the following words:

'The capacity of human beings to wish their neighbours dead is unlimited. Now, mind you! I don't say that everybody wants everybody dead. We all belong to little clubs. We want the members of other clubs dead; we only want the members of our own club *stunted*. A man wants his wife stunted and vice versa; a father wants his son stunted and vice versa'.

There is still a lot of work to be done in the field of mental health promotion.

References

Adorno, T. Frenkel-Brunswik, E. Levinson, D. & Sanford. R, (1950). *The Authoritarian Personality*. New York: Harper.

Bateson, G. (1972). *Steps to an Ecology of Mind*. New York: Ballantine Books.

Carpenter, C.C. (1978). Ritualistic social behaviors in lizards. In N.Greenberg & P.D.MacLean (Eds.), *Behavior and neurology of lizards* . Rockville, Ma: NIMH. (Pp. 253-267).

Chance, M.R.A. (1988). Introduction. In M.R.A.Chance (Ed.), *Social fabrics of the mind* (pp. 1-35). Hove: Lawrence Erlbaum.

Editorial (1988). Self-esteem. *Lancet, 2,* 943-944.

Eibl-Eibesfeldt, I. (1975). *Ethology: The biology of behaviour (2nd edition).* New York: Holt, Reinhart and Winston.

Gilbert, P. (1989). *Human nature and suffering.* Hove: Lawrence Erlbaum.

Greenberg, N., & Crews, D. (1983) Physiological ethology of aggression in amphibians and reptiles. In B.B.Svare (Ed.), *Hormones and aggressive behavior.* New York: Plenum Press, (pp.469-506).

Harris, V.A. (1964). *The life of the rainbow lizard.* London: Hutchinson.

Leff, J.P. & Vaughn, C. (1985). *Expressed emotion in families: its significance for mental illness.* New York: Guilford.

McLean, P.D. (1976). Depression as a specific response to stress. In I.G. Sarason & C.D. Spielberger, (Ed.), *Stress and Anxiety.* New York: John Wiley.

McLean, P.D., Ogston, K., & Grauer, L. (1973). A behavioral approach to the treatment of depression. *Journal of Behavior Therapy and Experimental Psychiatry, 4,* 323-330.

MacLean, P.D. (1985). Evolutionary psychiatry and the triune brain. *Psychological Medicine, 15,* 219-221.

Maslow A. (1937). Dominance feeling, behavior and status. *Psychological Review, 44,* 404-429. Reprinted in: Lowry, R.J., (Ed.), *Dominance, self-esteem, self-actualisation: Germinal papers of A.H.Maslow.* Monterey: Brooks/Cole, (1973), (pp. 49-70).

Maslow, A. (1943) The authoritarian character structure. *Journal of Social Psychology, 18,* 401-411. Reprinted in: Lowry, R.J., (Ed.), *Dominance, self-esteem, self-actualisation: Germinal papers of A.H.Maslow.* Monterey: Brooks/Cole, (1973), (pp. 139-149).

Maynard Smith, J. (1982). *Evolution and the theory of games.* Cambridge: University Press.

Parker, G.A. (1984). Evolutionarily stable strategies. In *Behavioural ecology: An evolutionary approach.* Second Edition. J.R. Krebs & N.B. Davies (Eds.), (pp. 30-61), Oxford: Blackwell.

Price, J.S. (1988) Alternative channels for negotiating asymmetry in social relationships. In M.R.A.Chance (Ed.), *Social fabrics of the mind,* (pp. 157-195). Hove: Lawrence Erlbaum.

Price, J.S. (in press). Homeostasis or change: a systems theory approach to depression. *Journal of Medical Psychology.*

Raush, H.L., Barry, W.A., Hertel, R.K., & Swain, M.A. (1974). *Communication, conflict and marriage.* San Francisco: Jossey-Bass.

Ricci, C. & Selvini-Palazzoli, M. (1984). Interactional complexity and communication. *Family Process, 23,* 169-176.

Rippere, V., & Williams, R. (1985). *Wounded healers.* Chichester: John Wiley.

Robson, P.J. (1988). Self-esteem - a psychiatric view. *Brit J Psychiatry, 153,* 6-15.

Sluzki, C.E. & Beavin, J. (1965). Symmetry and complementarity: an operational definition and a typology of dyads. *Acta psiquiatrica y psicologica de America Latina*, 11, 321-330. Reprinted in Watzlawick, P. & Weakland, J.H. (Eds.) *The Interactional View*. New York: W.W. Norton, 1977. Pp. 71-87.

Tannen, D. (1990). *You just don't understand: Women and men in converstation*. New York: William Morrow. (Also London: Virago Press, 1991).

Watzlawick, P, Beavin, J.H., & Jackson, D.D. (1967) *The pragmatics of human communication: A study of interactional patterns, pathologies and paradoxes*. New York: W.W. Norton.

12 The role of affective education in society

M. Sunderland and P. Clarkson

Abstract

We will present a case for affective education being implemented in Western Society within mainstream schooling, as both a preventative and growthful measure. At present, affective education is largely only available as an integral part of programmes of repair, such as psychotherapy or counselling. We will argue that the implementation of a formalised affective education programme may prevent or alleviate much unnecessary suffering, where the cause has been largely due to chronic ignorance of ways of coping with intense emotion. This in turn may lessen the need for programmes of repair. Because of our heritage in Western society of a pervasive feeling of danger around emotionality, learning about emotions has been left to psychologists as opposed to educators. Consequently, the present education system colludes in a mass deflection from 'self', from pupils' internal reality, their world of feelings and phantasies. On entering adult life therefore, many people functioning 'adequately' are hampered from functioning 'excellently', by their lack of skills and information about how to handle their emotionality in effective and creative as opposed to painful or destructive ways. A case will be presented against the argument that we learn about both emotional hygiene and literacy simply by virtue of living. What is learnt about emotionality from life is often highly questionable or grossly incorrect, a misinforming which in some cases is actually dangerous. The comprehensive understanding of emotion requires the deliberate act of education. We will also explore the inherent implications in this argument for professionals in the world of psychotherapy to render up their monopoly on their substantial body of knowledge about human emotion, and be prepared to make it more palatable for the general public. They have found some excellent answers to ease the business of living, but these now need to be more widely shared. The aims, objectives and content of the affective education programme will be examined. The specifics and limits of the role of the affective educator will be differentiated from that of the counsellor or psychotherapist. The paper will explore the practicalities involved in the implementation of such a programme.

Introduction

This paper offers an adaptation of a model used by Petruska Clarkson in her article on

103

'The scope of counselling in organisations conceptualised around stress.' (1991)

In *this* paper, Table 1 adopts the idea of the four quadrants used by Clarkson, and relates them specifically to the role of affective education in society.

Affective education is concerned with the development of emotional literacy. Its aim is to enable people to deal effectively and creatively with emotional experience in everyday life.

The paper presents the argument that if there are to be emotionally healthier and happier individuals, and a more well balanced society at large, more people must be offered affective education. It is suggested that this should become part of all school curricula and should also

be offered as an adult or further education programme for those people over school age. The paper will explore the view that affective education should be implemented in Western society, as both a preventative and growthful measure, rather than being seen as relevant and necessary only in programmes of repair (e.g. psychotherapy).

Table 1 and definition of the four quadrants

As introduction, Table 1 will be explained. Each of the four quadrants is considered as a different level of functioning. The left half of the diagram delineates the area which focuses on the individual, whilst the right half of the diagram focuses on society, on the culture or group, to which the individual belongs. The lower half of the diagram represents areas of difficulty and potential danger for the individual and the group, and the upper half, areas for growth, development and evolution. Unfortunately, as will be explored fully throughout the paper, 'much of society seems to only concentrate on the lower part of the spectrum and appears to believe the upper part will look after itself.' (Clarkson 1991)

Quadrant One

This quadrant is characterised by individual excellence, and ranges from normal functioning, and overall mental health, to what Maslow termed 'self-actualisation.' A self-actualised person is potent and pro-active in her life. She is able to take full charge of her life, and fulfils her potential because she has accessed or achieved the wherewithal to do so. The paper will present the argument that in order for more people to live their lives at a Quadrant One level of functioning, there would need to be a far more substantial input of affective education in society, and that affective education should be seen as a preventative as opposed to a solely curative measure.

Quadrant Two

This quadrant is characterised by personal difficulties. A person who has fallen below the level of normal functioning will be experiencing the constraints of her own emotional damage, in terms of its interference with the smooth running of her life and the resultant distress. The input necessary here is counselling, psychotherapy or psychiatry.

Quadrant Three

At the upper level of this quadrant, the group and its members function in an aware,

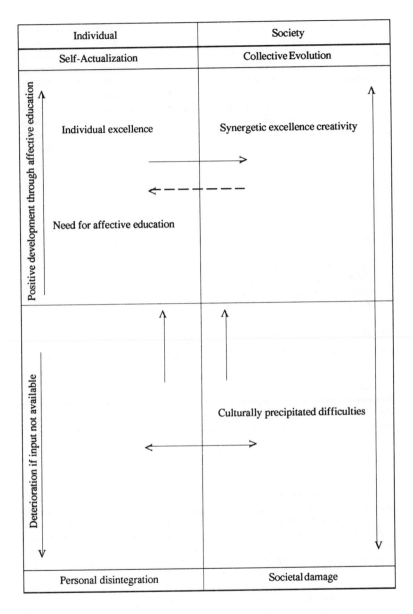

	Individual	Society
	Self-Actualization	Collective Evolution

Positive development through affective education

Individual excellence   Synergetic excellence creativity

Need for affective education

Deterioration if input not available

Culturally precipitated difficulties

| Personal disintegration | Societal damage |

Table 1

actualised and creative manner. Ideally at this level, across Quadrants One and Three, the individual will advance the potential of the group and the group will enhance the potential of the individual. In other words, an increased input of affective education in Quadrant One may well influence the likelihood of more systems functioning effectively at Quadrant Three. In contrast to this, a programme of repair at Quadrant Two is unlikely, on its own, to significantly enhance the level of creativity in the wider society.

Some so called primitive or simple societies have their own inbuilt affective education programmes, where dream sharing, ritual to express and communicate intense feelings, and formalised community support appear to be available on a daily basis. It would, however, be unrealistic to attempt to import this sort of 'emotional hygiene' into Western society on a grand scale. It is, on the other hand, conceivable for people to gain access to a programme of affective education in schools and colleges. Such a programme, which could quite easily be implemented, would inevitably affect the health of the social systems to which individuals belong.

Quadrant Four

This quadrant is characterised by various degrees of culturally precipitated difficulties. A group in breakdown destroys its own potential and resources and could cause widespread damage. In order to repair damage at this level of functioning, and to enable systems and groups to have more possibility of reaching a Quadrant Three level of existence, the appropriate input here would be organisational help, couple or family therapy, and/or intervention from Social Services.

Further consideration of affective education as recommended input at quadrant one level, positively influencing quadrant three

At present, there seems to be a significant lack of input at the level of Quadrant One or Three in any form. There is a great deal of input at Quadrant Two and Four. It seems that many people believe that functioning at One or Three will somehow take care of itself, hence the absence of any formalised input at these levels. Due to this absence, there are arguably far too many people who have fallen below the level of normal functioning *unnecessarily*, and who are, therefore, in need of programmes of repair at the level of Quadrant Two and Four. In many cases, damage could well have been prevented had there been some input of affective education at a Quadrant One level.

In terms of emotional pain, vast sums of money are poured into cure rather than prevention. Because of the acute imbalance of input at the levels of Quadrant One and Three, and the levels of Two and Four, cynics have sometimes referred to social work and psychotherapy as growth industries. Rather than affective education being offered to people at Quadrant One as a preventative measure, it seems to be offered only to people in a damaged state. (Quadrant Two). As a result, positive and healthy functioning at Quadrant Three would seem far less likely, and maladaptive behaviour at Quadrant Four, far more likely. Furthermore, people who are functioning at Quadrant One, but who are functioning 'adequately' at the lower level, as opposed to 'excellently' at the higher level, may not be fulfilling their potential, due again to the lack of any formalised input in this quadrant. They may remain in this unactualised state unnecessarily for the rest of their lives, hampered on a daily basis by the lack of information about how to handle their emotionality in creative as opposed to painful or destructive ways.

The present position of affective education as a quadrant two rather than quadrant one level intervention. The fear around human emotionality per se

Over the past decades, the worlds of psychotherapy and psychoanalysis have been steadily accumulating a substantial body of knowledge on the subject of human emotionality. Unfortunately however, by and large, the only people at present who are privy to this information are those who are functioning at a Quadrant Two level, and who seek a programme of repair. Many people receive affective education as a part of their psychotherapy or counselling, within a setting of problem solving and acute pain. Psychotherapists and their clients often seem, therefore, to have a monopoly on this most important body of knowledge. Moreover, there seems to be a somewhat collusive silence and absence of dialogue between educators working with people at the level of normal functioning and the lower section of Quadrant One, and psychotherapists who intervene at a Quadrant Two level, thus maintaining the status quo. The often unspoken covert communication goes something like this:

Psychotherapists: 'You need many years of training before you work with people's feelings. You can do a lot of damage otherwise.'

Teachers or Educators: 'Yes we know. Emotions are potentially very dangerous, so we will not even mention them. We'll leave it to you.'

By and large schools teach about external reality, the world *outside* the pupil. Children spend much of their time at school, learning about the life of *others*, in *other* countries, in *other* times, of *other* religions.

Sometimes feelings may be discussed in education, but from one remove. It is always for example, someone else's pain and distress-VanGogh's, Beethoven's, or Joan of Arc's, or that of the African slaves, or the Jews in Nazi Germany. The child's *own* pain and distress seem to be made a taboo subject.

It seems therefore that the present education system colludes in a mass deflection from 'the self' , from focusing on the pupil's internal reality, her world of thoughts, feelings, and phantasies. As a result, the child may learn that her emotions are seen as unimportant and valueless. She remains emotionally illiterate.

This overcautious and uninformed attitude to emotional expression is also prevalent in the home. Many parents are uncomfortable talking about feelings. As a result some children bottle up feelings instead of speaking out, or telling mother or father (or anyone else for that matter), that they are scared, angry or sad.

Throughout history, many people have been over cautious about emotional expression. Ever since Plato's time, emotions have, in some arenas, been regarded as dangerous, needing to be contained and suppressed at all times. Such views are often based on irrational fears of people being out of control, falling to pieces, or going mad. Many people have learnt to fear their own emotionality and that of others. This heritage may well be a major factor contributing to the lack of emotional education in a system where most other aspects of human life seem to be given adequate coverage. Should we then be surprised that so few people function at a Quadrant One level, and even fewer reach the level of self-actualisation, and so many need help within a Quadrant Two or Four position?

It is important to emphasise here however, that in spite of such a heritage, many people DO talk about their feelings to each other, over the garden fence, in the pub, with their friends, their neighbours and partners. By offering development in emotional literacy at school or college however, the education system could enable people to talk about, and subsequently act upon their feelings in a more informed way, with more creative, potent and less destructive outcomes.

A case against the argument that we learn about emotional literacy simply by virtue of living

Some people believe that we gain information about our emotional life simply by virtue of living. However, both the quality and truth of what is learnt from everyday life are highly questionable. Many of the beliefs which people acquire abut emotions are simply incorrect. This incorrectness is in some cases actually dangerous, leading to the psychological damage of self or others. Consider the acquisition of certain parental belief systems. Some people may for example have 'learnt' from their parents that it is better to swallow feelings than to express them, or that when you get angry the only thing you can do is to hit someone, or that anger is dangerous, or that it is not O.K. to cry. People also often 'learn' that they have no option but to suffer loneliness, anger, fear, envy, shame, that emotions act upon them, rather than being able to see, through education, that they can actually act upon their emotions.

In gaining knowledge of emotions from everyday living, often unthinkingly and without question, the person has gained no knowledge of 'why' or 'how', or given herself the time and space and the necessary information to consider the validity of her beliefs. *Moreover, experiencing or re-experiencing an emotion does not necessarily lead to learning something new about emotion.*

The comprehensive understanding of emotion requires the act of deliberate education. Awareness of emotions is not enough. One can 'know' that one feels jealous when mother takes in a new lover, or one can 'know' from watching a 'T.V. soap' that jealous people often feel bitter and tend to act aggressively. For education to ensue however, to understand *what* one knows and to then apply such understanding to the business of more effective living, there must be an understanding of 'why' and 'what for' and not just 'how' and 'that' jealousy is expressed.

In summary, in order to understand about emotions, knowing and learning about emotions are necessary and yet not sufficient conditions. Learning isolated unarranged facts about emotions from life is not education, whereas understanding emotional experience, *through an organisation of a body of knowledge which leads to seeing connections,* is.

It seems inconsistent to leave emotional experiencing to chance. The number of people functioning at a Quadrant Two level of mental illness and personal difficulty, is increasing in a world which paradoxically is more efficient than ever before, in catering for physical and material wellbeing.

It is agreed therefore, that emotional literacy through a programme of affective education is an essential step towards self-actualisation. It offers the necessary emotional health and hygiene without which people can find it difficult to reach a higher level of existence. With no education about the creative and effective handling of emotions, many people will tend to enter adult life emotionally illiterate, devoid of skills in how to cope with what they feel, and often chronically ignorant of creative ways in which to express and explore their emotions. Thus for many, this deficit becomes a major obstacle in ever achieving inner peace and self-actualisation.

The aims, objectives and content of the affective education programme offered as input at a quadrant one level

So what would affective education as input in Quadrant One actually look like? How would it and should it differ from a psychotherapeutic input in Quadrant Two? In answer to such questions, the following model is offered for a programme of affective education.

To reiterate, affective education is centrally concerned with the understanding of emotions so that the participant develops conceptual frameworks for considering emotional experience, one that equips her to deal more effectively and creatively with such emotional experience in everyday life.

It is advised that the following areas are covered in any programme of affective education:

1. An understanding and overview of human emotionality per se, and practical information about how to deal effectively with specific feelings and phantasies.
2. An overview of human relationships per se, and practical information about how to deal effectively with relationship issues.
3. An empathetic, compassionate and nonjudgemental space in which to communicate feelings.
4. An exploration of ways to access or reaccess positive affect.
5. Art as information about, and a vehicle for, the communication of emotional experience.

I will now outline some of these areas in more depth.

1. Practical information about how to deal effectively with feelings

Firstly, the affective education programme should include factual information and suggestions about how to deal effectively with all forms of emotional arousal. With an experience of anger, shame, or fear for example, it can be very useful to be informed as to the various common accompanying thought and feeling processes, and what specific actions may be taken to enable someone to feel better. Also, information may be offered as to why someone may feel a certain way.

People should also be offered information about common human phantasies including, for example, reassurance of the normality and commonality of sexual and murderous phantasies. An affective education programme should also offer relevant information to help people understand the origin of such feelings as emptiness, fears of invasion or exclusion, fears of breaking up inside, falling apart or exploding.

109

Clarkson and Gilbert (1990) refer to three main areas in which clients work in psychotherapy; confusion, conflict and deficit. Affective education is very much concerned with confusion and has the potential to offer considerable relief to the person who has been suffering from a high level of emotional confusion, e.g. 'You mean it's normal for me to feel at times like destroying the people I love!' 'You mean it's normal for me to cry even if I am a man!' 'You mean it's O.K. not to stay in every Saturday night and look after my mother.' 'You mean I'm not bad because I was sexually abused!' 'You mean other people feel empty and worthless at times too!'

Through the offering of information about emotions, there may well be an improved level of cognitive response to emotional arousal generally. People may be able to think more clearly and creatively after acknowledging a feeling and so explore more options for action. Such informed thinking may, for example, enable people to avoid wrongly labelling a feeling, to jump to the conclusion that they are angry, when maybe with more thought, they would realise it was actually not anger they are feeling, but hurt.

Thus affective education is concerned with the cognitive experience immediately *succeeding* the emotional arousal:

OBJECT APPRAISAL ▶ EMOTION ▶ THOUGHT ▶ CHOSEN ACTION

Benefit of affective education

Figure 1

In other words, the reactions, responses and thoughts immediately succeeding the experience of an emotion can benefit from greater understanding through the deliberate and conscious act of education. This may result in:
1. a better ability to perceive subtle distinctions between one emotion and another
2. an increased awareness of emotion generally
3. an increased ability to make more appropriate and rational judgements about one's own emotions and those of others
4. an increased ability to avoid inappropriate destructive or self-defeating emotional responses
5. an increased ability to avoid incorrect labelling of feelings
6. more informed thinking leading to more appropriate social behaviour

2. Practical information about the effective handling of relationships issues

There is a whole wealth of information embodied in the world of psychotherapy, about the effective handling of relationship difficulties, ways of fulfilling the potential inherent in relationships, and ways of achieving creative as opposed to destructive contact. Again this is often the input offered at a Quadrant Two or Four level, by the psychotherapist or a social worker. It is usually provided at a time when people are experiencing difficulties or even breakdown in their relationships, instead of it having been offered to them as a preventative measure.

In contrast, it would appear that people who do not seek this sort of help, who function

110

normally at the lower level of Quadrant One, are not usually privy to this sort of information. They are just supposed to know or to see what a full and rich relationship looks like, and how to achieve it; maybe by modelling on parents (who themselves have not had affective education) or through the media or the arts, by watching people's relationships on the television for example. (These are often portrayed as either highly abusive or idealistic i.e. 'I hate you so I'll kill you' or 'I'll fall in love with you for ever and we'll have no relationship difficulties for the rest of our married life'). Unfortunately, however, this sort of information is often people's main source of relationship education.

Through offering more informed knowledge about relationship skills, affective education can significantly reduce the level of unnecessary pain many people suffer both at home and in the wider community.

3. An empathetic, respectful and nonjudgemental space in which to communicate feelings

Many people could survive and recover from the hurt they have suffered if they could communicate about it to someone who will listen, if they could express and have acknowledged difficult and painful feelings intrinsic to human existence. Alice Miller (1984, 1987) in her books about abuse, speculates how, if only there had been a kind Aunt in the family, to whom the abused child could have turned and said 'I hurt'., 'I'm scared' 'I hate,' 'I feel shame,' then the child would not have needed to harden, often resulting in a communication of his feelings to the world in the form of a similar abuse to the one to which he was subjected.

If there is no informed situation such as an affective education programme in which to talk about feelings, there will again need to be much more input at Quadrant Two.

Unexpressed hurt often turns into hate, then at a second stage, if there is nowhere to express this hate, it may well be acted out on other people (ranging from argument to murder) or internalised, (ranging from self criticism to self-mutilation or suicide.)

It is also equally important to have a place in which to communicate about the joys of living. To say 'I love..' 'I delight in..' 'I am in awe of..' and to feel that you are truly heard, understood, rejoiced and celebrated with. This is the role of the affective educator as opposed to again being the sole property of the therapist or analyst.

Life is too hard, confusing painful, mystifying and beautiful, without the added difficulty of having nowhere to talk about these feelings, to someone who will really listen.

4. Ways to access or reaccess positive affect

This leads on to the next point, that many adults lose touch with the positive feelings intrinsic to human existence, such as awe, wonder and delight, joy, serenity which as children they may have been able to feel both fully and often. Again, the education of positive affect is essential, if more people are to achieve self-actualisation.

People need help in developing their ability to be fascinated with or absorbed in the moment; they need help in the awakening of their ability to perceive something fully, to lose themselves in the present, to notice beauty, to play and have fun. They often need reminding of, and/or practice in the experience of human tenderness, both emotional and physical. They need help to be able to see and experience the heavens on earth as well

111

as the hells. Many people are oversensitive to the latter and desensitised to, or unaware of, the former.

People also need help in rediscovering productive imagination, to develop imaginative capacities which can then be transferred to creative living. In this part of affective education, art is an obvious tool. Artists are people who have taken the time and/or have been inspired to capture the emotional moment, the moment of beauty, the moment of calm, the minutiae of the tender exchange. In contrast, many other people often seem too busy, preoccupied, or weighed down by confusing unexpressed emotion, to be internally free to notice and imbibe the truth and richness of such moments. And if they do, they often lose the feeling-memory very quickly and so are unable to use the image to enrich their soul.

5. Art as information about, and a vehicle for, the communication of emotional experience

As stated above, it would seem both relevant and worthwhile for the arts to become an integral part of the affective education programme. The arts offer opportunities for the forming of feeling in ways which can enhance understanding. Expression through art media can often transform vague, confused, or dimly aware feelings into communicable, clear and insightful statements.

Sometimes literal verbal expression cannot accurately encapsulate the specifics, quality, and multi-layered aspects of an emotional experience. Words may be chosen to convey a feeling, which actually distort the meaning of the experience or offer it emphases which are over-generalised or insufficiently impactive. Thus choosing to simply relate feelings verbally can sometimes leave a person feeling misunderstood. Certainly this is often the case with young children whose most fluent language for expressing feelings can be through the use of metaphor or symbol. Expression through art media can also be used to contain or free emotional energy as appropriate, to offer a safe channel for explosive feeling, to rehearse change, and in so doing offer people the opportunities to try out new ways of being and doing. Such rehearsal can help people to feel that they can take a pro-active as opposed to a passive stance in their lives. Moreover the role of creativity in the effective handling of the emotions is crucial, the ability to see a variety of options in response, as opposed to only one.

This suggested multi-faceted education programme has certain implications for the role of the educator. The educator of such a programme must take many decisions about the appropriateness and correct timing for the different sorts of input as outlined above, in terms of the particular needs of the individual or group. The educator must, for example, decide when it is appropriate to offer factual information, when she should simply hear the emotional statement of the student or pupil with compassion and respect, and when she should offer ways of making a metaphorical symbol of the emotional statement, so that the participant can clarify or identify what she feels etc.

The handling of emotional disclosure in affective education

In order to ensure that the educator is clearly offering affective education as opposed to covert psychotherapy, it is advised that the following code of ethics and guidelines are adhered to:

1. The educator offers unconditional acceptance and positive regard. The educator never criticises anything offered by the person with whom she is working. All images and feeling statements are accepted nonjudgmentally and unconditionally, with both compassion and respect. The educator does however, offer corrective information where there is a confusion or distortion of reality.

2. The educator simply listens and acknowledges the feelings expressed. She offers the dignity and respect of both time and space, and does not interrupt or invade either.

3. The educator stays with the emotional statement in the present. Excavation of how the present reflects the past is the job of the psychotherapist and not an appropriate intervention in Quadrant One for the affective educator.

4. The emotional statement (verbal, metaphorical or artistic) *is kept intact.* The educator does not try to excavate or dig deeper. If however the participant spontaneously feels anger or sadness and expresses it, the educator stays with this, and is with the person until she has come to a natural closure point.

5. A clear contract is offered as to what is and what is not being offered e.g. empathy, compassion, respect, information, non-judgmental listening, as opposed to cathartic or regression work, interpretation or analysis of feelings in terms of childhood events.

6. The educator knows when to refer to a psychotherapist. She has learnt how to recognise when a person needs an entirely different sort of input, requiring the expertise of professional therapists or counsellors. She has learnt to recognise and differentiate damage, from the difficult and painful feelings and issues intrinsic to human existence, in the normal person who is functioning healthily.

7. The educator does not interpret at any time. Interpretation from someone without clinical training can be dangerous. It can add to or exacerbate the initial damage and trauma many people have suffered as children when they were told who they were, what they felt and thought, and even why (e.g. 'you are stupid', 'you are just jealous.') The participant should always say what something means to her, never be told or given a suggested meaning.

8. Self-disclosure may sometimes be used in affective education, with the proviso that the statements are truly owned. e.g. 'When I look at your painting I feel sad.' 'I feel moved at your painting. I remember when I lost a friend too.' Such statements may help the defended or emotionally illiterate participant to begin to talk more easily about *her* feelings, through the educator having provided a norm, a permission and sometimes even a vocabulary in which to do so.

9. In affective education a person's defence systems, and her resistance to talking about or experiencing painful emotions should always be respected.

A note on the selection procedure for affective educators

The educator, like the therapist, should be emotionally literate, and have sufficient life experience, maturity, compassion and capacity for empathy, before being accepted into an affective education training. Emotional communication is dangerous in the hands of

113

the insensitive judgemental educator, just as it is in the hands of the insensitive judgemental psychotherapist.

Summary

It has been argued that input at a Quadrant One level will help to obviate the need for input at Quadrant Two and Four. A case has been presented stating that it is likely that without affective education as a preventative measure, more people will suffer damage from personal difficulties, confused feeling states and feelings of impotence, and therefore there will be a much greater need for input at Quadrants Two and Four in the form of psychotherapy and repair.

It has been suggested that more knowledge presently being offered at Quadrant Two should be translated into input at Quadrant One. Psychotherapists must render up their monopoly on information about human emotion to other professionals in education, and also be prepared to make it more easily understood, so that it may be used as palatable input at Quadrant One. The therapists must then actively support the affective educators.

The lack of any formalised affective education at Quadrant One may be preventing or handicapping a great many people from reaching a level of self-actualisation in their lives. The analogy is the person who sits in a sailing boat, spending years trying to find the way to get the sail up and then more years, trying to understand how to sail the boat, and so consequently never experiences the feeling of exuberance of sailing swiftly and easily on the open seas. Meanwhile other people on the bank have the information about how to put up the sail and about how to sail the boat. If they would simply give the person in the boat this information, she could get on with the sailing. Similarly, if people had the information about how to handle their emotions creatively and effectively, many would be able to use such information well and quickly, and be able to get on with running a far smoother life and sail towards self-actualisation, rather than being bogged down with basic difficulties.

Life is so much of a riddle anyway. It seems grossly unfair when a large body of people have found some excellent answers, answers which really help to ease the business of living, that these are not widely shared or made available through education.

Many people long for the day when the world's food is more equally shared amongst all people and famine is a thing of the past. It is arguable that of similar importance is the day when the world's knowledge of emotional literacy is shared out more equally, so that *unnecessary* and *uninformed* emotional struggling, pain and confusion, are a thing of the past.

References

Arnold, M.B. (1970). *Feelings and emotions*. London: Academic Press.

Arnstine, D. (1966). Shaping the emotions. *Journal of Aesthetic Education* 1.

Boas, G. (1968). Art, morals and the teaching of art. *Journal of Aesthetic Education*. 11, (3).

Clarkson, P. (1991). The scope of counselling in organisations conceptualised around stress. *Employee Counselling Today*, 2(4), 3-6.

Clarkson, P. & Gilbert, M. (1990). Transactional Analysis. In W. Dryden (Ed.), *Handbook of Individual Therapy in Britain*. (pp199-225). Milton Keynes: Open University Press.

Lowen, A. (1967). *The betrayal of the body*. New York: Macmillan.

Maslow, A. (1976). *The farther reaches of human nature*. Harmondsworth: Penguin.

Miller, A. (1985). *Thou shalt not be aware*. London: Pluto Press.

Miller, A. (1987). *For your own good*. London: Virago Press.

Neil, A. S. (1945). *Hearts not heads in schools*. London: Herbert Jenkins.

Oaklander, V. (1978). *Windows to our children*. New York: Real People Press.

Wilson, J. (1969). *Education and the concept of mental health*. London: Routledge.

Witkin, R. W. (1974). *The intelligence of feeling*. London: Heinemann.

Yarlott, G. (1972). *Education and children's emotions*. London: Willmer Brothers.

13 Breaking the single continuum

D. Trent

Introduction

I took the position of Director of the Mental Health Promotion Unit approximately eighteen months ago on the first of April, 1991. Almost immediately I realised that I didnt know what I was talking about. The more people asked me what mental health was, the more I realised that I was trying to promote an idea that was ill defined. Like most psychologists when faced with a problem, I went to the literature. I discovered that I was not the only one who was unsure of what mental health was.

Over the past eighteen months I have looked at many books, articles and papers. The one consistent pattern throughout them is that while they advertise an exploration of mental health in their titles, they invariably discuss only mental illness. The net result of this is that while I learned much about mental illness, I was still in the dark about mental health and what it was I was supposed to be promoting. Throughout my searches, however, I spoke to many people and asked them what mental health was and two assumptions continually came out of those discussions. The first was that mental health was the absence of mental illness. The second was that mental health was a state of well-being.

In trying to explain either of these ideas, I was continually shown a single straight line. The demonstration was accompanied by an explanation that argued that mental halth and mental illness were opposite ends of the same continuum. The line had mental health at one end and mental illness at the other end. As one approached the end away from mental illness there was an ever increasing degree of mental health. This was so simple. It gave a structure to the idea that anyone could understand. All one had to do to stay mentally healthy was to move along the continuum away from mental illness and toward mental health. I was even told of ways this could be done. Depending on the profession and interests of the individual speaking, I was told that I could reduce my stress, go into therapy or just become self-actualizing.

While I am sure that it was clear to those who were trying to explain it to me, it was becoming less and less clear to me as they spoke. I was beginning to feel the same as I imagined many had felt when I had tried to explain the same idea in the past. The blank stares that I so often saw on the faces of students slowly began to have new meaning. I began to believe that a new approach was needed.

Problems with a single continuum

There are many problems encountered any time one tries to define or explain an idea, and the idea of mental health is no exception. The first major problem with placing mental health and mental illness along a single continuum is the assumption that mental health is the absence of mental illness. The farther away from mental illness I remain, the healthier I am. The problem with this is that, if this is true, I can only be mentally healthy if I am at the extreme of the continuum. Anywhere else I am tainted with some degree of mental illness. This is not a pleasant thought for many people, and one that many of my non-psychologist friends are unwilling to accept.

There is also the problem of movement on the line. Believing, as many of us do, in Euclidean physics, it is impossible to head in two differing directions along the same line at the same time. Therefore, if I become more ill, I cannot attempt healthy behaviours at the same time. The best I can do is to try to momentarily halt the slide for a long enough period to change direction. Any continuation along the original direction then becomes a failure. Just what I dont need when Im feeling more and more out of control over my life. It would be like trying to put my car into reverse while driving down the highway when I dont even feel as though I can apply the brakes.

Euclidean physics also accounts for the third problem. It is impossible to be in two different places simultaneously. This means that not only can I not be headed in two different directions on the line at the same time, but I also cannot be co-located concurrently on the line. This means that I cannot be healthy and ill at the same time. I have to be either healthy or ill. I am now faced with being either one or the other. The idea that I can be healthy during periods of illness makes the whole issue even more confusing. It also suggests that I am either one or the other and that brings up the fourth problem.

The fourth problem is in trying to define where along the line one crosses from mental health to mental illness. The very fact that it is a single continuum suggests that there is a point at which that crossover is made. When I have asked others, and when I have been asked myself, the answer is always that there is no one point at which this occurs. Not only is there no one specific point, but the range or area of the line often varies between people and can frequently change from time to timefor any given person. At this point we as psychologists and therapists are often baffled at the reticence of people to tell us where they are on the line. As I thought about this, it became clear that no one is going to state where they are on the line until after I have defined where the mental health and mental illness crossover point is for fear they may inadvertently place themselves on the wrong side of the line. Even those who are willing to acknowledge current or past mental illness histories are wary since they often do not wish to place themselves further into a category than they feel is accurate.

Finally, there is the problem of trying to relate mental health and mental illness to other situations such as physical health and illness, social environments, etc. Since these parts make up what a friend of mine often refers to as the rich tapestry of life, it is important to find a way to integrate mental health and mental illness into that overall assumption called the human experience. There needed to be a way to tie both ends of a single continuum into a concept of life with equal degrees of concern or importance without the continuum doubling back on itself.

This concept of a single continuum raises many questions in the minds of both the professionals and the non-professionals. If a continuum is built with zero being total health and one hundred being total illness, at what point does a person stop being healthy? If we assume it to be at 50 - or 37 or 63 for that matter - why is a person at 49 healthy and a person at 51 sick? Worse yet, if I am at 10 and then go to 12, am I still healthy or am I becoming sicker?

At what point on the continuum do we hospitalise? Is one person at 71 as sick as another at 71? How do we quantify the illness to come up with such a number? If an illness returns as many mood disorders tend to do, has it ever been absent or only dormant? If the latter is the case then the publics worst fear of once mentally ill always mentally ill is going to be realised. Since, as we have noted, by definition one cannot be at two points on a continuum at the same time, not only will I always be ill, but by definition I will never be healthy.

If we accept that an illness is absent, then why continue medication? How do we explain repetitive illnesses? Does the reestablishment of an illness mean that I have done something wrong to drive myself toward the illness end of the continuum or is the entire process out of my control? Either of these assumptions can be devastating to the individual. The first can lead to feelings of guilt for having done something Wrong. The second leaves me at the mercy of Fate which at best will lessen the likelihood of my trying to alter the situation since I have no control over it.

If we are going to look at the idea of mental health, we need to have a starting point, and as Maria said in *The Sound of Music*, Lets start at the very beginning, a very good place to start. What is mental health? Historically, since mental health has always been seen as the absence of mental illness, it has always been subsumed into the domain of the psychiatrist, psychologist, psychiatric nurse, occupational therapist, and many others. The result is that we have tended to professionalise mental health to the point where some believe that if you dont have a professional you cant be mentally healthy.

I'm reminded of the cartoon in *Punch* that showed a rather dejected man leaving a psychiatrist's office. The psychiatrist is leaning out of the door after him and saying, 'Now don't try to cheer yourself up Mr. Jones.' These things are best left to us professionals. The professionalisation of mental health has caused some problems and the tendency to define it as the absence of illness is not the least of them.

Threshold confidentiality

American psychiatrists and psychologists are the greatest in the world. In 1980, the American Psychiatric Association published the *Diagnostic and Statistical Manual of Mental Disorders, 3rd Edition*. In the attempt to more accurately describe what was

119

happening they did away with the category of neurosis. It did not describe the process since there was no nerve or neuron that was definitively responsible.

Think of it; there are no neurotics in America. It sounds a bit like the cat song in Speilbergs *An American Tail* doesnt it? With one fell swoop of the pen, American psychiatry completely cured all neurotics by simply changing what they were called. Dont let this get you down, however. We have done them one better. About five to ten years ago we did away with all mental illness in Britain! Almost overnight we changed from treating mental illness to mental heath.

The problem is that we are still treating it in the same way we did when it was mental illness. People know that we have not changed what we are doing or to whom we are doing it. The only thing that we have accomplished is the tarring of a new term with the same old brush. By making mental health a euphemism for mental illness we now have people who will not discuss either idea in public. We have effectively put mental heath into the closet with mental illness rather than taking mental illness out.

This brings up the concept of threshold confidentiality. It works like this: if I go to my GP, I sometimes go because I am ill. Perhaps I have something simple like the flu or maybe something more serious. I also may be going because I am healthy. I may want my blood pressure checked or I may want my cholesterol count checked. It is safe for me to do this because my GP provides services for both physical health as well as physical illness.

Since most Mental Health facilities only provide services for mental illness, however, when I step across the threshold I have broken confidentiality in that anyone who sees me enter knows I am going for mental illness. Even if this is not true, the perception holds, based on the assumption that mental health facilities only treat mental illness.

The medical model

To understand why mental illness has historically been the focus we must look briefly at the medical model of health care. The basis of the medical treatment is the diagnosis. Now much has been written about the pros and cons of diagnosing. The problem with it resides not in what it is designed to do, but in how it is used.

A diagnostic system is designed to provide a shorthand method for passing a great deal of information in a short space and time. It should provide the practitioner with insight into four basic areas. The first is the history of the condition. Whichever theoretical orientation one holds, a diagnosis should suggest the history based on that theoretical orientation. For example, if one is depressed, a clinician steeped in Freudian theory may argue that it is anger turned inward and understand the history of how that takes place. At the same time, a behaviourist may understand that it is based on increasingly more depressed-like behaviours that have been reinforced over time. A cognitivst may understand that this condition comes from a faulty belief structure and repetitive self-deprecatory statements made by the individual. And so it goes for any theoretical orientation. For each, however, there is a sense of history understood in the condition of the patient.

The second thing that a diagnosis should give insight into is the syndrome which one may expect to see. As a clinician I can expect to see different groups of symptoms or syndromes when looking at a depressed person than I might if I am looking at a person who is manic. If I dont see what I would expect, then it is incumbent upon me to look for a new diagnosis rather than search for some symptom that I can use to qualify the original diagnosis.

Any good diagnostic system should give the clinician an idea of what treatment should be given. A clinician hopefully will not treat a person who is having an anxiety attack the same as a person who is demented or as one who has a severe personality disorder. Even in similar conditions such as depression and loneliness a difference in treatment protocol is not only necessary, but can result in a far worse outcome for the patient if not recognised and treated differently.

Finally, a diagnostic system should give some idea of the prognosis. If a clinician expects to see results of treatment of a personality disorder as quickly as those seen in the treatment of a grief reaction, a degree of disappointment is likely to occur. Likewise, if a major change of behaviour in the treatment of a case of dementia is expected, again the clinician may be disappointed.

The problem is that a differential diagnostic system such as *DSM-III-R* is very good at describing what is currently there to be seen. It is designed for the classification of disorders, not for the classification of the absence of disorders. As such, it distinctly does not work for a single continuum. At best, it is only applicable to one end of the continuum. This leaves nothing to describe the other end and the point at which it begins to describe is still very woolly at best.

Another possibility

If, however, we begin to look at the ideas of mental health and mental illness as separate ideas, then we can resolve some problems we have faced with the single continuum. To begin with, if mental health and mental illness are two separate ideas, they can be placed on two separate contina. While they undoubtedly are very closely linked, by looking at them as separate contina we have several advantages.

The first is a spin-off in that it affects mental illness more than mental health. It begins with the acknowledgement that since there are two continua we all not only have a mental health continuum, but we all also have a mental illness continuum. By having mental illness as a continuum from zero as no mental illness and one hundred as total mental illness, we now can see that, since the conditions of all or nothing are seldom met, we must acknowledge that we are all somewhere along the continuum of mental illness. The idea that abnormal behaviour is nothing more than an extension of normal behaviour makes the idea of mental illness far more understandable.

It also tends to normalise the mentally ill. We all worry. We also all daydream from time to time. It is only when I lose the ability to control and put limits on those processes that I become either neurotic or psychotic. It is well established within the professions that we will not see anything in an abnormal population that wont be see in a normal one. The only difference is in the degree or appropriateness of the behaviour at the time it is exhibited. The demystification of mental illness and the inherent reduction in fear as the unknown becomes understandable, then, becomes the first advantage.

The second advantage is that it continues to allow the medical model to be used and to be effective since it no longer needs to be applied against something it is not designed for. Looking back at the four areas of information given by a diagnosis, it becomes quickly clear that these have no real bearing on health. How does the history of health help in the treatment of health? Worse yet, why would one want to treat heath in the first place? How is health treated? Since the treatment of illness is the removal of that illness, is the treatment of health the removal of health? And what of the symptoms of health? Or the prognosis of heath?

The problem with the medical model is that it is an illness model. By separating mental illness from mental health, the medical model can be used where it is appropriate, ie illness, while not being used where it is not appropriate, ie health.

Thirdly, the focus on illness is an attempt to get rid of what is, while the focus on health is to expand or amplify what is. We dont treat what we dont have. I would never take penicillin to get rid of an infection I dont have. Health on the other hand is the prevention of illness. We take a polio vaccine not to cure our health but to remain healthy. As such, illness can be seen to be reactive while health is pro-active.

Finally, the shift between health and illness creates a shift between the loci of control over the concept. When I become ill, I turn to a doctor to get me well. When I want to be healthy, I begin to do things on my own. To go back to our physical metaphor, physical health and illness are not the same thing. If I decide to become a couch potato and lie on my couch eating crisps, drinking beer and smoking heavily, I may not be ill, but few would describe me as being very healthy. If I want to be physically healthy I may choose to lose some weight, stop smoking, get more exercise or change my diet. As with physical health, a shift in the focus from a mental illness continuum toward a mental health continuum as a discrete concept may have the same effect.

I mentioned earlier that the two concepts of health and illness are separate but closely linked. An analogy might be that of a cable in which the strands are separate but discrete. Each is a part of the whole and if one strand is pulled all other strands will come along with it. If the strands are taken out of the cable, the cable ceases to exist. Likewise, our health will affect our illness continuum as our state of illness will affect our health continuum.

Mental health

So what kinds of things does one need to focus on to increase one's mental health line? To remain with the physical analogy, I believe there are five senses which are inherent to the human condition. While the decrease or loss of any will not incapacitate the individual, it will create limitations on the individual and if too many deficits occur, the individual will become unable to function normally.

The first is a sense of trust. If I were to have to choose another word for trust it undoubtedly would be predictability. To trust is to be able to predict. I can trust my psychologist or priest or doctor because I can predict that they will not use the information I give them against me. I trust my partner because I know that I can predict how my actions and thoughts will be received. People need to be able to trust or predict their environment and others within it. Close your eyes a moment and imagine this morning as you were awakening. Picture yourself bringing your leg out from under the covers and placing it on the floor. Now imagine the terror you might experience if you could not predict that the floor would hold you.

One hallmark of abused children is that they never play. They spend their time testing the limits placed on their lives. They are not able to predict because the rules and limits are always in a state of flux. As an abused child I dont know when my parent may accept my behaviour or become highly enraged by it. I have lost the ability to predict and therefore have continually to test to find where the limits are at any given time.

This does not mean that situations cannot change. Giovanni Fagiuoli lived from 1660 to 1742 and was the court clown to Archduke Cosimo III. It has been reported that he once brought Cosimo a list of names. When asked by Cosimo what the list was, Giovanni replied that it was a list of all the fools in the Dukedom. Why, asked Cosimo, is my name on the list? Giovanni explained that it was because he had ordered goods from a man and had paid for them in advance. But what if he delivers as he has promised?, asked Cosimo. Then, replied Giovanni, I will remove your name and add his.

The second sense we need is a sense of challenge. In the 1920s George Mallory, when asked why he wanted to climb Mt. Everest, gave the classic response, Because its there. Challenge gives us the spice in our lives. It provides the interest in life without which boredom would prevail. Think of the challenges that you regularly build into your life. We know that repetitive work such as that often seen on assembly lines leads to boredom, loss of concentration, absenteeism and increased accidents due to inattentiveness. We often build challenge into our lives through sport, hobbies and leisure activities. Can you imagine a football game without a sense of challenge? Why watch it?

Again this does not mean that a person wont get bored. One of the most important men in the field of psychology was Charles Darwin. It has been reported that Darwin was fond of going to many public and scientific talks. As you are all aware, some scientific talks can be less than awe inspiring. While Darwin found many of the drier talks to be quite inspiring his wife did not. After taking her to yet another such talk, he turned to her in the middle and said, This must be very boring for you. No more, she replied, than all of the others.

The third sense is the sense of competence. Competence gives us a sense of power and control over our lives. A sense of power is imperative. The reason we study and become proficient in our profession is to be able to affect our environment. Why does a doctor practice medicine? Why does a salesperson sell? We need a sense of power and control. Mental Hospitals are full of people who feel they have no power or control over their lives. Without a sense of power and control we are reduced to total submission.

A psychologist by the name of Seligman did studies with mice in which he removed all their ability to exercise power and control over their environment. The result was what he termed learned helplessness. If I have no control over my life or if I feel I have no sense of power in life, I will shy away from it.

A sense of accomplishment is the fourth requirement for mental health. Accomplishment gives us our self-esteem and identity. This has been shown throughout all of history. Look at the classic literature. Recall the story of Snow White. The villain of the story was the wicked step-mother. She was given the most important line in the entire story. It was when she looked at the mirror and said, Mirror, mirror on the wall, whos the fairest one of all?

We all get our own idea of ourselves from the reflection we get from our environment and the people in it. If I do things well I may tell myself how good I am. On the other hand, if I do things poorly I may tell myself that I should never have tried, or that I was dumb or stupid for trying. If I tell myself often enough, I will begin to believe it.

We tend to dote on our accomplishments. If asked, I am far more likely to tell others that I am something I do well rather than something I do poorly. If I enrapture you with this talk, I may describe myself as a lecturer. I probably wouldnt if you all were to fall asleep while I was talking.

I will make these determinations separately, based on the activity. I may see myself as a good prent but a poor mechanic. Perhaps Ill see myself as a good driver but a poor cook. As many things as I do, so will I have an image of myself based on my ability to accomplish the goal of the activity.

The fifth sense is a sense of humour. Humour allows us to see the absurdity in life. Like it or not, people are funny, We do funny things all of the time. If we cannot laugh at ourselves and with each other, we run the risk of taking both ourselves and life far too seriously. I have heard, and I tend to believe that it is a physical impossibility to get an ulcer while laughing. Humour puts perspective in our lives.

Mrs. Patrick Campbell was once asked why women have no sense of humour. So we will love our men rather than laugh at them, was her reply. Life is not fair, and with unfairness comes inequity and irrationality. We must be able to take the knocks we are given without letting them crush us. Humour is the grain of salt with which we need to take life. That is not to say that we will not experience periods of great pain in our lives. But to laugh in the face of adversity is to make it far less adverse.

Harry Truman was the President of the United States at the end of World War II. He was very fond of saying, Horse manure whenever he disagreed with something. One day a Washington hostess came up to Bess and said, Bess, you have to get Harry to stop using the term manure. Bess is supposed to have replied, It has taken me twenty-one years to get him to use it!

Many people believe that there is a sixth sense, and I would not state categorically that there isnt. If there is a mental health sixth sense, however, I believe that it must be a sense of balance. It is achieving a balance between the other five senses. We all need water to live. Water is a good thing. Without it we would all die. If you were thrown into the middle of the North Sea, however, you again may die. That would be too much of a good thing. If you begin to lack one of the five senses for a specific reason, increasing another may be effective in maintaining balance, rather like increasing your exercise after eating a heavy meal.

A contagious state

Finally, I would like to say that mental illness is not contagious. I have never known dementia to spread solely because of proximity. Nor have I ever known paranoia to be caught solely by being near one who is experiencing it. If mental illness were contagious, our hospital staff would be in far greater risk than they are.

Mental health, on the other hand, is highly contagious. Think of the last time you were at a party and there were two people there, one of whom was unhappy and one of whom was full of life and enjoyment. Which person attracted the greater group? Which one did you gravitate toward? Think of the times you have awakened in the morning and thought, I dont want to go to work, not today. After you dragged yourself in and became involved in a project how many of you have looked up to find that you have spent the entire day and possibly even overtime without realizing it?

Mental health is contagious. It is one of the few contagious conditions that is better spread than contained. We must stop treating mental health and go back to treating mental illness. I remember once seeing a sweatshirt on an individual that said, Help stamp out mental health. Do we really want to? Or is it possible that by promoting mental health, we can help stamp out intolerance to mental illness. We at the Mental Health Promotion Unit believethat it is not only possible but that it is the way to go forward. Become a carrier. Become contagious. Mental health and mental illness are not the same. Dont treat mental health, spread it.

14 Community mental health promotion: A paradigm approach

K. Tudor

Abstract

Based on his research into community mental health promotion, funded by the Health Education Authority, the author presents a summary of his conceptual and developmental work on mental health promotion. Locating his work within the transdisciplinary tradition of sociopsychology and drawing on recent work on paradigm analysis, the author surveys and locates different and differing approaches to health and health promotion, mental health and mental health promotion, drawing out their implications for practice. He presents a 'paradigm map' as a conceptual and practical tool with and within which policy makers, managers and practitioners in the field of mental health can understand, respond to and use such different approaches. Using this paradigm approach, mental health promotion is seen to operate and be described on three distinct, although interrelated, levels of: content, process and meta-theory or theory about theories. On a meta-theoretical level paradigm analysis provides a framework for locating different and competing theories and 'models'; on a process level the paradigm map provides a framework with which to understand and bring about 'paradigm shifts'; whilst in terms of content the paradigm map is shown to be a practical tool for intervening with individuals, groups and in communities to enable people to achieve personal movement - from diagnosed patient to mental activist - from psyche to society. The author highlights in these terms a number of current debates within the field of mental health, including the role of Community Mental Health Centres and the development of the User movement. He also distinguishes mental health promotion from the concept and practice of mental illness prevention. He concludes that the three levels of mental health promotion identified each have highly practical implications for the implementation of national and local policy and practice in mental health.

Introduction

The government's recent green paper *The Health of the Nation* (Department of Health, 1991 and the Labour Party's strategic document *The Better Way to a Healthy Britain* (The Labour Party, 1991), have put health promotion on the political agenda. Unfortunately, neither document or party has any coherent notion of mental health, let alone mental health promotion: the government equates mental health with mental disorder and, in defining both physical and mental health objectives and targets, confuses promotion with prevention; the Labour Party, capitalising on the privilege of opposition, makes more political points on health promotion. Nevertheless their 'action on mental health' amounts to a limited three-point plan comprising: the reduction of the use of tranquillisers; the appointment of a Minister of State for Community Care; and the implementation of remaining sections of the Disabled Persons (Implementation and Consolidation) Act 1986, concerning the right to assessment and advocacy.

Such conflation, confusion and limitation of terms, ideas and ideologies is widespread in the new and emerging field of mental health promotion. My research in this field, funded by the Health Education Authority (HEA) and conducted through King's College, London, aims to clarify a number of issues and debates in the field as well as proposing a framework within which to locate different and competing theories and practices. Here I will briefly introduce the theoretical - paradigm - framework, describe its use on both theoretical and practical levels, through the clarification of four important debates - on prevention vs. promotion, the role of Community Mental Health Centres (CMHCs) in mental health promotion, the User movement, and the politics of community mental health promotion.

Theoretical resources

In recent years sectors of social theory have moved with centrifugal force away from the functionalism and systems theory that once ruled the discipline, fragmenting the resources of theory and offering a bewildering array of possible approaches to understanding and intervention. If the initial dogma of systems analysis was set at such a high level of abstraction that it could fit in, somehow, all 'lower level' activities, thereby conserving its legitimate authority, the situation now is more like a consumer orientated 'market' in that there is a piece of social theory to suit all different tastes and purposes. Practitioners, not being able to afford the luxury of knowledge for its own sake and seeking a useful theory, are confused by the variety of positions taken up, and unable to account for the tenacity with which they are defended. Understandably the response is sometimes a rejection of all theory and resort to experience and common sense (Holland, in press).

The situation in psychological theory is very similar: the initial dogmas have been attacked (though not disposed of by any means) and various alternative approaches have been proposed. For understandable reasons, related to the division of labour in intellectual work, there has been little in the way of substantial integration of sociology and psychology, and this means that the practitioner is now faced with a dichotomy of personal (individualist) and structural (collectivist) approaches, each containing a diversity of theoretical positions.

This opening out of theoretical possibilities is exciting and welcome but it carries with it a question: are there deep structures and commonalities both within and across disciplines? If so then this may be a matter of importance for theory, as well as providing for practitioners an overview of theoretical resources and therefore better opportunity for informed choice between alternatives, (as opposed to ill-informed eclecticism). By informed choice is meant not some objective scale of merit but rather, choice made with full awareness of the explicit and implicit consequences of a particular theoretical stance.

Paradigms

Holland and Tudor (1991) have summarised the history and development - through research, teaching, community action and psychodynamic psychotherapy - in drawing together the 'disciplines' of sociology and psychology using Burrell and Morgan's (1979) four paradigms.

Burrell and Morgan (1979) stated that 'all approaches to the study of society are located in a frame of reference of one kind or another' (p.10). They suggested that ' assumptions about the nature of science can be thought of in terms of what we might call the subjective--objective dimension, and assumptions about the nature of society in terms of a regulation--radical change dimension' (p.21). Taking these two dimensions together as axes Burrell and Morgan defined four distinct sociological paradigms, or sets of ideas.

The sociology of radical change

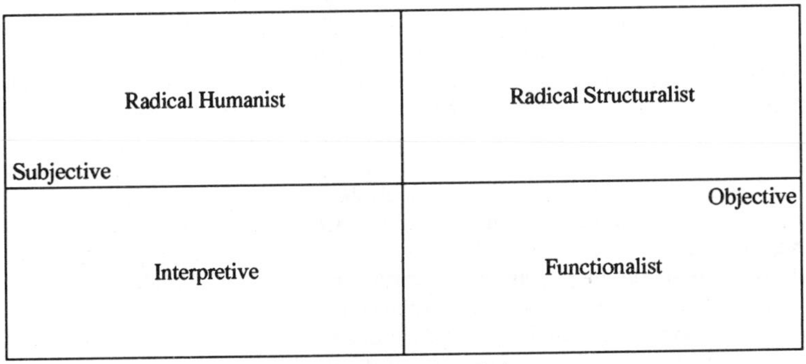

Radical Humanist	Radical Structuralist
Subjective	
	Objective
Interpretive	Functionalist

The sociology of regulation

Four paradigms for the analysis of social theory (Burrell and Morgan, 1979, p.22)

Figure 1

I have used the paradigm framework to survey the literature and ongoing activities in and around mental health promotion (Tudor, 1991). Four current and salient debates were also addressed in relation to the paradigms in which they - as debates - are located: prevention and promotion; the development of Community Mental Health Centres; the User movement; and the politics of community mental health promotion. In the following section these debates are briefly summarised and located as representative of the respective paradigms.

129

From theory to practice

Functionalist approaches

Prevention When appraising a particular contribution it is generally found that it can be located within one paradigm, although elements of the approach may suggest another location. It is necessary to look carefully at the project or text for statements claiming to be self-evident or consensual: these will usually determine the basic location, even though other incidental borrowings are in evidence. In this way the seminal work in community mental health of Klein (1968) was classified as functionalist because of the following passage on change in the community:

> certainly in the mental health approach there is an implicit value attached to the reduction of conflict and the management of conflict through rational means. Emotional well-being could hardly be expected to thrive in a conflict-laden social environment (Klein, 1968, p.145).

I interpreted this passage as follows:

> This is classic functionalism: there is implied one 'right' way, 'the mental health approach', an objective approach to knowledge; a statement about conflict *management* which implies a view about social regulation: and both supported by an unsubstantiated statement about emotional well-being (Tudor, 1991).

Using this analysis other examples of this approach identified include: the *Northampton Mental Health Project* (Gatherer, 1963); the *Greater Easterhouse Mental Health Project* (Kennedy, 1988); and the West Lambeth Health Authority Mental Health Unit Mental Health Education Group's (1989) booklet on *Mental Health problems*.

After mapping several contributions to the prevention approach it was concluded that these tended to cluster within a limited area: firstly because they derive from the natural sciences and, in particular, medicine; secondly they were located in the institutions of public health/welfare, having a functionalist approach, at a particular historical time and place in the development of the welfare state, its theories and practices, i.e. post war in the USA; and thirdly, they imply a set of assumptions essentially about ideals and *norms* of mental health. As Fernando said of health promotion,

> illness-prevention may be involved but that is not the point of it. Thinking and planning in terms of 'illness' merely confuses and distorts the issue; and in the name of health promotion you end up with an illness-relief service (Fernando, 1990, p.14).

Interpretive approaches Interpretive approaches include not only the wide range of studies in symbolic interactionism which deal with the sick role, the insanity of place, etc., but all those areas of counselling and psychotherapy which attend to the explicit and implicit meanings of human interaction and build a humanistic practice based on untangling these meanings. Micro-sociology encounters issues of health and so does psychotherapy. Social models of mental illness can be seen in terms of mental disorders defined either as problems of socialisation (Martindale, 1961); as problems of social control (Scheff, 1966); or as due to what Siegler and Osmond (1976) referred to as the conspiratorial model of mental illness in which the mad person is a victim of labelling (Szasz, 1961). There is here a complex interface between psychiatry, theories of the

130

individual and the law, nowhere more acute than in local policing policy in relation to section 136 of the Mental Health Act 1983 (Rogers & Faulkner, 1987) under which a police constable has the power to remove to a place of safety a person 'who *appears to him* to be suffering from a mental disorder' (Mental Health Act 1983 S.136(1)) (my emphasis).

The principal example of community mental health promotion within this paradigm is the work of the first Mental Health Promotion Officer in the country, based in Salford. The post (and the Officer) takes a community perspective, arguing that 'at the heart of health promotion is the empowerment of communities... community development encompasses a commitment to a holistic approach to health which recognises the central importance of social supports and social networks' (Adams & Holroyd, 1989). The Officer is struggling to influence policy and shift others to a greater awareness of the meaning of their work in relation to mental health. Since my initial research the Officer concerned has elaborated the emphasis of his work and argued that the assumptions underlying the mental health promotion work in Salford lies within more radical paradigms (Tudor & Holroyd, 1991).

Community Mental Health Centres With reference to Community Mental Health Centres (CMHCs) - nominally at least a focus for mental health in the community - Sayce and Field (in press) in their national survey of CHMCs commented that 'substantial community development activity, such as developing self-help or engaging with community action groups, was rare, as was accountability to local people through management groups or other structures'. Elsewhere (Tudor, 1990/1991) I have argued that CHMCs have their origins in policy which, as Holland, S. (1988) has observed, 'has elements of both progressive reform and reactionary opportunism' (p.127). The meaning that CMHCs carry into the community and promote (if at all) is essentially a medical model of illness, community and individuals. Something far more radical is required if significant change in the community's perception and understanding of mental illness and health, let alone community care, is to be achieved.

Radical humanist approaches There is a wide range of alternative approaches which might seem to answer, in various ways, condemnation of the medical profession and which finds its most powerful expression in the work of Illich (Illich, 1975).

> Alternative/complementary medicines, whilst covering a wide spectrum of body and mind as well as more spiritual therapies, nevertheless, are essentially both radical and humanist by virtue of: their challenge to dualism - the notion in Western thought of a 'split' between mind and body; their belief in the organism's capacity for healing; their focus on the patient/clients' subjective experience of the 'illness'; and their positive view of the 'healing crisis' and the patient/clients' ability to respond to it (Tudor, 1991).

The emphasis on change is reinforced by the World Health Organisation:

> At a general level, health promotion has come to represent a unifying concept for those who recognise the need for *change* in the ways *and* conditions of living, in order to promote health (WHO, 1986, p.37).

A practical example from this perspective is Davidson's (1987) ten-week health education programme designed to increase participants' awareness of the psychological and physical aspects of health, enabling them to choose their own individual health pattern. The Mid-Staffordshire Mental Health Promotion Team stands as an example of health promotion based on radical humanism:

> The promotion of mental health is not solely for the purpose of disease prevention. It is to improve the quality of life for the whole population at all stages during their life; particularly at times of transition which are times of high risk (Murray, 1989, p.2).

This work helps to define the relation between content and process, so essential to any attempt to map movement between paradigms. If the Team, operating within the Health Authority, receives a series of specific requests for, say, stress training for nurses, it considers the deeper reasons for their emergence. Then perhaps by linking nurses to other groups they facilitate understanding and change. If they intervene it may be at some appropriate institutional or organisational level.

Users There are many examples of individual therapies which emphasise and celebrate change, but for brevity I select some points within the user movement and advocacy, as typical of radical humanist approaches. The many terms used to describe or label people - patient, client, sufferer, victim, survivor, user, recipient, consumer, customer, member, resident, trainee - all carry particular implications. And there are different types of advocacy which might be mobilised in support of those whose case is to be argued: self-advocacy and citizen advocacy; and professional advocacy and patients' advocacy (Sang, 1989). The former pair of terms implies a defensive, grass-roots quality, the latter pair a professional or 'top-down' approach. Rose and Black (1975) have developed a practice theory which 'validates the person, reconnects her/him to the *objective context* in which she/he lives, legitimates the impact of psychiatric history or self-expression, and engages the person in a process of transformation' (p.40).

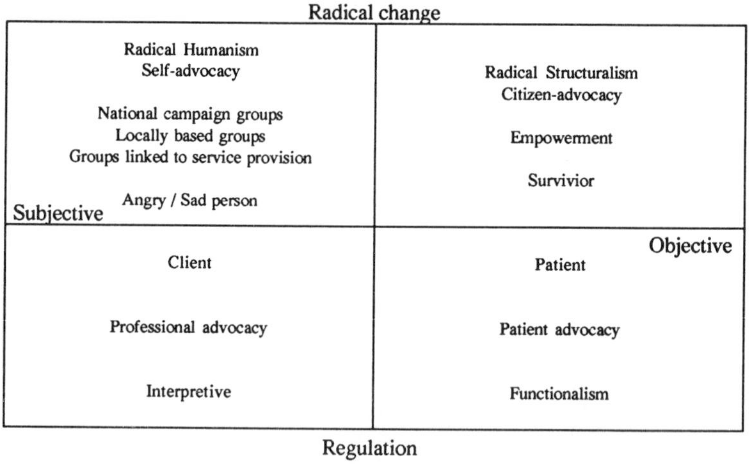

Radical change

Radical Humanism Self-advocacy National campaign groups Locally based groups Groups linked to service provision Angry / Sad person	Radical Structuralism Citizen-advocacy Empowerment Survivior
Client Professional advocacy Interpretive	Patient Patient advocacy Functionalism

Subjective ... Objective

Regulation

Four paradigms for the analysis of social theory, locating different forms of advocacy and terms (with reference to Burrell and Morgan, 1979, p.22 and Tudor, 1991).

Figure 3

Radical structuralist approaches

The politics of community mental health promotion The view that the relation between (the individual) psyche and society is a central problem in addressing mental health promotion is represented by attempts by theorists such as Reich (1970), Marcuse (1968, 1969) and Mitchell (1975) to develop a theory of the politically contextualised person. More recently, Leonard (1984) has attempted to build such a theory using the principal concepts of historical materialism. As Fernando (1990) has said, 'health promotion is not an academic exercise - it is political action' (p.14). (WHO, 1986) has recognised that 'health promotion programmes may be inappropriately directed at individuals at the expense of tackling economic and social problems' (p.75).

If the radical humanist paradigm generates anti-psychiatry, the radical structuralist paradigm is exemplified in the 'non-psychiatry' of the Italian psychiatrist and reformer, Franco Basaglia (1924-1980) and the work of the reform movement Psichiatria Democratica (PD).

> The importance and significance of Basaglia's theoretical contribution lay in linking: the social construction of madness and the social control of medicine (interpretive), and the notion of the tendency to chronicity (radical humanist), together with a praxis of de-institutionalisation (radical structuralist) (Tudor, 1991).

The marxian roots of Basaglia's work are clear:

> medicine, entrusted with the treatment of everything that has been set within the sphere of illness, conceals the fundamental contradiction between the separation of the productive and the unproductive which then becomes opposition between 'sane' and 'sick' (Basaglia, 1980, p.18).

Elsewhere (Tudor, 1988, 1990/91) I have reviewed the theory and practice of the Italian psychiatric reform movement, with its grounding in legislation, and shown that Law 180/1978 was the culmination of a process of deinstitutionalisation and dehospitalisation. Its three principles were:

> Concern not for categories of disease but with the forms of and reasons for treatment.

> An emphasis on, where necessary, compulsory 'treatment' rather than hospitalisation, and for this to be undertaken in the local Community Mental Health Centre.

> A shift of emphasis from the behaviour of the 'mad' person to the provision of appropriate services, together with the shift of financial administration to provide these.

It is within the radical structuralist paradigm that issues of race, class and gender are seen as implicated in mental health. From the work of Fanon (1967) through to the recent work of Fernando (1988), and Littlewood and Cross (1980), comes evidence of misdiagnosis and mistreatment of black people.

From Hollingshead and Redlich (1958) to Brown and Harris (1978) comes evidence of class differences in the incidence and treatment of the mentally ill. Holland, S. (1985, 1988, 1990) has consistently built issues of race, class and gender into her social action psychotherapy on an inner city estate. Busfield (1988), in a recent review of gender influences has identified patriarchal power and oppression as implicated in the higher incidence of diagnosis, admission to hospital, and prescription of tranquillisers, suffered by women.

In terms of the practice of mental health promotion within this paradigm, radical projects can be identified as long ago as the 1930s when Reich established his *Psychoanalytic Polyclinics*. Echoes of this tradition can be found in the more recent *Battersea Action and Counselling Centre* (Holland, S. & Hoggett, 1977; Holland, S., 1979; Hoggett & Lousada, 1985); in the *White City Mental Health Project* with its sister organisation, *Women's Action for Mental Health* (Holland, S., 1988, 1990), and its offshoot, *Shanti* in Lambeth. No doubt there are many people working quietly to achieve similar objectives in many parts of the world under many disciplinary banners. For example, in the area of family therapy there is in New Zealand a small unit devoted to what they call 'just therapy'. They build into their work accountability for class, gender and ethnic identification, recruiting and encouraging the people for and within whom they are working (Waldegrave, 1990).

Lively political analysis of related fields such as social policy and social work has appeared over the years in the *Bulletin on Social Policy, Critical Social Policy, Case Con, Radical Health Promotion, Humpty Dumpty Radical Psychology Magazine, Free Associations,* and in the work of *The Radical Therapist Collective,* the *Black Workers in Mental Health* group and in *The Politics of Mental Health* (Banton, Clifford, Frosch, Lousada and Rosenthal, 1985).

Movement within and between paradigms

It is incumbent upon those who recommend self-critical analysis and reflection to make clear the commitments and assumptions they have espoused, and the present project - of developing a paradigm approach to mental health promotion - is premised above all on the idea of movement between theoretical stances and their attendant practices. It is further contended that analogies between significant personal change (of mind, attitude, stance or mental condition) and change in theoretical positions, are useful for understanding and for teaching. At the highest level there is acceptance of the relevance of a sociology and psychology of knowledge which offers, by means of metatheory - that is, a theory of theories or framework for theories - greater awareness of what we do in holding, teaching and using knowledge in problem interventions of any kind.

The paradigm framework which runs through this project could have been merely a device for exposition of theory. In this respect it is a powerful and informative abstraction. The shift into conceiving the paradigm spaces as signposted routes for theoretical and personal journeys, has linked sociology to psychology (psychotherapy) as well as theory to practice. Sue Holland has developed her therapeutic work with depressed women and their families on an inner city council housing estate as 'social action psychotherapy', describing the movement in psychotherapy from 'symptoms', through knowledge ('insight') and 'desire' into 'social action' (Holland, S., 1988, 1990). (See Figure 3.)

Holland, R. (1990b) has questioned and challenged himself and others to develop an overview of 'conflicting criteria, embedded in the forms of knowledge we rely on to guide practice, and ...(to) find a way of moving beyond stalemated conflicts' (p.2).

My research, entitled *Psyche and Society* responds to that challenge and presents three

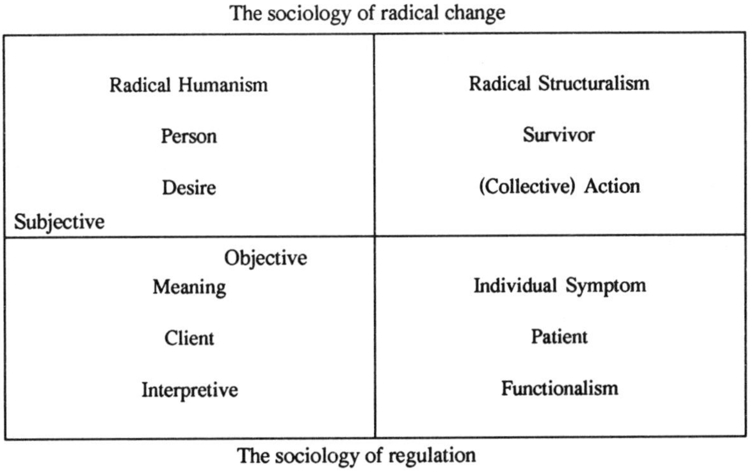

The sociology of radical change

Radical Humanism Person Desire Subjective	Radical Structuralism Survivor (Collective) Action
Objective Meaning Client Interpretive	Individual Symptom Patient Functionalism

The sociology of regulation

Four paradigms for the analysis of social theory, locating terms and describing the
movement between paradigms (with reference to Burrell and Morgan, 1979, p.22;
Holland, S., 1990, p.258).

Figure 3

definitions of community mental health promotion:

Community mental health promotion is that work done to promote the positive
mental health and well-being of individuals, groups and communities, whether
geographical or organisational - work carried out by a range of professionals
involved in the field of mental health and of health promotion as well as by members
of that particular community - and mental health and well-being as defined by those
individuals, groups and communities (Tudor, 1991).

This is a content or descriptive definition of community mental health promotion, of
which there are many examples - some noted - and not least represented by the various
and varied workshops at this Conference.

A process-level definition of community mental health promotion refers to paradigm analysis: community mental health promotion is a way of understanding those
processes at work within groups and communities which both promote and restrict
the promotion of mental health, and is a way of using that understanding in order
to help individuals, groups and communities to make 'paradigm shifts' individually, in groups and/or at the level of community action (Tudor, 1991).

Within this definition I have noted Sue Holland's work in helping people to move
through the paradigms; it should also be noted that there are current debates about other
possible movements and directions of movement between the paradigms (Holland, R.,
1990a).

135

Finally, community mental health promotion is a transdisciplinary epistemological framework with and within which: to locate and understand different and competing theories, paradigms and models of community, health, health promotion, mental illness and mental health, and community mental health promotion; and to promote the content - and process - definitions of community mental health promotion (Tudor, 1991).

This is a meta-definition, which describes the paradigm framework itself and within which I have looked at and located particular projects, work and debates in terms of this present paradigm analysis.

Acknowledgements

My thanks and acknowledgements to Ray Holland, Senior Lecturer in Sociopsychological Studies, King's College, who not only supervised the research on which this article draws but also has encouraged further self-critical reflection and writing.

References

Adams, L., & Holroyd, G. (1989, Spring). Promoting mental health. *Health For All News*, 8, pp. 5-6.

Banton, R., Clifford, P., Frosch, S., Lousada, J., & Rosenthal, J. (1985). *The politics of mental health*. Basingstoke: Macmillan.

Basaglia, F. (1980). Problems of law and psychiatry: The Italian experience. *International Journal of Law and Psychiatry*, 3, 17-37.

Brown, G.W., & Harris, T.O. (1978). *The social origins of depression*. London: Tavistock.

Busfield, J. (1988). Mental illness as social product or social construct: A contradiction in feminists' arguments? *Sociology of Health and Illness*. 10, 541-542.

Burrell, G., & Morgan, G. (1979). *Sociological paradigms and organisational analysis*. London: Heinemann.

Davidson, J. (1987). Health education in a psychiatric setting. *British Journal of Occupational Therapy*. 50, pp. 311-315.

Department of Health. (1991). *The health of the nation*. London: HMSO.

Fanon, F. (1967). *Black skins and white masks*. (C.L. Markmann, Trans.). New York: Grove Press.

Fernando, S. (1988). *Race and culture in psychiatry*. London: Croom Helm.

Fernando, S. (1990). Mental health promotion - the way forward. In *National Mental Health Promotion Conference*. (pp. 13-17). London: Health Education Authority.

Gatherer, A. (1963). *The Northampton mental health project 1961. An experiment in mental health education*.

Hoggett, P., & Lousada, J. (1985). Therapeutic interventions in working class communities. *Free Associations*, 1, pp. 125-152.

Holland, R. (1990a). The paradigm plague: prevention, cure and inoculation. *Human Relations*, 43(1), pp. 23-48.

Holland, R. (1990b). *Sanity, necessary complexities and mental health promotion.* Unpublished manuscript.

Holland, R. (in press). Reflexive analysis and usable theory in family work. *Issues in Social Work Education.*

Holland, R., & Tudor, K. (1991, March). *Psyche and society: Mental health promotion in theory and practice.* Paper presented at the Annual Conference of the British Sociological Association, Manchester.

Holland, S. (1979). The development of an action and counselling service in a deprived urban area. In M. Meacher (Ed.), *New methods of mental health care* (pp. 95-106). London: Pergamon.

Holland, S. (1985, June). *Loss, rage and oppression. Neighbourhood psychotherapy with working class, black and national minority women.* Pam Smith Memorial Lecture, Polytechnic of North London.

Holland, S. (1988). Defining and experimenting with prevention. In S. Ramon & M.G. Giannichedda (Eds), *Psychiatry in transition* (pp.125-137). London: Pluto.

Holland, S. (1990). Psychotherapy, oppression and social action: Gender, race and class in black women's depression. In R.J. Perelberg & A.C. Miller (Eds.), *Gender and power in families.* (pp.256-269). London: Routledge.

Holland, S., & Hoggett, P. (1977). People's aid and action centre. *Humpty Dumpty Radical Psychology Magazine, 8*, 18-23.

Hollingshead, A.B., & Redlich, F.C. (1958). *Social class and mental illness.* New York: Wiley.

Illich, I. (1975). *Medical nemesis: The expropriation of health.* London: Calder & Boyars.

Kennedy, A. (1988). *Positive mental health promotion - fantasy or reality?* Glasgow: Greater Glasgow Health Board Health Education Department.

Klein, D.C. (1968). *Community dynamics and mental health.* New York: John Wiley.

The Labour Party. (1991). *The better way to a healthy Britain.* London: The Labour Party.

Leonard, P. (1984). *Personality and ideology.* London: Macmillan.

Littlewood, R., & Cross, S. (1980). Ethnic minorities and psychiatric services. *Sociology of Health and Illness, 2*, 194-201.

Marcuse, H. (1968). *One dimensional man.* London: Sphere.

Marcuse, H. (1969). *Eros and civilisation.* London: Sphere.

Martindale, D. (1961). *The nature and types of social theory.* London: Routledge.

Mitchell, J. (1975). *Psychoanalysis and feminism.* Harmondsworth: Penguin.

Murray, M.C. (1989, November). *Mental health promotion team.* Document available from Mid Staffordshire Mental Health Promotion Team, Mental Health Unit, St. George's Hospital, Stafford ST16 3AG.

Mental Health Act 1983. London: HMSO.

Reich, W. (1970). *The mass psychology of fascism.* (V.R. Carfagno, Trans.). Hardmondsworth: Penguin.

Rogers, A., Faulkner, A., (1987). *A place of safety.* London: MIND.

137

Rose, S.M., & Black, B.L. (1985). *Advocacy and empowerment*. Boston: Routledge.

Sayce, L., & Field, V. (in press). *Community mental health centres in the UK: A national survey*. London: Research and Development for Psychiatry.

Scheff, T.J. (1966). *Being mentally ill*. Chicago: Aldine.

Siegler, M., & Osmond, H. (1976). *Models of madness, models of medicine*. New York: Macmillan.

Szasz, T. (1961). *The myth of mental illness*. London: Secker & Warburg.

Tudor, K. (1990/91). One step back, two steps forward: Community care and mental health. *Critical Social Policy*. 30, pp. 5-22.

Tudor, K. (1991). *Psyche and society*. Manuscript submitted for publication.

Tudor, K., & Holroyd, G. (1991, September). *Between psyche and society - the role of the mental health promoter*. Paper presented at the First Annual Conference on the Promotion of Mental Health, Keele.

Waldegrave, C. (1990). Just therapy (special issue). *Dulwich Centre Newsletter*. 1, 1-47.

West Lambeth Health Authority Mental Health Unit Mental Health Education Group. (undated). *Mental health problems*. Booklet available from Mental Health Unit, West Lambeth Health Authority, Tooting Bec Hospital, Church Lane, London SW17 8BL.

World Health Organisation. (1986). A discussion document on the concept and principles of health promotion. *Health Promotion*. 1, 73-76.

15 Between psyche and society: The role of the community Mental Health Promotion Officer

K. Tudor and G. Holroyd

ABSTRACT

At present neither the mental health professions nor health education or health promotion provide a career structure or systematic training for those working in mental health promotion. There is, in addition to this lack of professional ownership, no specific or required training or qualification for working in this emerging field.

The authors, uniquely involved in both theoretical and practical perspectives and concerns in mental health promotion, and drawing on recent research in this field, suggest a transdisciplinary knowledge base for the emerging profession and practice of mental health promotion. Within a framework of paradigm analysis they identify a number of different approaches to the role of the community mental health promoter.

In conclusion the authors explore the need for and propose an outline of a training course in mental health promotion for Health Promotion Officers which takes a developmental and reflexive view of learning, education and training in this field; suggest and present their outline of a Job Description for Mental Health Promotion Officer; and present a model for supervision/consultancy, an important aspect of the mental health promoter's role.

Introduction

Health promotion and health education are in a state of flux. The government's green paper (Department of Health, 1991) and the Labour Party's strategic document (The Labour Party, 1991) have put health promotion on the political agenda; the government's community care policies and legislation have introduced the concept of, and split between, the purchaser and provider in health and social welfare services. However, such publicity has brought no oxygen to this subject, rather; terms such as promotion and prevention are conflated, theoretical debates are obscured and practice becomes eclectic and pragmatic (Tudor,1991a). In contrast, this paper explores and proposes a clear theoretical and practical framework for mental health promotion and the mental health promoter.

Fifteen years ago McPheeters noted that 'none of the mental health professions provides any amount of systematic training for prevention and promotion' (McPheeters, 1976, p.197). More recently, Holland (1990) has reflected that,:

'since professions are defined partly by their possession of a body of knowledge, health educators need to assemble a credible, saleable corpus of knowledge capable of legitimizing their practice. To their embarrassment, nearly everything they need already belongs to other professions. Epidemiology belongs to the public health areas of the medical profession. although some part of it can be gained from demographers. Personal intervention theories belong to clinical psychologists and social workers, family intervention theories belong to family therapists, and mental health knowledge belongs to psychiatrists and clinical psychologists. The only bodies of knowledge without strong commitment to professional sectors of activity are the academic disciplines of education, psychology, and sociology, and the two latter disciplines are notoriously unpractical in their academic form. How can the group aspire to professional status on a knowledge base which is fragmented, incoherent, and in may aspects already spoken for?' (Holland, 1990, p.30).

Mental health promotion, as a new and emerging field of theory and practice, falls short of this remark: currently, no one profession, social work, psychology, medical, nursing, etc., has the monopoly on the field of mental health promotion; neither does it draw on a (one particular) body of knowledge. These apparent lacks can be turned to good advantage as, and if, the emerging profession lays claim to 'transdisciplinarity'.

Transdisciplinary theories and ways of working start, Caplan, R. (1989) suggested, 'from the premise of the holistic nature of knowledge which cannot be mechanically separated into different disciplines' (p.3.) Murphy (1986), in tracing the historical development of transcultural psychiatry, has acknowledged the different connotations of different terms, such as 'cultural', 'ethno- cultural', 'cross-cultural', etc.: 'the 'trans' part of the term even caused some unease, since it appeared to imply that the field would be concerned only with features that transcended cultural boundaries, not those that remained within them; but on the other hand it could be taken as implying intercultural comparison' (Murphy, 1986, P.13). Reason (1977) proposed 'a positive, concrete conception of knowledge, understanding and enquiry which would be interdisciplinary in all but name' (p.206) for, he argued, that once interdisciplinarity is named it becomes in essence another 'discipline'. In so far as he named or defined the term Reason proposed an interdisciplinarity which is a methodology of 'the continual confrontation of the problem of methodology' (. 206), so that the *way* we do things becomes as much a part of our study or consideration as *what* we do - this reflection on *process,* as well as the process of reflection, it essential to our method and enquiry.

Before we look at different approaches to community mental health promotion, two points are worth noting.

The first is one of terminology and role confusion. People are appointed - at present, mainly within the health care professions and Health Authorities - as Health Promotion Officers (sometimes with Mental Health in parentheses), or with a special interest or specific brief in mental health. Not only that, but rather than 'Officers' they may be 'Workers', 'Specialists', 'Advisors', 'Consultants', 'Facilitators', or even, in the current 'contract culture', 'Providers'. These terms are important: they often carry an organisational and theoretical significance beyond a mere title. Whilst 'Officer' has a professional ring to it, the term 'Worker' implies an active activist, especially when linked to 'community', the focus for much mental health promotion work. 'Specialists' are special, their expertise can exclude, whilst the advice of 'Advisors' can be taken or left. The terms 'Consultants', 'Facilitators' and even 'Supervisors' all describe aspects of a person's role. We do not propose any one term over another - and for present purposes use the terms 'Promoter' (despite its perhaps pugilistic associations) or 'officer'; we merely point out all terms are significant in terms of their meaning and their implications for aspects of a person's role.

The second point is one of focus. The focus of community mental health promotion is both on individuals, (including groups), and on the community. McPheeters's (1976) strategies for the promotion of positive mental health are (as are his strategies for primary prevention) directed to both individuals and the environment; the former, education and developmental, both concerned with 'improving the ability of people to deal more effectively with everyday life' (McPheeters, 1976, p.195), the examples concerned with being more productive and more tolerant; the latter directed at the environment and increasing resources.

Community mental health promotion.

Klein (1986), in his work on community dynamics and Mental health identified the functions of the community, including: the provision and distribution of living space and shelter; the distribution of necessary goods and services; the maintenance of safety and order, and the facilitation of the resolution of conflicts; the education and acculturation of newcomers (e.g. children and immigrants); the transmission of information, ideas and beliefs; the creation and enforcement of rules and standards of belief and behaviour; and the provision of opportunities for interaction between individuals and groups', summarising that 'much of a community's existence is taken up with the distribution and use of space' (Klein, 1968, p.58). From this it follows that the role of the person promoting community mental health is essentially a functional one: maintaining the boundaries of the community and its functions; and educating and instructing individuals and groups in how to maintain their own and the community's mental health.

Elsewhere Klein (1968) suggested that 'it is important that the mental health worker raise the question of meaning with himself' (p.25) - the meaning, that is, of community, his/her own sense of community, his/her attitudes and responses. This then raises the interesting and important issues and questions of: What sense the mental health promoter/officer makes of the community? How does s/he communicate that and to whom? These issues have been raised and discussed by Caplan, G. (1970) in his development of the notion of mental health consultation: 'the consultee's work problem must be defined by him as being in the mental health area - relating to (a) mental health disorder or personality idiosyncrasies of the client, (b) promotion of mental health in the client, (c) interpersonal aspects of the work situation' (Caplan, G., 1970, p.28). Caplan is very clear that the consultant is the expert: 'the consultant must have expert knowledge in those areas' (Ibid., p.28). There is a strong tradition in the field of community mental health of mental health workers - whether psychiatrists, psychologists, social workers,

141

community psychiatric nurses, youth workers, counsellors or others - offering consultation and supervision of individuals and groups within a community. In establishing contacts within a particular community professionals may, in an attempt to work with 'the community', identify community 'leaders' and work with them, thus developing a lay professional and professionalised leadership. The Artemis Trust (undated) has identified these people as opinion leaders as key individuals in any network. It studied the various roles of people in the change process and identified the practitioner, the adopter (client), the change agent (promoter) and change agency, and the potential adopter, as well as attitude formers and specific opinion leaders on various activities, arguing that such opinion leaders are the best change agents. Although limited and limiting in the roles it identifies and ascribes, the Artemis Trust's work is unique in identifying and developing how the field of 'personal growth' is promoted through networks, channels of communication, decision-making processes and targeting populations. There is, within these approaches, often a shift away from a narrow 'medical' view, represented by Ashton and Seymour (1988), who, working within a 'Health for All' framework, advocated such a shift through a expansion in the five areas of: self-care; integration of medical care with other related activities; integration of the promotion of health with preventive medicine, treatment and rehabilitation; meeting the needs of 'undeserved' groups; and community participation.

Another approach to mental health promotion emphasises a participative and collaborative relationship with individuals, groups and communities. The mental health worker/ promoter works with, rather than for or on behalf of individuals and the community; 'promotion' and 'education' - literally, 'leading out' - take on a more libertarian, problem-solving perspective. The mental health worker takes account of people's subjective experience of themselves, others and the environment and their views about what it is that they want to change. Whilst the radical therapist may focus on individual change, the radical mental health worker and community mental health promoter are concerned to begin to generalise and to 'collectivise' individuals' experiences and, in terms of McPheeter's strategies, may be more concerned with the environment and its relation to mental illness and health. Much of the mental health promotion work undertaken in Salford over recent years - through the appointment of the first Mental Health Promotion Officer - has been based on fostering the notion of the competent individual acting and active within a competent community (Holroyd, 1991).

Yet another approach, and one which militates against much traditional community work which contacts and attempts to influence the opinion leaders within the community, identifies the most distressed members of the community as potential community activists and 'leaders'. Community mental health workers/promoters operating from this perspective understand the relationship between dis-ease and distress in terms of oppression and exploitation arising from structural differences and conflicts within society - on the basis of, for instance, class, race and gender - and promote awareness of such relationships. Approaches to this work are influenced by the notion of empowerment, developed by users and survivors of the psychiatric and mental health system (Survivors speak out, undated) - and, more recently, taken on by organisations in the field, such as the Health Education Authority (HEA) (Hagard, 1988) and MIND (MIND, 1990). Mental health workers promote initiatives which make exiting services more accessible, develop new services, and which empower user of services - often by forming alliances with users and by challenging authorities and social structures. This approach is at the heart of mental health promotion work in Salford where there has been an emphasis on the involvement of users of services and other members of the community. To enable effective communication and consultation a self-help network has been established. Holroyd (1991) has reflected that 'minimised dependence on statutory care and maximising self-coping mechanisms will diminish the likelihood of future need--- one of the most effective ways of doing this has proved to be through a series of self-help groups co-ordinated by a central body, the Salford Forum for Mental Well-being' (p.10). He has also suggested that the strengthening of community action aids effective mental health promotion precisely through the participation and involvement of the community, taking control and power over its activities and initiatives.

On reflection

How do people, faced with these different, and, at times, conflicting approaches to community mental health promotion understand the differences and choose and develop their own theory and practice? For mental health promotion to have any form and meaning, let alone become a 'discipline' or profession it must comprise more than ill-informed or a theoretical eclecticism; *it is very important to recognise that choice of a particular theoretical stance is not merely a technical decision: in the human sciences it implies moral commitment to a certain interpretation of what is to be human and to be involved in various kinds of social structure'* (Holland, 1991, p.3).

A framework for practice

Burrel and Morgan (1979) stated that 'all approaches to the study of society are located in a frame of reference of one kind or another' (p.10). They suggested that 'assumptions about the nature of science can be thought of in terms of what we call the subjective -- objective dimension, and assumptions about the nature of society in terms of a regulation -- radical change dimension' (p.21). Taking theses two dimensions together as axes Burrell and Morgan defined four distinct sociological paradigms, or sets of ideas (See Figure 1).

This framework has been developed in a number of fields, including that of health education theory which Caplan, R. (1986) 'mapped', identifying the core views of society, the identified source of the problem, and the implications for approaches to health eduction - all within each paradigm (See Figure 2). Tudor (1991b) has further developed this in relation to the role of mental health promoter (See Figure 3).

Using this framework as a 'paradigm map' it is possible, and indeed useful, to identify and locate different and differing approaches to the role and work of those promoting community mental health and thus to locate the different approaches discussed. Elsewhere, Tudor (1991b) has located the current different and differing practices of community mental health promotion in Britain - from educative projects and booklets on mental illness and health to social action psychotherapy.

143

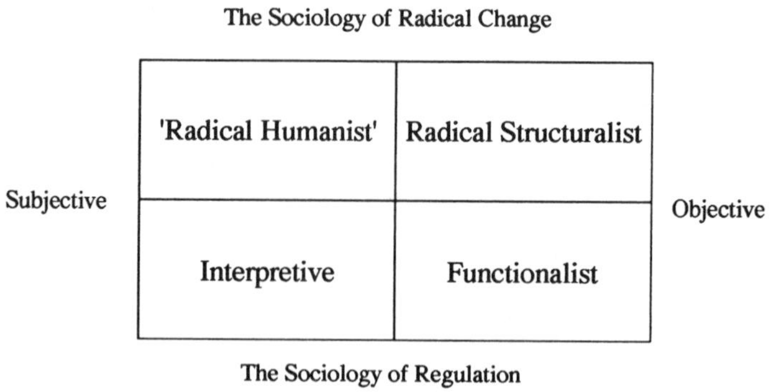

The Sociology of Radical Change

'Radical Humanist'	Radical Structuralist
Interpretive	Functionalist

Subjective   Objective

The Sociology of Regulation

Four paradigms for the analysis of social theory (Burrell and Morgan, 1979, p.22)

Figure 1

Training, job establishment and supervision

Finally, we focus on three developments for mental health promoters: training; the establishment of the work/profession; and supervision/consultancy.

The first National Mental Health Promotion Conference, held in Salford, 22-25 July 1989, was funded by the HEA and organised by Salford Mental Health Promotion Unit. Two of the recommendations identified by the Conference (HEA, 1990) concerned the need for more research into mental health promotion and for further follow-up conferences at regional as well as at a national level. Research into the field of mental health promotion, funded by the HEA, and carried out by one of the authors (Tudor, 1991b), under the auspices of King's College, London, has begun to address the issues of a lack of theoretical and professional base for mental health promotion and promoters. It has done this in two ways: firstly, through an investigation into the conceptual issues in mental health promotion (-work which is due to be published by the HEA); and secondly through the establishment of the first Training Course in Mental Health Promotion for Health Promotion Officers - a course designed by the author of the research and set up through the Management Centre and the Continuing Education Unit, at King's College, London. Details of the (second) forthcoming course are available/appended to this paper (Appendix 1).

The establishment of mental health promotion posts or officers for whom a part of their job is mental health promotion is increasing. We have already noted the lack of theoretical, professional or training base for such promoter. The Job Description presented (Appendix 2) is an attempt to elaborate elements of the mental health promoter's job - using the paradigm framework outlined above.

We have stressed the centrality of reflection in our presentation. Supervision is

Radical health education

Core view

Society is oppressive and alienating. It is characterised by hierarchial and authoritarian institutions of the state, business corporations, the professions, science, work and the family, which cognitively dominate people, (political and ideological domination). The very language we have to speak creates and sustains our participation in this form of oppression.

Sources of problems

Institutions we inhabit, which socialise and train us, and in which we work. The order which these institutions define devalues, discredits or invalidates alternatives. It affects human consciousness, relationships, and potential, producing alienation and frustration of full personal and communal fulfilment.

Health ed aims

Self-discovery through mutual aid and non-hierarchical cooperative projects which challenge the necessity of institutional processes. Radical self-help and deprofessionalisation of health care which changes social control systems instead of so-called deviants. Reveal and challenge the 'political' in health.

subjective

Core view

Social life is meaningful and proceeds on the basis of the subjective interpretations of participants. Social structures, institutions, roles and concepts of normality are socially created, sustained and changed by people through their interactions with one another. Implicit orientation to integrated, harmonious and enduring social units since it does not focus on political or economic consequences, or causes.

Sources of problems

Meanings and definitions that people give to their actions or identities are disrupted by events, or reinterpreted or so labelled by others that disorganised or deviant roles, identities and health careers are created. Loss and disruption of taken-for-granted reality produces disorientation and distress.

Health ed aims

Improve understanding of self and others; improve communication by exploring the meanings of problems and events to all relevant parties, reconstruct identities by reframing accounts, representing unheard or unexpressed

Radical structuralist health education

Core view

Fundamental conflicts and contradictions arising from the economic system which give unequal wealth, power and opportunity to different classes. This determines broadly, the form of social institutions and the state, of which the health and welfare services are but one example. Society is characterised by class conflict and struggle to redress the economic basis of class inequality.

Sources of problems

The demands of production and the reproduction of the conditions for capital accumulation (or which profits are a part). Production-occupational diseases and injuries: unemployable and unemployed: occupational stress. Consumption-lifestyle patterns and consumer habits determined by what is produced. e.g., advertising which induces consumer preferences. Distribution-artificially maintained scarcity for basic needs, e.g., inadequate housing, heating, food and clothing.

Health ed aims

Provide a theoretical analysis of the relationship between health, illness and the economic class structure. Link health education to those initiatives which challenge capitalism.

objective

versions, challenging key labellers, correcting stereotypes.

Core view

An enduring and integrated system based on a harmony of interests and common value system. Models and methods of natural science applied to the understanding of human affairs (medical science and epidemiology). The social whole is sustained by social institutions which function in the interests of individual and society, and which is adaptable to change.

Sources of problems

Pathological, maladaptive or incorrect (irresponsible) behaviour, habits or lifestyle; or, pathological or faulty functioning of organisational and environmental processes.

Health ed aims

Behaviour and attitude modification: or, administrative, legislative and environmental change (social engineering). Social change is not precluded so long as it is based on acceptance of the rules and legitimate institutions of liberal democracy.

regulation

Theoretical approaches in health education

Figure 2

	RADICAL HUMANIST MENTAL HEALTH	RADICAL STRUCTURALIST MENTAL HEALTH
Core view of society	Society is oppressive and alienating. It is characterised by hierarchical and authoritarian institutions of the state, e.g., business, science, work, family and language.	Fundamental conflicts and contradictions arise from economic system giving unequal distribution of wealth, power and opportunity. Society characterised by class, race, gender conflict.
Source of problem	The institutions we inhabit affect human conciousness, relationships and potential, producing alienation. The invalidation of alternatives.	Production: occupational injuries and diseases; distribution: artificial scarcity, inadequate housing; consumption: habits determined by what is produced.
Mental health promotion	Self-discovery as an individual with the ability to respond (response-ability);and with a social self within cooperative projects. Challenge the political in mental health. Conscientisation.	Provide a theoretical analysis of the relationship between health, illness and class structure. Link mental health promotion to initiatives which challenge social structures.

	INTERPRETIVE MENTAL HEALTH	FUNCTIONALIST MENTAL HEALTH
Core view of society	Social life proceeds on the basis of the subjective participation of participants. Social structures and institutions are socially created and changed by people's interactions.	An enduring and integrated system based on harmony of interests and common value system. Models and methods of natural science applied to mental illness/health.
Source of problems	Meanings and definitions that people give to their actions are disrupted by events or reinterpreted/labelled by others.	Pathological, maladaptive or incorrect (irresponsible) behaviour.
Mental health promotion	Improve understanding of self and others, reconstruct identities by reframing and correcting stereotypes. Promote understanding and meaning of mental health.	Behaviour and attitude modification based on an ideal/norm of mental health. Boundary maintenance and instruction.

Theoretical approaches to the role of the community mental health promoter(Tudor, 1991b)

Figure 3

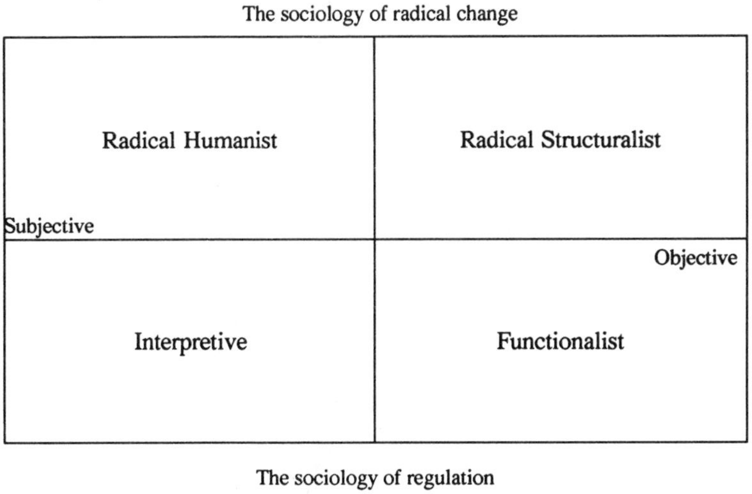

The sociology of radical change

Radical Humanist	Radical Structuralist
Subjective	
	Objective
Interpretive	Functionalist

The sociology of regulation

Four paradigms for the analysis of social theory (Burrell and Morgan, 1979, p.22),
locating theories of community mental health promotion

Figure 4

essential in facilitating this process; good supervision is crucial to the development of a
reflexive process in mental health promotion work. Another reason for focusing on
supervision is the element of mental health consultations, as Caplan, G.(1970) summarised it, in the mental health promoter's role. Thus, we may be called upon to consult a
community group; a local religious leader may come to you to ask advice about how to
approach a particular mental health problem; a mental health social worker might ask for
non-managerial supervision of her/his work; you may yourself have managerial and
supervisory responsibility for others.

Hawkins and Shohet (1989) have developed a model or matrix of supervision and
therapy which we have adapted for and found useful in mental health promotion work
(see figure 5).

    6 -Focus on the supervisor/consultant's feelings.

    5 -Focus on the 'here and now' process in the supervision/ consultation sessions as
        a mirror or parallel of the 'there and then' process.

    4 -Focus on the supervisee's feelings.

    II. Focus on the supervisee's work as it is reflected in the supervision/consultation
        process.

    3 -Exploration of the supervisee's work - process and relationship.

    2 -Exploration of the strategies and interventions used by the supervisee.

147

1 -Reflection on the content of what the client presents/the issue.
I. The work presented by the supervisee is reported and reflected upon in supervision/consultation.

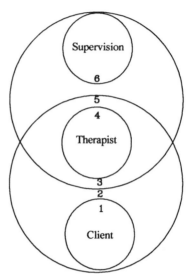

The domains of supervision/consultancy (from Hawkins annd Shohet, 1989)

Figure 5

The 'domains' of supervision/consultancy are explained:
I. The work presented by the supervisee is reported and reflected upon in supervision/consultation
1. *Reflection on the content of what the client presents / the issue.* This is supervision/consultancy at the level of the content of someone's work, i.e. what they are doing in practice. The aim of this form, level or domain of supervision/consultancy is to help focus the supervisee on the client and/or issue presented.
2. *Exploration of the strategies and interventions used by the supervisee.* Here the focus is on the choices of intervention used by the supervisee, an example of which is when the mental health worker helps a mental health care planning group to explore the different options and implications of community and user involvement and/or developing professional preventive strategies.
3. *Exploration of the supervisee's work - process and relationship.* Here, the focus is on the process - both conscious and unconscious - of the supervisee's work in order to enable her / him to develop greater understanding of the dynamics of their work.
II. Focus on the supervisee's work as it is reflected in the supervision/consultation process

148

4. *Focus on the supervisee's feelings* Here the supervisor attends to the conscious and unconscious in the work presented, e.g. focusing on the language and metaphor used in supervision a worker in a Community Mental Health Team highlights their own ambivalence about the ethos and work of the Team.

5. *Focus on the 'here-and-now' process in the supervision/ consultation session as a mirror or parallels of the 'there and then' process.* E.g. an Officer working in a Health Authority is a consultant to a Social Worker having a similar brief in Social Services. Through acknowledging and reflecting on the competitiveness in their own relationship they identify areas of competition and conflict between the two organisations in which they work.

6. *Focus on the supervisor/consultant's feelings.* Here the supervisor reflects on her/his own feelings evoked by the supervisee's work 'to provide reflective illumination for the therapist' (Hawkins & Shohet, 1989, p.58).

Such reflexive self-critical awareness is a pre-requisite for positive and critical mental health promotion.

References

Ashton, J., & Seymour, H. (1988). *The new public health.* Milton Keynes: Open University Press.

The Artemis Trust. (Undated). *Spreading personal growth in society.* Available from: The Artemis Trust, 19 Park Hill, London W5 2JS.

Burrell, G., & Morgan, G. (1979) *Sociological paradigms and organisational analysis.* London: Heinemann.

Caplan, G. (1970). *The theory and practice of mental health consultation.* London: Tavistock.

Caplan, R. (1986). *The implications of socio-theoretical constructs for the evaluation of health education theory.* Unpublished MSc dissertation, King's College, University of London.

Caplan, R. (1989). *Proposal for the establishment of a fellowship to investigate conceptual issues and implementation of community mental health promotion.* Paper. Available from the Health Education Authority, Hamilton House, Mabledon Place, London WC1H 9TX.

Department of Health. (1991). *The health of the nation.* London: HMSO.

Hagard, S. (1988, October). *Is mental health promotion possible ?* Lecture to the annual general meeting of the Cambridgeshire Mental Welfare Association.

Hawkins, P., & Shohet, R. (1989). *Supervision in the helping professions.* Milton Keynes: Open University Press.

Health Education Authority. *National Mental Health Promotion Conference.* London: Health Education Authority.

Holland, R. (1990). The paradigm plague: Prevention, cure and inoculation. *Human Relations,* 1, 23-48.

Holland, R. (1991). *Reflexivity.* Unpublished manuscript.

Holroyd, G. (1991). Promoting mental health - the Salford experience. In *Community development and health.* Milton Keynes: Open University Press.

Klein, D. C. (1968). *Community Development and Health.* Milton Keynes: Open University Press.

Klein, D. C. (1968). *Community dynamics and mental health.* New York: John Wiley.

The Labour Party. (1991). *The better way to a healthy Britain.* London: The Labour Party.

McPheeters, H. L. (1976). Primary prevention and health promotion in mental health. *Preventive Medicine, 5,* 187-198.

MIND. (1990). *Advocacy. Different forms of empowerment.* Paper available from MIND, 22 Harley St., London W1.

Murphy, H.B.M. (1968). The historical development of transcultural psychiatry. In J.L. Cox (Ed.), *Transcultural psychiatry* (pp. 7-22). London: Croom Helm.

Reason, D. (1977). The red queen's estate; or, grounds for interdisciplinarity. *Studies in Higher Education, 3,* 2-3-209.

Survivors Speak Out. (Undated). *Where are we now?: An overview on mental health self advocacy.* Self advocacy action pack available from Survivors Speak Out, 33 Lichfield Road, London NW2 2RG.

Tudor, K. (1991a). *Health promotion: Paradigms for theory and practice.* Unpublished manuscript.

Tudor, K. (1991b). *Psyche and society: Community mental health promotion.* Manuscript submitted for publication.

SECTION THREE
RESEARCH

16 Quality of life issues in the evaluation of mental health services

M. Barry, C. Crosby and D. Mitchell

Introduction

The changes in policy concerning the design and delivery of mental health services have been accompanied by a growing awareness of the impact of services on the lifestyles of their users. One of the major concerns with regard to hospital care was that through the process of institutionalisation, the services had lowered the quality of life of its residents. Jones (1988), for example, points out that improved quality of life is one of the most frequently cited justifications for deinstitutionalisation. Researchers evaluating the new services have therefore increasingly concerned themselves with the broader impact of the services on clients' lives, looking beyond illness-related outcomes to quality of life issues.

However, looking to improved quality of life as a criterion for evaluating a service, one could argue that the very generality of the concept makes it a problematic guide for effective evaluation. Issues such as what constitutes a good quality of life are far from clear. Can single definition be broadly applied across different groups in society? As researchers we are confronted with the problem of developing quantifiable indicators of quality, i.e. adequately defining quality of life in measurable terms. The issue of how client-derived assessments of life quality can be appropriately integrated into programme change and policy development also needs to be considered.

Looking to quality of life in the context of service evaluation, one needs to consider the utility of the construct as an outcome measure and examine its meaning and implementation in the evaluation and planning of services. As a construct, quality of life accents a holistic approach to the client's life, embracing physical, social, cognitive, and material dimensions of well-being and directs awareness to an examination of needs and standards. In this respect, as an evaluation measure, it holds much promise. However, certain definitional and methodological obstacles need to be overcome before definitive conclusions can be drawn from research in this area.

Methodological issues

Providing a single definition of quality of life is rather difficult, but generally it refers to the sense of well-being and satisfaction experienced by people under their current life conditions. Quality of life is usually evaluated with some combination of life satisfaction measures and objective indicators of external life circumstances. The methods used for assessing quality of life have taken their lead from a number of national surveys on quality of life in the USA. The approach adopted by researchers such as Andrews and Withey (1976); Campbell, Converse, and Roger (1976), was to consider general or global measures of well-being as well as measures of satisfaction with respect to particular life areas. Though the specific domains used to describe quality of life have varied, they tend to include life areas such as work, finance, social and family relations, leisure, health, safety etc. A number of measures such as satisfaction rating scales and semantic differential scales have also been designed for this purpose.

This approach to assessing quality of life has been adapted by researchers in relation to psychiatric patients. Lehman (1983a) outlines a general quality of life model based on the national survey data. According to this model, quality of life is ultimately, 'a subjective matter reflected in a sense of global well-being' (Lehman, 1983a, p.369). Three types of variables are delineated as components; personal characteristics such as age, sex, etc., objective quality of life in various life domains and subjective quality of life in the same life domains. From this model Lehman developed a scale for assessing the well-being of chronic psychiatric patients. The schedule, which consists of a structured interview format, collects objective and subjective data covering nine life domains in addition to measures of general well-being.

Lehman (1982) carried out a major study of 278 chronic patients living in supervised community residences in Los Angeles. In a series of publications in 1982, 1983, Lehman reported that chronic psychiatric patients were able to provide statistically reliable responses to the quality of life interview. High internal consistency reliabilities were reported for the satisfaction scales, and a factor analysis of the satisfaction items revealed that respondents differentiated among their feelings about the various life areas. Lehman also reported that subjective quality of life indicators in specific life domains were much better indicators of global well-being compared with objective indicators in the same life domain. Areas of particular importance were health, leisure, social relations and finances. In fact, finances were the most consistent source of dissatisfaction. With regard to the effects of psychopathology on the analysis of the quality of life data, Lehman reported that, while psychopathology was not found to introduce bias into the overall structure of the data, the study did suggest the importance of controlling for mental health effects, particularly in relation to in-patients' assessment of health and satisfaction with health care.

Lehman's scale is probably the most widely used scale in this area. However, in examining the research work with chronic psychiatric patients, a number of questions ought to be addressed. For example, how well does the general model of quality of life translate to a psychiatric population and how suitable are the measures devised for national surveys for use with chronic psychiatric patients? Lehman's model of quality of life is founded on a conceptual base which integrates access to resources and opportunities, fulfilment of social roles in multiple life domains, and expressed satisfaction with life in various domains. The application of these concepts to a chronic psychiatric population needs to be considered. Access to resources for chronic patients is likely to be constrained by virtue of them being hospitalised.

The hospitalised psychiatric patient may be seen as the occupant of an ascribed and all encompassing social role, that of being 'mentally ill' (Goffman, 1961). The average long-stay patient rarely has an occupational or domestic role apart from that of psychiatric patient, and the usual segmentation of life into domestic, occupational and recreational sections rarely occurs. In this respect, looking at the dimensions that are being used to define quality of life in Lehman's scale, one has to question if these dimensions are especially central in the assessment of quality of life of psychiatric patients who have spent a substantial proportion of their adult life in a psychiatric institution.

Research on the quality of life of long-stay patients at north Wales Hospital

The present study concerns itself with the use of quality of life as one of a range of outcome criteria being used to evaluate the resettlement of long-stay psychiatric patients. Details of the research project are described in full elsewhere (Crosby et al., 1989). Briefly, the study is concerned with monitoring and evaluating the degree and direction of change in patient functioning related to the move from hospital into the community and attempts to relate these changes with changes in patients' quality of life. Employing a repeated measures longitudinal design, the study follows up a cohort of patients as they are discharged from hospital, permitting a direct evaluation of quality of life under the different modes of service delivery. Therefore, the quality of life of the residents is assessed on the hospital ward prior to discharge and follow-up assessments are carried out following their discharge from hospital, thus allowing a comparison to be made between the hospital and community settings. The following discussion draws on findings from the baseline phase of the data collection conducted in the hospital setting, a detailed description of which may be found in Barry et al. (1990).

Sample

A quality of life schedule was administered to 62 patients resident at North Wales Hospital. The majority of the sample (83%) had a clinical diagnosis of schizophrenia, and patients ranged in age from 27 to 87 years with a mean age of 56.2 years. The mean length of present hospitalisation was 21.7 years (range .4 to 62 years) and total years hospitalised ranged from 1 to 62 years with a mean of 25.6 years. The sample, the majority of whom were male (N=54), comprised two sub-groups representing both the 'old' and 'new' long-stay patients. One group consisted of relatively old individuals who had been in hospital for a large proportion of their lives and with few admissions, and the second group consisted of relatively younger patients characterised by frequent, shorter stays in hospital. A more detailed description of the psychiatric and behavioural characteristics of the sample may be found in Mitchell et al. (1990).

Quality of life schedule

Lehman's quality of life scale was modified and adapted for use in the present study. The redesigned schedule retains the same basic structure as Lehman's scale i.e. subjective and objective indices for nine life areas, plus measures of general life satisfaction. Following pilot trials, the wording of the items and their response formats were modified and refined to increase comprehensibility and ease of implementation. The result is an interview schedule which takes on average 30 - 40 minutes to administer and covers objective and subjective indices of both life domains and general well-being. Also included are questions concerning residents' attitudes to their discharge from hospital. In addition to the interview schedule for residents, a list of questions concerning the objective indicators of life quality for each of the residents was also completed by a member of the care staff. This information was obtained in order to cross-check the reliability of data derived from residents concerning finances, health, family contact etc.

Discussion of findings

Objective indicators of quality of life

The quality of life of the patients, as measured by the objective indicators, appears to be severely restricted. Levels of independence and privacy on the hospital wards tended to be low, with the majority of residents not having their own bedrooms or adequate facilities for self-catering. Many of the residents were socially isolated with few social contacts within or outside the hospital. Roughly half the residents (47%) reported having friends within the hospital, whereas only 26% reported having friends who resided outside the hospital. Although some patients reported having friends, further questioning revealed that they rarely met or had contact with such friends.

The most frequent source of daily interaction was with staff, with a surprising 39% of residents reporting not interacting socially with other residents on the ward. Social interactions outside the hospital were infrequent, as was contact by phone and writing. Further analysis of the data showed that levels of interactive contact were higher for the younger patients. Generally, however, the frequency of contact with close or intimate friends was low and apart from family there were few sources of social support outside the hospital. The frequency of family contact tended to vary between residents, from very regular i.e., weekly to twice monthly visits (39%), to very infrequent e.g. once a year (16%), with 26% not receiving any visits in the past year. However, maintaining family contact was important to the majority of residents and many expressed a desire to see their relatives more often.

Few of the patients engaged in active leisure activities, and none was in employment at the time of the interview. However, 36% of the sample carried out work within the hospital for which they received a small payment. The majority of residents (71%) received less than £20 per week and for many this was a source of dissatisfaction. Residents reported being in good physical health, but few had insight into the nature of their psychiatric illness or the purpose of their medication. Personal safety issues did not appear to be a problem for the residents and only two had involvement with the police, in relation to minor incidents in the previous year.

The information obtained from patients concerning the objective indices of the quality of life was found to concur with that derived from staff who also completed a quality of life schedule for each of the patients. This finding places confidence in the ability of patients to report on their life experiences and supports the validity of the objective indicators being used in the study.

Subjective indicators of quality of life

Despite the objective living conditions, self-reported levels of satisfaction were high in most life areas. The levels of expressed satisfaction in each of the life domains are depicted graphically in Figure 1. Overall, reported levels of satisfaction were quite high with greatest satisfaction being reported in relation to social relations (73%), religion (73%) and living situation (72%). The life areas that elicited the highest levels of dissatisfaction were finance and family relations, but even in these areas the majority of the residents appeared to be satisfied with their current situation. Reports of general life satisfaction were also high (61%), but were somewhat lower than those expressed in the specific life domains.

With regards to patients' attitudes toward discharge, the majority (52%) did express a desire to leave the hospital, despite the fact that some 42% were unsure if they would be better off as a result of the move. However, patients' attitudes were found to be influenced by such factors as length of stay, with the older residents who had been hospitalised for lengthy periods tending to hold negative attitudes towards resettlement.

Relationship between the indices of quality of life

Spearman rank correlations were computed to assess the relationship between the different indices of quality of life used in the study. The intra-domain correlations between subjective and objective indicators of quality of life are displayed in Table 1. Consistent with findings from previous studies (Andrews & Withey, 1976; Campbell et al., 1976; Lehman, 1988), the results revealed a lack of correlation between the majority of the subjective and objective indices in each life domain. From the total set of 16 correlations, only two emerged as significant; a positive correlation between satisfaction with social relations and frequency of contacts within the hospital ($r = 0.32$, $p < 0.01$), and a negative correlation between satisfaction with living situation and independence ($r = -0.32$, $p < 0.01$).

The correlation between frequency of contact with residents in the hospital and satisfaction with social relations is not altogether surprising as so few residents had frequent social contacts outside the hospital. However, the negative correlation between independence and satisfaction with the living situation is more difficult to explain as it is not what might be expected. This suggests that those residents who had their own personal belongings, cared for themselves and occasionally cooked their own meals, expressed greater dissatisfaction with their living conditions than did other residents. One possible interpretation of this finding is that those residents who experienced greater levels of independence in the hospital may have had as a result higher expectations and desired even more independence, leading to a dissatisfaction with restrictions of the hospital. On the other hand, the more dependent, institutionalised residents are likely to have had lower expectations (Jones, 1988) and be more resigned to and accepting of

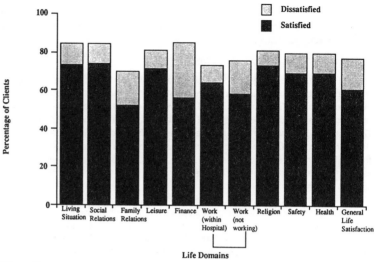

Levels of Satisfaction: Domain-specific and general life satisfaction (N = 62)

Figure 1

hospital life (Wing and Brown, 1970). In this context it is interesting to note that general life satisfaction was found to be positively correlated with a desire to remain in hospital (r = 0.38, p<0.01), and was negatively correlated with positive expectations concerning discharge (r = -0.23, p<0.05). In this sense, higher levels of dependency and institutionalisation may be associated with higher levels of expressed satisfaction. Statements of satisfaction in this context therefore need to be interpreted cautiously.

Correlations between general life satisfaction and the domain-specific indicators were also carried out. Consistent with previous reports in the literature, the domain-specific subjective indicators were found to be significantly related to general life satisfaction. The strongest correlations were in the areas of social relations (r = 0.61, p<0.0001), living situation (r= 0.57, p<0.0009), and health (r = 0.46, p<0.0001).

The relationship between general life satisfaction and a number of demographic variables such as age of residents, current length of hospital stay, and ward setting was also explored. Spearman rank correlations indicated a significant correlation between age and general life satisfaction (r = 0.23, p<0.05). Older residents tended to report greater satisfaction with life overall. This finding has been reported in the general quality of life literature, suggesting that in general, the elderly are known to express greater satisfaction with life (Campbell et al., 1976). Apart from age, no other significant correlations emerged.

The relationship between general life satisfaction and indices of psychopathology was also explored. The measures of psychopathology used were those rated on the Brief Psychiatric Rating Scale (Overall and Gorham, 1962). In all, seven indices of psycho-

158

Correlation between Subjective and Objective Indicators of

Quality of Life (N = 62)

Subjective Indicator	Objective Indicator	Spearman Corr Coefficient	Significance
Living Situation	Privacy	-0.03	0.41
	Independence	-0.32	0.01**
Social Relations	Total No. of Contacts	0.16	0.12
	Contacts in Hospital	0.32	0.01**
	Contacts Outside Hospital	-0.12	0.20
	Close/Intimate Contacts	0.22	0.06
Family Relations	Frequency of Contact	0.18	0.12
Leisure	Number per week	-0.03	0.40
	Yearly activities	-0.10	0.24
Finances	Spending money per week	-0.18	0.11
Work	Work in Hospital	0.01	0.47
	Pay	0.30	0.11
Health	Illness in past year	-0.08	0.28
	Use of Health Care Services	-0.29	0.08
Religion	Attendance at Church Services	-0.01	0.47
Safety	Victim of Crime	0.21	0.07

** $p < .01$

Table 1

pathology were correlated with general life satisfaction, two of which were found to be significant; depression ($r = -0.30$, $p<0.05$) and thought disorder ($r = -0.52$, $p<0.0001$). As expected, residents with higher ratings of depression and thought disorder were more likely to report lower levels of overall life satisfaction.

Implications of findings

The overall impression from the baseline results is of a group of residents who rate low on quality of life as objectively measured, yet evaluate their subjective life quality in a positive manner. As a group, the residents present as unemployed, economically disadvantaged, with few leisure activities and few sources of social support outside the hospital setting. This is a very dependent and institutionalised group, who experience many social problems in addition to the limitations associated with their psychiatric disorders.

The frequently reported lack of correlation between the objective and subjective indices of quality of life is usually interpreted as testimony to the fact that the two sets

159

of indices are measuring different aspects of quality of life (Lehman, 1988). However, one could argue that the lack of correlation between the two sets of measures implies that, from the data, we are unable to specify what aspects of residents' lives are related to expressed satisfaction in each life area. In this respect, the influence of such factors as positive response bias, and the effects of institutionalisation on residents' evaluation of living conditions and expression of satisfaction need to be considered.

The problem of positive response bias is frequently encountered in relation to satisfaction measures in this area, both in the quality of life literature and consumer satisfaction research, with levels of reported satisfaction ranging from 60-100%. Should these high levels of expressed satisfaction be accepted at face value as an expression of satisfaction with the current quality of life, or should they be interpreted as an indication of dependency needs, a consequence of the effects of institutionalisation which changes the nature of the relationship between living conditions and their evaluation? Alternatively they might represent residents' desire to please the interviewer. Clearly the demand characteristics of the interview situation are relevant. The influence of the interview setting is important in that one is tempted to question whether the social environment of the hospital is conducive to the expression of dissatisfaction and demands for change. Residents may experience a certain amount of pressure to suppress feelings of dissatisfaction, as this may be a necessary part of the process of adapting to institutional life. As a result, aspirations and expectations may be lowered. An additional factor to be considered in interpreting the subjective data is the observed influence of age and psychopathology on the general life satisfaction measures. The influence of these variables needs to be examined further.

These points have quite serious implications concerning the validity of the self-report measures and how the data should best be interpreted. However, despite the clustering of positive responses, the subjective measures do appear to be sensitive to the effects of psychopathology and they do succeed in highlighting areas of dissatisfaction. It was also found that the information obtained from patients concerning the objective indices of quality of life concurred with the information derived from staff, which gives some confidence in the validity of reportage by residents.

The information derived from the quality of life schedule, as well as providing a useful baseline against which to measure changes in life quality following a move to the community, also provides a rich array of information on residents' perceptions of their lives and what areas they perceive as important. This information is of considerable value to service practitioners directly involved in the planning and implementation of services programmes for this group. With this purpose in mind, the research team is developing a Needs Assessment strategy which aims to use research data, such as quality of life assessments, to identify areas of patient need. This work is being conducted in collaboration with members of care staff and will use a needs case conference as a primary source of information and communications.

The findings to date suggest a number of life areas on which intervention and rehabilitation strategies may focus. The objective quality of life indices suggest that the resettlement programmes should direct attention to the non-medical needs of this group, focusing on life areas such as maintaining and encouraging any existing family contact, since this emerged as an area of considerable importance and relevance to residents' life

160

quality. The data on patients' social relations also highlights the need to assess carefully patients' abilities to relate socially and develop friendships during the preparation and planning of community placements. The prospect of social isolation following discharge, as a result of patients' restricted social contacts during years of hospitalisation, presents as an area of concern. Expressed dissatisfaction regarding finances highlights the importance of assessing and monitoring patients' abilities in budgeting their limited funds. The need for structured recreational and educational/vocational activities for patients following discharge is also suggested from the quality of life data, particularly in relation to the younger patients.

In addition, the findings from the subjective indices of life quality point to the necessity of addressing patients' attitudes and expectations. It would appear that the experience of long years of hospitalisation may have robbed patients of their expectations, aspirations, and desire for achievement. Although the ability of patients to make choices and decisions concerning their own lives cannot be ignored, these abilities may be severely curtailed by past experiences and patients' basic dependency needs. Attempting to overcome the damaging effects of institutionalisation may be a long and slow process that will require skill and sensitivity on the part of care staff.

Conclusions

The gathering of data on how residents perceive their lives is obviously a central part of assessing quality of life. It would appear, however, that residents' self-assessment of quality of life does have certain limitations and this is one reason for attempting to assess quality of life from a variety of different perspectives, using different methods. The influence of residential setting, psychopathology, staff attitudes and operational policy also need to be recognised. It is therefore important that the information derived from the quality of life schedule should be related to these other variables. Such an approach permits the monitoring of the impact of changes in services, i.e. residential location, operational policy, etc. on residents' self-assessments of life quality and the impact of quality of life on other client measures and vice versa. In this way quality of life may be related to many other measures being used in this study.

In developing adequate outcome measures of quality of life for evaluation purposes, attention needs to be given to the validity of the measures being used, elucidating factors that influence judgements of subjective well-being, and monitoring the sensitivity of the measures to change. The observed lack of correlation between the objective and subjective indicators raises the question of which set of indicators should be used for evaluation purposes and/or if both sets are used how much weight should be given to each in terms of informing policy decisions. As pointed out by George and Bearon (1980), 'if quality of life is to be an organising rubric for research, planning and practice, the distribution, predictors and correlations and implications of life quality need to be carefully delineated' (p.202).

The design and scope of the present study, with a comprehensive range of data being collected at repeated intervals before and after the move from hospital, provides a unique opportunity to carry out a detailed investigation of these issues. The relationships between and within the dimensions of life quality will be monitored over time and the extent to which life satisfaction is responsive to changes in external conditions will be explored. Likewise, the pattern of relationships between quality of life and other outcome measures e.g. psychiatric functioning, staff practices, economic measures, will be catalogued and examined. It is intended that further usage of the schedule in this manner will inform both the conceptualisation and measurement of quality of life in this research area.

Acknowledgements

The work reported in this paper forms part of a longitudinal study commissioned by the Welsh Office, The Department of Health, Clwyd and Gwynedd Health Authorities, and Clwyd and Gwynedd Social Services Departments. The cooperation and assistance of patients and staff at North Wales Hospital, Clwyd is gratefully acknowledged, in particular the collaboration of Dr. F. A. Horrocks and Dr. C.S. Littlejohns in carrying out psychiatric assessments. The authors wish to thank Professor Fergus Lowe and Dr Gordon Grant for their comments on an earlier draft of this paper. The views expressed in this paper represent those of the authors and do not necessarily reflect those of the sponsors or others who have commented on the work.

References

Andrews, R.F., & Withey, S.B. (1976). *Social indicators of well-being: Americans'perception of life quality.* New York: Plenum Press.

Barry, M.M. (1990). In Crosby C., Barry, M.M., Mitchell, D.A., Horrocks, F.A., & Littlejohns, C.S. *Evaluation of the Clwyd Mental Health Community Service: An Interim Report.* Health Services Research Unit, Department of Psychology, University of North Wales: Unpublished Manuscript.

Crosby, C., Barry, M., Mitchell, D., Grant, P., Horrocks, F.A., & Littlejohns,C.S. (1989). *Evaluation of the Mental Health Community Service in Clwyd: Research Protocol and Manual.* Health Services Research Unit, Department of Psychology, University College of North Wales: Unpublished Manuscript.

Campbell, A., Converse, P.E., & Rodgers, W.L. (1976). *The quality of American life.* New York: Russell Sage Foundation.

George, L.K., & Bearon, L.B. (1980). *Quality of life in older persons: Meaning and measurement.* London: Human Sciences Press.

Jones, K. (1988). *Experience in mental health: Community care and social policy.* London: Sage Publications.

Goffman,E. (1961). *Asylums: Essays on the social situation of mental patients and other inmates.* Chicago: Aldine.

Lehman, A.F., Ward, N.C. & Lynn, L.S. (1982). Chronic mental patients: The quality of life issue. *American Journal of Psychiatry.* 139,10, 1271-1276.

Lehman, A.F. (1983a). The well-being of chronic mental patients: Assessing their quality of life. *Archives of General Psychiatry*. 40,369-373.

Lehman, A.F. (1983b). The effects of psychiatric symptoms on qualify of life assessments among the chronically mentally ill. *Evaluation and Program Planning,* 6, 143-151.

Lehman, A.F. (1988). A quality of life interview for the chronically mentally ill. *Evauation and Program Planning*, 11,51-62.

Mitchell, D.A. (1990). In Crosby C., Barry, M.M., Mitchell, D.A., Horrocks, F.A. & Littlejohns, C.S. *Evaluation of the Clwyd Mental Health Community Service: An Interim Report.* Health Services Research Unit, Department of Psychology, University College of North Wales: Unpublished Manuscript.

Overall,J. & Gorham,D. (1962). The Brief Psychiatric Rating Scale. *Psychological Reports,* 10,799-812.

Wing,J.K. & Brown, G.W. (1970). *Institutionalisation and schizophrenia: A comparative study of three mental hospitals, 1960-1980.* London: Cambridge University Press.

17 The health promoting potential of a College of Further Education

P. Broad

Abstract

Whilst an extensive literature exists about stress amongst school teachers, there is comparatively little in the field of teaching in Further Education. In examining the literature on workplace health promotion initiatives, references to 'large educational institutions' suggest that as part of their philosophy there are assumptions made about caring for students and that this might make it easier to suggest that this caring attitude should be extended to the health of the staff. A hypothesis was developed that there may be a huge potential for Health Promotion initiatives in Colleges of Further Education. Such initiatives could provide a unique opportunity, not least that the college could demonstrate to students in its charge, by its own policies as an employer, the ideals of a caring and health promoting workplace. A study was undertaken on one college of Further Education in the Midlands to examine its health promoting potential, dealing with it as a workplace. Interview schedules were designed, examining areas most likely to cause distress to the workforce, drawing on the work of Jee & Reason (Action on Stress at Work, HEA 1988). [1] The three broad areas identified by Jee & Reason, of the physical environment, the job itself and the organisation, were examined in detail. Selected groups of management and staff were interviewed to examine the impact of the organisation, structure and culture of the college on the mental, physical and social well being of the staff. A 'Health Promotion Audit' was subsequently drawn up identifying areas where the organisation was found to be positively contributing to well being. Adopting an empowerment model of health promotion, suggestions were made as to how existing policy could be improved and new policy could be developed, using the existing framework of the health and safety committee as the vehicle of change.

Introduction

This is a study of the health promoting potential of a college of Further Education, concentrating upon the college as a workplace. Whilst there was an extensive literature about schools, notably about stress in schools, FE was an area that was not well researched and on which there was little literature.

In the existing literature, Perkins [2] suggested that for 'large educational institutions', having as part of their philosophy assumptions about caring for students, it made it easier to suggest that care should be exercised about the health of students and that this attitude should extend to the health of all staff. Expertise in occupational health and counselling was likely to be available. The organisational structure would already have a health and safety network and decisions on issues related to health, like food purchasing or provision of suitable facilities, would be made centrally. 'The structure could therefore be used to promote health if the will to do so existed.'

Allegrante and Sloan [3] in considering the ethics of workplace health promotion recognise that factors under the control of the individual are rarely solely responsible for the development of disease. They suggest that any use of behaviour change strategies must be balanced with enlightened management practices designed to address organisational factors contributing to health risks. They argue that health promotion approaches should be adopted to foster self empowerment of the workers to enable them to engage in system challenging responses. To avoid conflict, it would be necessary for the workplace to become a self empowering system.

A hypothesis was developed that there was potential for health promotion in colleges of further education. The Health and Safety committee was identified as the most appropriate vehicle in which to discuss and initiate health promotion programmes. It had the potential to develop the 'welfare' aspects of the employer's responsibilities beyond those envisaged when the Health and Safety at Work etc. Act was drawn up in the early 1970's.

A unique opportunity existed since a college could demonstrate to the students in its charge, by its own policies as an employer, the ideals of a caring and health promoting workplace.

To test the hypothesis, an in-depth study was designed to examine the organisation of a college of Further Education in the Midlands, in the rapidly changing educational environment of the late 1980's.

It was necessary to look at how the college was organised, the environment in which staff worked, both physical and social, detailed aspects of individuals' jobs, to gain an insight as to the impact of these on the mental, physical and social well being of the staff. The following aims and objectives were drawn up:-

Aims

To examine the organisation, structure and culture of a college of Further Education with a view to exploring its potential as a health promoting institution.

Objectives

1. To develop a picture of the organisation highlighting any of its aims, structural and cultural aspects having implications for the mental, physical and social well being of members of the college

2. To develop a picture of the management style of the organisation and its implications for the mental, physical and social well being of members of management and teaching staff.

166

3. To assess the impact of the physical environment on mental, physical and social well being of members of management and teaching staffs

4. To identify the impact of the whole range of duties expected of a lecturer on the mental, physical and social well being of the incumbent

5. To identify any health initiatives in the organisation and their impact on the mental, physical and social well being of members of management and teaching staffs

6. To identify the extent to which interpersonal relationships contribute to the mental, physical and social well being of members of management and teaching staffs

7. To identify the potential for the introduction of health promoting policy which might improve the mental, physical and social well being of members of the college

Finally, a health promotion 'Audit' was drawn up identifying areas that were positively contributing to staff well being and areas that needed positive interventions to make improvements.

Methods employed in study

The study was designed to examine the areas that had the potential to affect the well being of the teaching staff. Jee and Reason's [1] 'Action on Stress at Work' was used as a guideline for designing the study. They identified three broad areas of work to examine: the physical environment, the job itself and the organisation.

Two published studies on colleges of Further Education had used interviewing techniques to collect data, one as the main method, the second to develop a larger, in-depth study.

Tipton [4] acquired most of her information through interviewing methods particularly as she was interested in collecting information on the climate of interaction and staff attitudes to the college. She relied heavily on quotations from these discussions in presenting her material as she felt it was the only way that the 'feel' of the college could be conveyed.

Snape [5] used unstructured interviews with a third of the teaching staff with a view to identifying areas of concern. Later he used this information to design a questionnaire to measure quantitatively the amount of stress the lecturers experienced.

It may have been possible to design a detailed questionnaire to elicit some of the information, but to explore feelings would have required open questions asking the respondent to write freely and honestly. Given the number of areas to be explored, this would have required a very long questionnaire with the possibility of misinterpretation of answers. Questioning allowed the interviewer to ask for further clarification where there was ambiguity. Many of the questions were sensitive so it was important to build some kind of rapport with the interviewees to increase co-operation.

In June 1989, there were 234 full time lecturing staff in the college and between 170 and 200 part time staff, the numbers fluctuating throughout the year. These were supported by 53 technicians, 94 administrative and clerical and 86 manual staff. The author wished to examine 'traditional' craft areas and those that were innovative and part of the new, enterprise spirit of colleges. Therefore, the Heads of the Construction and Allied Trades Faculty and the Enterprise Directorate were approached and a sample of their staff was selected for interview.

167

Within the Enterprise Directorate, only three of the seven areas were undertaking teaching, or teaching within the confines of the college. These three units provided 12 members in full time teaching posts.

Within the Construction Faculty, the choice was wider. and the School of Building Crafts was chosen as a traditional craft area. The School contained 21 full time teaching staff, so to make the sample comparable to the other group, only three skill areas were chosen: Brickwork, Glazing, Painting and Decorating. There were 11 full time members of staff, including the Head of School.

Three more people with health and welfare interests were interviewed. The college nurse, a Health and Safety representative (in Construction) for the teaching union NATFHE, and another NATFHE Health and Safety representative who, in addition to her teaching of Physical Education, had promoted healthy campaigns around food and exercise on her own initiative.

In total, 29 people were approached to be interviewed and no one refused. Four slightly different interview schedules were designed - one each for the Senior Management (welfare), Heads of Faculty/Division, Full time Lecturing staff and Staff with health and welfare interests.

The interviews took place between the 9th June and 5th July 1989, at the college, in a place of the interviewees choosing. Typically, interviews lasted between one and one and a half hours.

Results of study

Objective 1: To develop a picture of the organisation

The lack of a unified perception of the ethos of the college caused people to feel isolated and struggling to keep teaching as the main purpose of their employment. Frustrations occurred because of the slowness to realise equal opportunity goals. Time restraints limited take up of research and publication opportunities. Lack of any substantial welfare function, having to rely on colleagues for support and lack of support for staff with health and safety remits, caused dismay.

In examining the health promoting potential of the college, within an empowerment model, the following observations were made:

The striving to achieve shared goals was recognised to be an element of a self empowering system, but the conflict in priorities and level of support in the new, enterprise, environment may have caused people to be depowered.

An empowering system existed to serve the development of individuals and the efforts on personal development and equal opportunities were mostly found to be very positive.

In an empowering system, individuals would give support and be open to receiving it from one another. However, where workers were able to do this little credit could be given to the system. Indeed, the perceived shortfall in welfare provision, of not being valued enough, served to depower people.

Objective 2: To develop a picture of the management style

Feelings of remoteness of management were expressed and many felt they were not being fully consulted nor communicated with about changes, desiring more decision making responsibilities. Efforts to reward by improved facilities or resources were welcomed but lack of promotion opportunities caused dismay. Motivation was reinforced largely by contact with students, but lack of positive feedback or constructive criticism was demotivating.

In examining the health promoting potential of the college, within an empowerment model, the following observations were made:

A system that encourages power sharing, enabling people to pursue their own directions within the context of shared goals is said to be empowering. From the responses to the openness of management, consultation and decision making it would appear that many people felt depowered by most aspects of their situation.

A system can be said to be empowering where there are effective and sensitive lines of communication. The amount of negative emotion generated by the issue of communications suggested that people felt depowered by the college's information systems. It was welcomed that some of these were being reviewed.

The helplessness and frustration caused by lack of flexibility in pay and promotion opportunities may have had a depowering effect. It was encouraging that ways to overcome these were constantly sought.

An empowering system will help people identify their strengths and build upon them. Some of the motivational factors served to empower the individual, but the disproportionate amount of negative feedback served to depower some.

Objective 3: To assess the impact of the physical environment

Frustration arising from lack of teaching space was frequently voiced. Overcrowded staff rooms led many to take work home, which was felt to be an undesirable response. The loss of a staff common room reflected a poor decision, failing to recognise the importance of private space to meet colleagues socially and professionally. The use of the bar as a meeting space led to pressures to resist alcoholic drinks in the working day. The lack of consistent security measures led to some groups feeling less important. Provision of exercise facilities was welcomed. Eating facilities were considered poor, both in choice and time that meals were available. The future introduction of a no-smoking norm was generally welcomed.

In examining the health promoting potential of the college, within an empowerment model, the following observations were made:

The helplessness arising from lack of space for work and relaxation and an uncontrollable environment could have had a depowering effect on people.

The loss of communal areas, seen as a negative comment on a valued facility, may have served to depower people.

The inconsistency in security provision produced a feeling of being less valued than others and may have served to depower people.

The frustrations encountered with parking, with no apparent plans to alleviate the problems, may have depowered people.

The presence of an exercise facility with qualified instructors, with a non victim blaming approach to those who did not wish to use this, could encourage self empowering behaviour.

The choice and availability of food did not meet with many people's needs and could lead to feelings of helplessness and depowerment.

The adoption of a no-smoking norm after pressure from the Health and Safety committee was an illustration of the system encouraging people to experience self empowered behaviour. However, without sufficient health education input as to the dangers of passive smoking and skills training to enable those who wished to give up smoking to do so, antagonisms would have remained and served to depower people.

Objective 4: To identify the impact of the whole range of duties expected of a lecturer

Many staff worked over their contractual hours on a regular basis due to pressures beyond their control. Relaxation opportunities were seen as necessary, but limited. Keeping up to date required a constant vigorous effort to stay ahead of the students knowledge and needs. Constant tiredness was often cited as a problem that interfered with both domestic and social life. Other health consequences were suspected to be caused by excessive hours and worry.

In examining the health promoting potential of the college, within an empowerment model, the following observations were made:

The additional hours required to keep pace with work demands, largely beyond the individuals' control, may have served to depower people. Those who kept these extra hours manageable were displaying empowered behaviour.

Lack of relaxation facilities and opportunities, mostly beyond individuals' control, caused people to be depowered.

Keeping abreast with new ideas and information was achieved by those displaying empowered behaviour.

Managing stress and anxiety such that domestic and home life did not suffer displayed empowered behaviour. Many were unable to do this.

Objective 5: To identify any health initiatives

A positive effect was anticipated when the no-smoking policy was introduced - both for smokers and non smokers. One-off initiatives to encourage the take up of exercise had had little impact. A more sustained and flexible approach to accommodate these into the working day was thought likely to be more successful.

In examining the health promoting potential of the college, within an empowerment model, the following observations were made:

The creation of a smoking policy, setting up a no-smoking norm, initiated by the Health and Safety Committee, was an example of empowered behaviour. The college, by being open to re-evaluation, to internal and external influence for change in this area displayed empowering values. Similarly, the use of problem solving strategies, instead of scapegoating, blaming or focusing on faults, was an example of an empowering system.

One-off initiatives on food had been welcomed but where these had ceased people were powerless to make healthy choices.

In acknowledging that making use of the gym facilities would contribute to improvements in their health, people were displaying empowering values that they were primarily responsible for what happens to them. However, lack of flexibility in the working day, largely beyond the individuals' control, and domestic commitments, hindered many from using the gym, thus displaying depowered behaviour.

Nervousness about taking up exercise or participating in end of term games may have been as a result of 'failure' in school sporting activities. This negative evaluation served to depower people and may have been one reason people did not take up exercise for health in adult life.

Objective 6: Contribution of interpersonal relationships

This area generated the most positive response in all areas under investigation. Apart from occasional, and inevitable, interpersonal friction, a very definite feeling of support and concern for one's fellow worker came over. The physical proximity of staff in the Construction Faculty (on a separate site and with their own staff room facility intact) had encouraged the building of a sense of community.

In examining the health promoting potential of the college, within an empowerment model, the following observations were made:

Where the organisation enabled people to work together co-operatively towards shared, identifiable goals, then it may have been said to be an empowering system.

By supporting others around them, the interviewees were displaying empowered behaviour in showing they valued and respected their colleagues.

Where pressures of work limited people from giving or receiving as much support as they desired from their colleagues, the organisation could be said to be depowering.

Lack of opportunity to meet with people in other disciplines to develop a wider support network may have served to depower people.

Objective 7: To identify the potential for the introduction of health promotion

Summary of potential Health Initiatives:

Improvements in communication systems, aiming to produce effective and sensitive lines of information exchange, as well as allowing people access to those whose decisions had a bearing on their lives, would make the system more empowering.

Improved management training would assist the organisation to monitor its own performance in a continuing cycle of reflection-action, thereby displaying empowering values.

Development of the welfare function of the personnel services would empower employees by giving support and help.

A system that sought to reward people for work well done, whether by increases in pay, resources or facilities, would contribute to self esteem and would serve to empower individuals.

Eliminating discrimination was a prerequisite for a empowering system and improvements in Equal Opportunities were needed.

Making healthy eating choices available would allow people to take more responsibility for their own welfare which would encourage empowering behaviour.

Giving people information on sensible drinking and providing non or low alcohol drinks, as well as a relaxation space other than in the bar, would allow people to make healthy choices and encourage empowering behaviour. A formal policy statement to set out the college's policy and procedures, including support for employees with drink related problems, needed to be developed.

Making a smoke free environment the norm would allow non smokers to maintain their healthy choice. Offering smokers places to smoke, without victimisation, and the chance of skills training to give up smoking, would help them develop self empowering behaviour.

The need for regular exercise to maintain health was widely recognised. By giving time and expert help the college could empower people to actively improve their health.

Enabling people to take rest and relaxation breaks during the working day, in surroundings conducive to this, was essential. By providing such opportunities the college would allow people to display empowering behaviour.

By undertaking HIV/AIDS training for all staff the college could raise awareness of the issue, provide information, seek to address prejudices and enable people to take more responsibility for their own and others' welfare. Thus the college would be promoting empowering behaviour.

Stress and anxiety could be managed. Stress management courses would enable people to become more self empowered. However, an empowering system would examine also itself to reduce and eliminate as many stressors within the organisation as possible.

By providing education and health screening for women the college would enable women to take more responsibility for their health and thus develop more empowered behaviour.

In developing its welfare function, in areas of counselling and pastoral care and in developing problem solving strategies, for individuals and the organisation, the college would be displaying empowering values.

The welfare function could be extended to provide regular health checks, combined with better information and understanding of the multifactorial nature of health, so that staff would be better able to make decisions about their lifestyles. Some decisions would require organisational changes, demonstrating an empowering system.

Discussion

The study examined in detail certain aspects of the organisation and the role of the lecturer within that organisation. It looked at the impact of these on well being of the interviewees

172

interviewees and identified areas that required attention.

It analysed the responses within a health promotion model of empowerment and sought to identify the ways the college could positively contribute to people's ability to act in an empowered manner. Ways to increase people's opportunities to act in an empowered fashion were suggested, that is, how the system itself could become more empowering.

The college was already displaying empowering values in its stated objectives. By being open to internal and external influences for change in its statements about Commercial and Enterprising Activity, Focus on Learning, and Contribution to the Development of Education it displayed empowering values. Statements on the Quality of Learning, External Relations, the recognition that individuals are unique, valuable and worthy in its Equal Opportunities statement and Pastoral Care and External Relations objectives, displayed empowering values.

An empowering system shows consistency between its goals and its methods of achieving them and this is illustrated in its final objective, Efficiency, Economy, Effectiveness and Equity.

Health Promotion Audit

The following 'Health Promotion Audit' is offered as a summary of the study. Each objective is dealt with separately, although there is an overlap in some areas, and is introduced by organisational issues that the author considers already contribute to promoting positive well being.

1. The organisation The college was striving to achieve a prominent position in the fast changing world of Further Education, recognising the new business context in education and accommodating this in its objectives. It had set bold targets to achieve in the field of Equal Opportunities, continued to stimulate personal development opportunities and recognised the need to develop its welfare functions.

Improved well being could be achieved by providing more information, support and training to meet the aspirations of the objectives; vigorous efforts to meet Equal Opportunity targets; substantial efforts to improve the welfare provisions.

2. Management style The college recognised a need to improve some of its methods of communication, and that reward systems needed improvement with a more structured approach to staff appraisal.

Improved well being could be achieved by providing better communication systems; wider consultation and involvement in decision making; improved pay, reward and promotion opportunities; positive feedback as well as constructive criticisms on performance.

3. The environment The college was constantly striving to improve its physical environment and allocations of space. Security measures were generally good. Exercise facilities were made available to staff and a no-smoking norm was to be introduced.

Improved well being could be achieved by providing improved allocation of space, for teaching, departmental duties and staff only relaxation; a more equitable approach to security and car parking arrangements; time during the working day to make use of exercise facility; a food policy to allow people to make healthy eating choices with food available at times that better fitted work patterns, in an environment conducive to relaxation; more education on the dangers of passive smoking and provision of smoking cessation classes.

4. The duties of a lecturer The college was positive in its provision of personal development opportunities and encouraging people to keep up to date with their subject areas.

Improved well being could be achieved by providing feedback on performance so that individuals may better assess the hours required to carry out their tasks well; reviewing workloads of teaching staff to eliminate the need for excessive hours; efforts to remove or reduce workplace stressors, stress management courses for managers and staff, including training in time management skills and relaxation techniques; quiet areas for relaxation and ensuring staff had mid-session and lunch breaks.

5. Health initiatives The college had realised the wish, raised at the Health and Safety Committee, to introduce a no-smoking norm into the college. Other initiatives, mostly at the instigation of enthusiastic individuals or groups, had been neither discouraged nor particularly encouraged.

Improved well being could be achieved by the college: by being proactive in introducing and facilitating health initiatives.

6. Interpersonal relationships The college had succeeded in building strong support-ive teams in the Schools and Units.

Improved well being could be achieved by ensuring time was available to enable teams to maintain and develop support networks; providing more opportunities to meet with staff across disciplines; developing its welfare function so the college could become a more personal, supportive organisation.

7. Health promoting policy The following were seen as desirable and feasible areas to develop existing, or draw up new, policy to improve mental, physical and social well being of members of the college:

Reviewing all its current policies and objectives with a view to ensuring they have a positive impact on well being.

Priority areas were identified as communications and information, consultation, management training, reward structures, appraisal and feedback, workloads, space allocation, facilities and opportunities for relaxation and exercise, smok-ing, formal and informal support networks, and welfare provisions.

Additional policy development, offering education and facilities in the areas of eating, alcohol, stress, HIV/AIDS, women's health, and health checks, was desirable.

The health promoting potential

The college was found to have a greater potential to promote health than it already displayed. A framework existed in which to develop health promoting policy, via the Health and Safety Committee, and this had been already demonstrated by the way concerns about smoking were being dealt with.

The author believes that 'soft' and 'hard' benefits could be demonstrated after the introduction of such policies, given a reasonable amount of time elapsing, It is recognised that many of the 'soft' benefits will be difficult to evaluate and that in an empowerment model self assessment by the participants is often necessary.

The college had already shown itself willing to take a close look at its potential to promote health by allowing this study to take place. If it adopted some of the ideas contained herein, it would further display the values of an empowering system, one always open to alternatives and never static.

References

1. Lee, M. & Reason, L. *Action on Stress at Work*. London: Health Education Authority, 1988.
2. Perkins, E.R. *Health Education in the Workplace : Guidelines for Action.* London: Health Education Council, 1984.
3. Allegrante, J.P. & Sloan, R.P. Ethical Dilemmas in Workplace Health Promotion. *Preventitive Medicine* 1986;15:317 - 318
4. Tipton, B.F.A. Conflict and Change in a Technical College. *Brunel Further Education Monographs*, Brunel Further Education Group. London: Hutchinson Educational Ltd., 1973.
5. Snape, J. Stress factors among lecturers in a college of further education. *Work & Stress*; 1988:2

18 Promoting mental health after childbirth

J. Gerrard and S. Elliott

Abstract

The birth of a child does not automatically confer Madonna serenity and contentment on a woman. Birth is an event which brings losses as well as gains. Parenthood is a role with a high level of demand and frequent stress as well as one of rewards. The transition to parenthood has long been acknowledged as one where preparation and support could reduce the risk of family crises or personal breakdown (eg Cowan & Cowan 1988, Shereshefsky & Lockman 1973, Gordon & Gordon 1960). The recognition that the birth of a second child may be equally demanding is rather more recent (Stewart, 1990).

A controlled trial with first and second time mothers has demonstrated that a psychosocial intervention begun in pregnancy can promote emotional wellbeing in the puerperium and reduce the prevalence of diagnosable postnatal depression (Elliott et al 1988).

Since 1987 a trial of training health professionals in this approach has been taking place in London, Stoke on Trent and Edinburgh. This paper will describe the problems and progress in implementing such mental health promotion programmes for mothers within the British NHS system.

The theory

For some people our title remains a contradiction in terms. Think of a newly delivered woman and what do you see? The serene Madonna and child as depicted in the NCT symbol? The beautiful woman and baby of TV ads and magazine covers? The congratulation cards and cooing relatives? Surely newly delivered women are happy by definition. Not only have they acquired this beautiful baby to cuddle and show off but they have just achieved the pinnacle of womanhood and are fulfilled and content. So what

177

needs promoting?

But what about Esther Rantzen? Nobody who's been exposed to the British media in the last few years could have escaped the 'news' that some women are ill after childbirth; about 10% of them get this illness called postnatal depression. True, but even supposing such an illness exists and can be prevented by drugs this is not promoting positive mental health, it is prevention of physical disturbance by medication.

The fact is that the first step in promoting mental health after childbirth is challenging such widespread beliefs about postnatal women. This is by no means as easy as it sounds. Although we are well past the era of post war propaganda encouraging women to believe that domesticity and fertility was the only way to contentment and fulfilment there still seems to be resistance to a new view. This is not confined to men who collectively have a vested interest in keeping women chained to the kitchen sink by perpetuating the view that that is where they 'should' feel happy, at least if they have small children. Pregnant women understandably prefer to look forward to life with the baby once they survive labour. Postnatal ones meanwhile don't wish to admit to not living up to whatever superwoman image their own particular social circle dictates for new mothers. If their unhappiness or coping difficulties can't be concealed then they'll take the 'ill' label thank you very much. The myth of motherhood is so powerful that anyone not presenting as a contented Madonna or not achieving all the current dictates for 'good mothers' feels they may be judged or indeed judge themselves, to be 'mad', 'bad' or a 'failure'. If offered the alternative of the label 'postnatal depression' defined as a socially acceptable physical illness precipitated by birth they will obviously opt for that in preference to the other three. In addition to that, it offers a simple explanation and the promise of a magic wand cure if only those doctors could sort out the right magic pill.

Of course, some postnatal women do have mood disorders of primarily physical origin, most of which would, in fact, achieve the label 'puerperal psychosis'. However, the repeated failure to identify a hormonal imbalance related to non psychotic depression along with the consistent findings of a relationship to psychosocial factors suggests that the majority of depressions in the puerperium do not have a primarily biological origin.

The majority of researchers into postnatal depression appear to accept that it is rarely the manifestation of a biological illness yet prefer to retain the medical model. That is, they view postnatal women as either having or not having 'it', and search for the cause or causes of 'it' and recommend a variety of treatments for 'it'. One function of prevalence studies is to determine whether 'it' exists and whether 'it' is caused by the event of birth. For certain audiences we too use the terminology from the medical model and describe our research as on the primary and secondary prevention of postnatal depression. We present the results of our controlled trial of a psychsocial intervention as a comparison of prevalence rates using diagnosis via Bedford College Criteria applied to the PSE (Table 1) and rejoice in the significant difference.

However, for ourselves and more importantly for the couples participating, we view our approach as promoting positive mental health. The pregnant women did not receive invitations to 'psychotherapy for the prevention of postnatal depression in at risk groups'. First timers were asked to 'Preparation for parenthood' groups and second timers to 'Surviving parenthood' groups.

The aims of the service were to provide continuity of care with the professionals

Percent	Invited	Not Invited
Not Case	81%	60%
Borderline/Case	19%	40%
Number		
Not Case	39	30
Borderline/Case	9	20
	48	50

Depression during first three months in more vulnerable first and second time mothers

p<.01

Table 1

responsible for postnatal support known from antenatal period. Social support was encouraged within and outside support group' meeting. Preparation for parenthood enabled women to reconsider expectations. Stress management consisted of encouraging women and their partners to apply problem solving approach to potential or existing problems. Women were informed of telephone access to individual support from group leaders and where to request education on postnatal depression and puerperal psychosis. First time mothers were the most keen to take up the offer of group meetings and most willing and able to attend regularly. Consequently the Programme had the greatest impact for first timers and this impact lasted.

It should be clear that the approach is based on the assumption of continuity from happy through normal and discontented to diagnosably depressed rather than the dichotomy normal v postnatal depression of the illness or medical models.

To go back to the need for a model. In cases where a simple illness model applies with a rapid descent into clinical depression due to physical factors such as biochemical disturbance, the treatment will be primarily physical. In this category I think of Depressive Disorders which are encompassed under the psychotic disorders.

However, my own view is that this illness model is applied too widely in depression. It has been applied to too many of the women with non psychotic Depression and has limited our choice of interventions.

It is true that many Clinical Depressions seen at psychiatric hospitals have so called endogenous or organic features, so physical or biochemical disturbance must be present in some form to produce such symptoms. However, adopting the simple illness model in which aetiology is viewed as purely physical and treatment as necessarily medical denies the variety of possible points of intervention in both prevention and treatment. I

179

have always viewed Clinical Depression, even with accompanying organic features, as the end point of a vicious spiral. This is crucial to everything we teach.

The depth and speed depends on a variety of factors including:

1. vulnerability to physical symptoms of depression - possibly indicated in a family history of major depression
2. current negative major life events, stressful demands and lack of support
3. cognitive style involving personal tendency to view events and difficulties as major, negative, aversive, uncontrollable and indicative of personal failings
4. the extent to which depressed mood enhances this tendency to view events negatively
5. expectations of life events and situations may also contribute to these perceptions since *failure of reality* to match expectations may lead to more negative views of reality. This is a particular problem for new motherhood, given the media images of Madonna and Child and of the mothers in advertisements. Both Ann Oakley and Vivien Welburn lay much blame for Postnatal Depression at the door of media images and unrealistic expectations of motherhood (Oakley 1980, Welburn 1980).
6. Expectations of emotions. Pregnant women not only have expectations about the life of new mothers but also about the emotions they will experience such as *instant love* for baby, contentment, happiness etc. Such expectations may render new mothers especially vulnerable to the 'Depression about Depression' component which many cognitive therapists such as Teasdale claim contribute to the maintenance of depression.
7. Status of relationships, a complex topic; relationships with others, particularly partners, play a crucial role in the lives of new mothers. Such relationships may be a *source of stressful demands* or of support at a variety of levels. Does she come out of hospital to a tidy home and a husband who tells her to put her feet up or does she return to a litter strewn house and a husband demanding his tea, meals and conjugal rights.
8. Finally, sleep disturbance, broken nights and physical exhaustion should never be forgotten in considerations of puerperal women.

If you picture the descent into depression in this way it is easy to see the *number* of points at which it is possible to intervene to reverse the trend as well as the fact that several *different* types of treatment may be called for in one individual.

This is how I believe people vulnerable to depression move up and down the continuum as opposed to jumping a chasm between ill and well mental states. Perhaps the most critical point is when a woman is experiencing depressed mood - almost certainly connected to postnatal fatigue. If she holds strong expectations of being a contented Madonna or of being a superwoman (especially common among women who mistakenly believe their jobs qualified them for motherhood) then she will feel guilty, or a failure, in fact depressed about being depressed, and she will spin down the spiral. Midwives and health visitors need to explore more ways to gently challenge unrealistic expectations.

My intention is to show that, not only are there several points of intervention for treatment but that there are several points at which the descent into non psychotic Depression may be prevented. Essentially, the aim would be to reduce the actual aversiveness and uncontrollability of events and situations through service changes to improve the lives and experiences of mothers and through facilitating preparation and problem solving by the women themselves. Also, preparation classes and support groups could serve to alter the perceived aversiveness and uncontrollability of such events and situations. Unrealistic expectations of ability to cope, of the nature of situation and of emotions would be challenged. Education about postnatal depression should remove the 'depression about depression' component. Incidentally, we would also have the opportunity for early detection of women requiring medical interventions.

Clearly therefore we need measures of mood outside the range leading to diagnosis of psychiatric disorder. That is of subclinical depression and positive mood levels. Our research tapped into these through the use of several questionnaires. (Table 2).

Ours is a model to be used alongside those for early detection and treatment where health promotion and prevention fails. Ideally, it involves integrating the aims of our service with existing antenatal education and postnatal care.

More Vulnerable Group	EPDS Total	Anxiety	CCEI Depression	Somatic
First-time Mothers				
Intervention	5.4	3.3	2.4	3.0
Control	8.4	5.7	4.2	5.1
Second-time Mothers				
Intervention	8.3	5.2	3.9	4.3
Control	9.7	5.7	5.0	4.7

Mean scores on the EPDS and the CCEI

Table 2

The practice

To us, the obvious next step was to take our theories and research findings to the front line professionals with a 'health for all' remit. With Jenifer Holden, who specialised in detection and treatment, (Holden et al 1989) we set up a 3 centre study, training health visitors in Stoke, Edinburgh and Lewisham. One training session focused on prevention. During this session discussion took place in order to establish what services were already on offer for antenatal and postnatal women locally.

Each Health Visitor received a copy of a prevention manual which described in detail how groups for mothers-to-be, continuing through pregnancy to the postnatal months, could be organized. Health Visitors were encouraged to do antenatal visits as part of a preventive strategy, also to raise the subject of psychological problems following childbirth at parent craft classes.

From each Sector one Health Visitor was identified as a prevention co-ordinator. Their task was to collate information from their colleagues regarding what was on offer in the way of services for antenatal and postnatal women. This information was subsequently passed on to the Health Visitor trainer and then mapped out to illustrate how and where these services were distributed. The prevention coordinator and trainer proceeded to explore ways in which services could be improved to meet the aims of a service promoting mental health.

As one of the trainers, I am now in a position to give a personal view of the feasibility of implementing earlier research findings into current Health Visitor practice. Is the gap between theory and practice closing or are constraints prising it further apart?

Firstly, it could be argued that in order to change practice, attitudes and beliefs need to be challenged. This does not necessarily mean attitudes and beliefs of Health Visitors as individuals, but of the system which trains and employs them. Health Visitors may have constraints on them which conflict with their own belief system and prevent them from changing their style of working.

We did not encounter anyone who did not consider promoting mental health of mothers to be part of a Health Visitor's role. There were, however, differences over prioritizing. Many Health Visitors would have liked to have given top proiority to antenatal visits but were under pressure to fulfil their commitment to children on the 'At Risk' register and Case Conferences etc. In other words although they operate in the field of primary care, priority was given to secondary prevention. Uncovered caseloads due to sickness, leave, etc., do not encourage successful, effective health visiting practice. The practicalities of finance ultimately control the level of health promotion done by Health visitors, who at times found their minimum commitments were becoming their maximum. As much as some Health Visitors wanted to carry out antenatal visits, other demands on their time left them having to omit these visits. However, this did not apply to all the Health Visitors, some of whom regularly managed to do antenatal visits. GP attachment rather than geographic allocation was facilitative here.

Health visiting intervention regarding antenatal education varies from area to area. In Lewisham, Health Visitors took a major responsibility for parent craft classes, at health centres. This is not the case in Stoke-on-Trent where Health Visitors on average (at the invitation of the Midwife) took 2 sessions of parent craft. Having discovered this significant difference, it then became obvious that in this area in particular it was essential to involve Midwives in our work regarding mental health promotion for mothers.

Here again we found differences in the amount of contact Health Visitors and Midwives had with one another. Some had regular informal liaison meetings or were involved in running groups such as antenatal and postnatal reunion groups together. Others due to geographical or other reasons rarely had contact with one another.

One way of dealing with this problem was to evolve a Health Visitor and Midwife liaison group which initially started out on a monthly basis at Charles Street Parent & Baby Day Unit, a unique local psychiatric facility catering for disorders before and after childbirth.

Health Visitors who were involved in the 3 centre study with a particular interest in prevention and whose caseload allowed them more time for this, attended these meetings together with the Midwife from their sector. These meetings are now held every 12 weeks and continue to be a vehicle for the sharing of information, new ideas and general support.

Education of Health Visitors and Midwives on mental health problems surrounding childbirth is relatively straightforward; but how could we be sure that they applied this knowledge to their practice? Here again we met individual differences; some Midwives openly stated that they were reticent to bring up the subject of postnatal depression for example, for fear of frightening mothers-to-be, also the belief that pregnant women do not 'take in' such information was used as a rationale for not talking about such matters. On the whole these views were held only by a minority of professionals and are not supported by research findings.

The Health Visitors were encouraged to look at their areas to see if there were any groups in the service provision for mothers of small children. We identified big variations, some had regular postnatal groups held every week and others had no provisions other than the usual 'baby clinics' for the purpose of weighing etc.

Some of the problems encountered in initiating and running groups for mothers were to do with:

a) Finances - nowhere practical at the Health Centre to run a group meant finding an alternative venue which involved paying a rental fee. This cost ultimately had to be met by the women themselves.

b) Health Visitors lacking in confidence regarding group work. Some Health Visitors developed a structured regime for their groups, inviting guest speakers to talk on topics ranging from diet to beauty tips. Others wanted a more informal arrangement. Group dependency was discussed and age limits to do with the babies. As with any group there are always teething problems. At the Health Visitors and Midwives liaison meetings it was possible to explore these problems and gain from fellow colleagues' previous experience in this field.

At the time of the 3 centre study Health Visitors were being encouraged by management to get involved in group work, so postnatal groups fitted well into their remit.

In Stoke-on-Trent there are now several flourishing groups for postnatal women as well as the groups run by Midwives such as 'early bird' where Midwives invite couples who have recently had confirmation of a pregnancy to an evening discussion etc. Also antenatal and postnatal reunion groups have been run for several years by Midwives to provide a forum for discussion and feedback.

At the end of the day it is down to the individual professionals style of working and level of motivation. In today's climate of NHS changes, uncertainty prevails for many professionals. Only time will tell if the recent NHS reforms are conducive to enabling Health Visitors and Midwives to provide an effective service regarding promotion of mental health after childbirth.

References

Cowan, P.A. & Cowan, C.P. (1988). Changes in marriage during the transition to parenthood: must we blame the baby? In G.Y. Michaels, W.A.Goldderg (Eds.) *The Transition to Parenthood : Current Theory and Research* (pp 114-156). Cambridge Studies in Social and Emotional Development.

Elliott, S.A., Sanjack, M. & Leverton, T.J. (1988). Parent Groups in Pregnancy : A preventive intervention for postnatal depression? In B. Gottlieb (Ed.), *Marshalling social support : Formats, processes and effects* (pp 87-110). Sage Publications.

Gordon, R.E. & Gordon, K.K. (1960). Social factors in the prevention of postpartum emotional problems. *Obstetrics & Gynaecology, 15* ; 433-438.

Holden, J.M., Sagovsky, R. & Cox, J.L. (1989). Counselling in a general practice setting: Controlled study of health visitors' intervention in treatment of postnatal depression. *British Medical Journal, 298* ; 223-226.

Shereshefsky, P.M. & Lockman R.F. (1973). Comparison on counselled and non-counselled groups. In P.M. Shereshefsky & L.J. Yarrow (Eds.), *Psychological aspects of a first pregnancy*, (pp 151-163). New York: Raven Press.

Stewart R. (1990). *Birth of a Second Child.* Sage.

19 Community Mental Health Centres: The natural setting for the prevention of mental health problems?

L. Goodbody

Abstract

This paper describes a questionnaire and interview survey of the preventive activities undertaken by the Community Mental Health Centres (CMHC's) in the South Devon Healthcare Trust area. In recent years, the primary prevention of mental health problems has come to be regarded as an important component of accessible and comprehensive mental health services, corresponding to an emphasis upon psychosocial models of mental health. However, there is an absence of information about policy implementation and achievements in prevention in Britain.

The survey results showed that a wide range of preventive work was being done. Attitudes towards the prevention of mental health problems were consistently positive, and staff rated it as an important CMHC task. However, only a very small proportion of the working week was being spent on prevention. The findings are discussed in terms of current policy, the necessary organisational conditions for prevention, and the conflict between proactive and reactive models of CMHC's. By way of conclusion, a number of recommendations for the development of preventive practices are made.

Introduction

The career of the concept of prevention, and its undulations in popularity on different waves of mental health politics and ideology, has been well documented elsewhere (eg. Ketterer, 1981; Felner et al. 1983). Whilst there have been calls for greater precision in both concept and application (Cowen, 1983), few real challenges have been made to the seminal theoretical propositions of Caplan (1964). He defined primary prevention as "lowering the rate of occurrence of new cases of mental disorder in a population... by counteracting harmful circumstances before they have a chance to produce illness." Preventive interventions are usually group- or mass-oriented, encompassing both the reduction of factors detrimental to mental well-being and the promotion of health and protective competencies. Edwards (1989) identifies three overlapping aims of primary prevention: 1) To foster the development of a 'competent community' though the facilitation of social support systems, 2) To design and implement early intervention for at-risk groups, and 3) To educate the public about mental health, and maximise the coping skills of the community.

Some of the arguments for diverting resources into the prevention of mental health problems are very similar to those favouring the development of more far reaching community mental health services. For instance, both arise from criticism of the medical model and its construction of mental illness, with its emphasis on rooted mental dysfunction and its limited treatment success. Both offer an alternative to the costly, time consuming, culture bound nature of the traditional mental health service, and its unavailability to major segments of the population. It is not surprising, therefore, that the developmental paths of Community Mental Health Centres (CMHC's) and the prevention of mental health problems are closely entwined.

Prevention was a central consideration in the early days of the American CMHC movement. It was one the five key tasks CMHC's were required to fulfil in the 1963 legislation, described by the heading "Consultation and Education" (C and E). However, it became apparent that demands for a reactive service were such that proactive activities remained marginal and poorly resourced and understood. A number of surveys showed that on average, only 4% of CMHC staff hours were spent on C and E services (Ketterer, 1981). In response to these kinds of findings, legislative amendments were made in 1980 and 1983 to make provision for a national prevention unit within NIMH, to provide a lead and to operationalise the terms for delivery of preventive services. However, preventive effort remains inadequately promoted and co-ordinated (National Prevention Coalition, 1989).

In Britain, the functioning of the CMHC's established over the last decade is starting to be reviewed and critiqued (eg. Goldie et al. 1989; Huxley, 1990). Sayce and her colleagues at Research and Development for Psychiatry have sought to monitor the development of CMHC's since 1987. In a recent paper (1991), they have documented the major aims stated by the 67 centres responding to their national survey. 45% of CMHC's reported "Primary Prevention of Mental Illness" as a major aim, 39% stated "Building Community Links", and 33% said that "Secondary Prevention" was a goal. However, there are no corresponding evaluations of the extent to which these aims are being realised in practice, and no preventive headings occur in this list.

Therefore, although prevention and the development of community mental health services make good conceptual bedfellows, the question remains as to whether or not the marriage works out in practice when the honeymoon is over.

The South Devon context

Torbay Health Authority was in the vanguard of the radical changes to adult mental health services, opening its first CMHC in 1984. Closure of the old hospital at Exminster followed in 1987. Currently there are five CMHC's in different towns throughout the district, serving a total adult population of 146,500 people. There is also a 60 bedded acute unit at the District General Hospital. The multidisciplinary teams are all exclusively based in the centres. For most of their history, the teams have been democratically structured. However, three of the teams now have Team Managers, all from different professional backgrounds. Referrals are taken from any source, and most of the centres offer a walk-in self-referral service. There are other, similar teams providing services to children, people over 65 and people with learning disabilities.

From the outset, local policy documents emphasised the importance of developing preventive practices, primary, secondary and tertiary, as an integral part of the new services (eg. Torbay Health Authority/South Devon Social Services, 1983). The ideas expressed were in tune with established conceptualisations, detailing the dual aspects of prevention of new cases and of "inoculation". Operationally, primary prevention is seen as involving "the design, implementation and facilitation of programmes designated:

> to enhance the long-term psychological functioning of those who are as yet unaffected, and/or
>
> to counteract the psychological, ecological or sociocultural causes of mental health problems (Torbay Health Authority 1990)

The operational policies of the five CMHC's are quite variable in respect of prevention. Whilst one has no written statement, it was decided at a recent team day that prevention was one of their core tasks. Another states that one of the main functions of the team is "to work with others to promote mental health education and prevention work within its locality". However, in marked contrast to face-to-face therapy and crisis work, none of the policies mentions how preventive goals are to be achieved and monitored.

The survey

In early 1991, the Community Unit management decided to initiate a major review of the CMHC's, as the service delivery model had been in place for a number of years without thorough evaluation. The Review Committee was made up of managers and representatives of the teams and professions. In the absence of any plan to review non-caseload activity, I offered to undertake the present piece of research, as an organisational intervention and in order to ensure that prevention was included in the Review's terms of reference. As secondary and tertiary prevention were at lest partially covered by other measures, I decided to concentrate on the primary prevention of mental health problems. Senior management gave it their backing, and the prevention questionnaire was circulated under their auspices.

The questionnaire was designed by me, in consultation with managers and members of the local Prevention Interest Group. It was based on issues raised in local discussions and in the literature. It yields both qualitative and quantitative information in four main areas:

> description of current preventive activities
> relative task priorities
> support and communication
> attitudes

Loosely structured interviews were also conducted with team managers and representatives. Their aim was to set the questionnaire data in the context of the immediate organisational climate of opinion and policy within which staff were working.

There was an excellent response rate, with only 3 of the 50 identified staff not returning

187

their questionnaires. The sample was as follows:
    20 Community Psychiatric Nurses (CPN's)
    11 Social Workers, 2 0.T's
    7 Psychologists
    3 Team Managers
    4 Psychiatrists/doctors.

Results

Staff were asked to list preventive activities they had been involved in during the previous six months under the headings of Mental Health Education, Developing the Work of Another Organisation/Profession, Community Development, Developing Social Support, Advocating Mental Health Needs to Providers and Planners, Staff Support and Other.

A total of 132 projects or activities were listed by staff, that is, roughly three per person. 12 members of staff were not engaged in any kind of primary prevention, 26 staff listed between 1 and 4 activities, and another 9 had 5-13 projects on the go, indicating that whilst there was a group of people who were especially interested in prevention, it is a broad based activity. Although CPN's and psychologists tended to be doing proportionally more, the only professional group to be involved in a consistently high number of activities were the 3 team mangers (median=6, range=4-7), reflecting the importance of community/inter-agency liaison and support in their roles (see Table 1 below).

Profession	n	Mean n of Projects	Range	Total n of Projects
CPN	20	3	0 - 13	61
Social Worker	11	1.9	0 - 5	19
Occ. Therapist	2	1.5	1 - 5	3
Psychologist	7	3.8	0 - 13	25
T. Manager	3	5.7	4 - 7	17
Psychiatrist/Dr.	4	1.5	0 - 3	7
Totals	47			132

Distribution of prevention projects by profession

Table 1

The distribution of activity across CMHC's was generally as might be expected, with the three largest CMHC's supporting the highest number of projects. However, it was very noticeable that the smallest CMHC was doing proportionally far more preventive work. This team had a distinctive service vision, which incorporates prevention into many aspects of routine work; for instance, its groups are open to all members of the community.

It must be said that these figures should be taken as indicative only, as the activities reported are not equivalent in terms of time, effort or size of target population. A one-off talk to volunteers, a course for GP trainees on "Education of the Emotions", and a project spanning a couple of years to develop psychological care of women undergoing medical procedures on the Obstetrics and Gynaecology wards each received a count of one. However, an interesting range of work was being done: here is a 10% sample of the activities:

> Stress advice at a Health Fair, Self-help leaflet on back ache, Talks to General Students on placement, Training in counselling skills of RGN students, Working group developing therapeutic services for children who have been abused and their carers, Support of open Relaxation/Yoga classes at local church, Involvement in Neighbourhood Councils, Self-help gamblers group with Addictions Team and Social Services, Advocacy of mental health needs to District Social Services planning, Various staff support groups at the hospital and hostels, Consultation to managers about staff personal problems, Gulf Support Group, Teaching to Homestart volunteers re mental health issues.

Staff were also asked how they evaluate their work. Most responses fell under the heading of feedback - from clients/target group, the team managers, supervisors and other organisations. This was generally done verbally and in qualitative, process terms rather than quantitatively. However, 10 people mentioned the use of written feedback, either through questionnaires and other formal evaluation procedures, or through goal setting and review.

What priority does preventive work have?

Staff were asked to indicate how important they thought certain CMHC tasks should be. There was little differentiation between the ratings: all the named tasks were thought to be important, with Assessment and Therapy coming out as most important, followed by Crisis Intervention.

Prevention/Community Development took third place, and Rehabilitation fourth (see fig.1). The only statistically significant difference between ratings was on Crisis Intervention, with Team Managers and Psychiatrists giving it more importance than Psychologists, and CPN's and Social Workers in between (Kruskal-Wallis, $p<.03$).

Fig.1 here

From their estimates of how much time they spent on each of the major tasks, it is evident that the bulk of staff time goes on Assessment and Therapy. On average, Prevention/Community Development accounts for 1.8 hours per person per week, or 5.7% of the working week (see Fig.2). This contrasts with the importance accorded to it, as indicated above. Although there were trends in the allocation of time according to profession, only one of them reached statistical significance. The amount of time spent

189

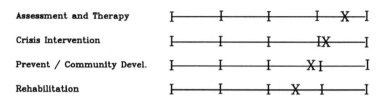

Mean ratings of importance of major CMHC tasks

Figure 1

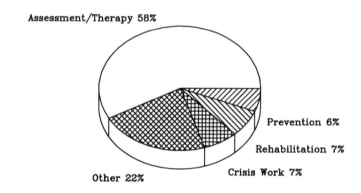

Average porportion of time spent on major CMHC tasks

Figure 2

on Crisis Intervention varied by CMHC according to whether or not a full "walk-in" service was operational and its urban/rural siting (Kruskall-Wallis, p<.02).

Question 6 asks staff whether they want to spend more, less or about the same amount of time on these activities as they are now. The clear finding is that the large majority if staff are content with the way their time is allocated to the major tasks. The notable exception to this is Prevention, on which 80.5% of staff want to spend more time, 19.5% the same, and 0% less (see table 2).

Support, training and communication

Staff most commonly discuss preventive work with their team (62%). 45% of

% of staff who want to spend	Less time	Same time	More time
Assessment and therapy	20.5	66	13.5
Crisis intervention	11	69	20
Prevention/Community Development	0	19.5	80.5
Rehabilitation	10	73	17

Staff satisfaction with current workload distribution

Table 2

respondents discuss it with their managers as part of workload management, but only 34% bring it up in supervision. Furthermore, 79% of staff ticked the response "true" in relation to the statement, "I do not currently have supervision about preventive work". As 76% of staff are involved in at least one preventive activity, these figures suggest that some of the preventive work goes unsupervised, either managerially or clinically.

About half of CMHC staff expressed the intention that they would use support and training. 47% said they would attend local training, 40% would use individual supervision, and 55% group supervision. None of these results differed greatly by CMHC or profession, with the exception of attending training which appeared to attract larger numbers of CPN's (Chi Square, p<.04) Interestingly, only 6 out of 20 nurses thought it was true that their professional training equipped them to do preventive work, although 13 out of 19 said they felt they had the necessary skills, presumably acquired through on-the-job experience as indicated by the relatively high number of projects they are involved in. Psychologists were the only group where a majority felt prepared by their training (5 out of 7).

Staff attitudes to prevention

Staff are overwhelmingly positive in their attitudes towards prevention. Only 16% of staff said they were not interested in prevention, although 30% thought that prevention was unrewarding because the returns are slow and difficult to see. 98% thought that prevention is a necessary aspect of a community mental health service. In terms of support and validation to do preventive work, responses were rather more equivocal. 76% of staff felt they had the support of management. 90% of respondents felt it was true that preventive work is not valued by the service. Finally, in consideration of opportunities to do prevention, 55% thought it was unrealistic to do prevention given the pressure of referrals, and 77% would only do more of it if there was more time.

Staff were asked what they thought the effects and implications of CMHC's not doing preventive work would be (Q10). Responses to this open-ended question fell into four main categories:

Increase in unnecessary mental health problems - more entrenched problems and hospitalisations, more social problems and distress, reduced quality of life.

Generational effects - more family difficulties and damaged children.

Narrow, stagnant 'illness model' services - increased stigma and labelling, short-sighted treatment strategies, community would not be encouraged to deal with problems well.

Lowering of staff morale and job satisfaction - specialist skills and creativity under used, more stress and sick leave and so, reduction in standards of care.

Discussion

A considerable amount and variety of primary preventive work is going on in South Devon's CMHC's, and to some extent therefore, the new style services can be said to be fulfilling their promise. Using a conservative figure that each project impacts upon an average of 10 people, then as a 'guestimate', 1,320 professional contacts were made as a result of the activities that staff listed in the questionnaire.

The ratings of importance of CMHC tasks are comparable to those reported in an earlier study of one South Devon CMHC (Whittle and Logan, 1988). Staff value prevention as an integral part of the mental health service, and their attitudes are very positive. A preventive perspective appears to be linked to staff commitment to the local service model, quality and job satisfaction. This reflects their effective socialisation to the mental health ideology expressed by the local policy documents over the last decade.

However, it was also apparent that the majority of preventive activities were quite small in scale. Relatively few of them could be considered as 'programmes' that have been designed, planned and implemented to modify specific social and individual factors contributing to mental ill-health, even if all of them contribute in some way to the development of a more competent community and population. Rather, prevention is more often woven into the web of CMHC activities when opportunities arise. Although there are no figures for comparison with traditional centralised, unidisciplinary services, it seems probable that this kind of serendipity will occur more richly within the structure and setting of a CMHC service where a psychosocial ideology is dominant and professionals are empowered to work autonomously and creatively through connection with a given community.

In this embedded way, primary prevention can be said to be an integral part of routine CMHC practices. Yet the survey results showed that staff spend very little time on it, the figure of 5.7% of CMHC hours being very similar to the average of 4% quoted by Ketterer (1981) in the States. Prevention is usually squeezed in, an invisible extra sometimes done out of hours, and it is therefore one of the first activities to go when the demands to be reactive are high. This was indicated by the number of staff who felt unsupported and that they could only do more preventive work if time were carved away from referrals, raising difficult political and ethical issues about the allocation of resources. However, as Long says in the report of the National Mental Health Association Commission on the Prevention of Mental-Emotional Disabilities (NMHA, 1986), "Success will be neither cheap nor rapid, but will be far less expensive than failure to act."

Although the philosophy of primary prevention is part of the CMHC model, its practice is not. In many ways it can be argued that the 'new services' are not radical, still being based upon individualistic models for the containment of social stress. For instance, the hub of team effort and multidisciplinary communication is the weekly referral meeting: no equivalent statement of importance is made through allocation of similar time and space to non-caseload work. The rhetoric of prevention policy is not legitimated in the organisational life of the CMHC's, as evidenced by the absence of operational criteria and strategies, and of management procedures for facilitating, monitoring and supervising preventive work. This local tendency is mirrored at a national political level, and is reinforced by the contract culture of the NHS where face-to-face treatment contacts are counted and costed, and the kind of work involved in the prevention of mental health problems is not.

In some respects, CMHC's are the natural setting for the prevention of mental health problems. Prevention is a contextual perspective that is applied as part of the overall service orientation and ideology. However, proactive activity is not the foundation of CMHC work, and will never achieve a foreground focus in what remains an essentially demand-led service unless there is some form of positive discrimination for primary prevention. This would include protected time for some specialist staff, prioritisation and targeting by management, and ultimately, a political climate conducive to its development.

As in many relationships, there is a struggle for power: in the structure and resourcing of CMHC's there is a latent conflict between the discourses of treatment and prevention. It will continue to be necessary to put prevention on the agenda and lobby for its recognition. In the meantime, staff deserve to be recognised for their efforts. It was notable that there were remarkably few differences between professions or CMHC's in the survey trends, and the overall picture is of practitioners who are interested, motivated and competent to work preventively but who struggle to find the time, support and structural permission to do so. I am reminded of "Waiting for Godot" (Beckett, 1971). A leitmotif throughout the play is the refrain between the two tramps when one says "Well? Shall we go?" and the other replies "Yes, let's go". The stage directions are always the same: "(They do not move.)"

Conclusions

Recommendations for the development of preventive practices in community mental health services.

The following recommendations are derived directly from the interviews with Team

Managers and Coordinators, from the comments made by the two thirds of staff who responded to the open-ended question, "Anything else?", and from my interpretation of the data set as a whole. The implementation of these recommendations would improve the standard of preventive work, thus enhancing its effectiveness, and also make it more accountable and marketable. They have been submitted to the Review Committee, and will be fed back to each CMHC with their individual profile of results. Whilst some of the recommendations may be of mainly local significance, most are of relevance as general systems issues central to the development of preventive practices.

1. Increased organisational recognition and monitoring

Prevention should be actively put on the mainstream agenda for action: Consensus is not enough to develop good practice. Nearly everyone is doing some prevention, albeit often secondary, (eg. education of individual clients, prioritising clients with children). These standards should be made more explicit and overt in team meetings, caseload management and supervision.

A policy statement is needed as to acceptable levels of time spent on primary prevention in CMHC's, with agreed areas targeted and reviewed annually. Prevention work should be monitored through being counted in caseload management and written forms alongside Korner, and incorporated into purchaser-provider contracting.

2. Developing the role of CMHC's as catalysts and partners

Teams should assess and identify the mental health needs/risks for the population in their locality, and negotiate a focused preventive strategy, including permission for team members to play certain roles within it. Whilst CMHC's are well situated to flag up causative processes in mental ill-health, they do not always have all the local knowledge, resources or particular skills to carry out preventive interventions. Therefore, work should be shared or contracted to other agencies or groups, such as Health Visitors, voluntary organisations, and Health Promotion in particular.

3. Well defined, planned and evaluated projects

Projects should be clearly thought out, including assessment, prior to intervention, of the likely costs and benefits, and be based on identified need rather than personal interest. They should be selective and focused, and contain a clear task definition and statement of aims, to which outcome can then be related. A variety of evaluation methods should be used whenever possible, as a greater degree of proof will probably continue to be required of prevention than of traditional clinical interventions. In order to achieve these standards, attention needs to be given to supervision, training and audit.

4. Specialist staff roles and responsibilities

Each team should have one member of staff with a reduced caseload whose responsibility it is to give a lead on prevention, communicate specialist knowledge and develop the preventive strategy of the team. Skills and interest in community work with organisations, consultancy, education and evaluation therefore need to be taken into account in considering the skill mix of a team. A district-wide-coordinator with "teeth" is also suggested to ensure a parsimonious use of resources, especially as some projects cannot be confined to one locality.

5. 'A lead from the top' - organisational initiatives

A statement on prevention from the CMHC Review is required. It is suggested that this should lead to two complementary initiatives: a district initiative, in the form of a working party set up from the Review, and local initiatives, whereby a person or persons discusses the issues with teams and their managers, and mobilises them in accordance with the directions of policy.

References

Becket, S. (1971) *Waiting for godot.* London: Faber

Caplan, G. (1964) *Principles of preventive psychiatry.* NY: Basic Books.

Cowne, E.L. (1983) Primary prevention in mental health: Past, present and future. in R D Felner et al. (eds.) *Preventive Psychology: Theory. resaerch and practice.* NY: Pergamon.

Edwards, G. (1989) Finding the broad street pump: Primary prevention in mental health. *Changes* 7 61-64.

Felner, R.D., Jason, L.A., Mortisugu, J. and Farber, S.S. (1983) Preventive Psychology: Evolution and current status. in R D Felner et al. (eds.) *Preventive Psychology: Theory. resaerch and practice.* NY: Pergamon.

Goldie, N., Pilgrim, D. and Rogers, A. (1989) *Community mental health centres: policy and practice.* London: Good Practices in Mental Health.

Huxley, P. (1990) *Effective community mental health services.* Aldershot: Avebury

Ketterer R F (1981) *Consultation and education in mental health.* Sage

N.M.H.A. (1986) *The prevention of mental-emotional disabilities.* Virginia: National Mental Health Association.

National Prevention Coalition for the Prevention of Mental-Emotional Disorders (1989) NPC Update October Virginia: National Mental Health Association.Sayce L Craig T K G and Boardman A P (1991) The Development Community Mental Health Centres in the UK Soc. Psychiatry Psychiatr. Epidemiol 26, 14-20

Torbay Health Authority and South Devon Social Services (1983) *The way forward.*

Torbay Health Authority (1990) Mental Health in the 1990's

Whittle, P. and Logan, V. (1988) Some comments on progress in South Devon CMHC. *Clinical Psychology Forum,* August, 33-37.

20 Promoting mental health: Whose priorities?

J. Harvey

Introduction

This paper is in effect a brief examination of the implications of the shift of paradigm in health promotion which involves 'a recognition of the sovereignty of people's own perceptions of their health and of the necessity to develop a new partnership between the public and professionals engaged in health work' (1). We work in two health districts in Tyneside, and it is appropriate to begin by referring to the events of last week when many of our communities experienced outbreaks of violence of a new intensity. As usual in such circumstances there was a queue of 'experts' and politicians who were ready to offer to anyone who would listen, and particularly to the BBC, an analysis of the problems, the causes, and even the feelings of local residents. One of the most difficult tasks in the past week has been to find ways in which the voices of local residents could be heard, and the collective perceptions of the community could be presented in a coherent way. The last people to whom the professionals and the media seemed ready to listen were the residents of the very communities who were affected.

For those who were prepared to listen, several factors were easily identified. These include fear - 'I don't feel safe on the street at night'; anxiety - 'we don't know what is going to happen next'; intimidation - 'I dare not get involved'; and depression - 'it's all hopeless'. The intimidation is the product of the attitudes that stigmatise people for various reasons. These may be race, employment status (not just whether you work but who you work for), being active in community work, or being known to oppose the values of the local culture. The forces at work in this context are very powerful within the communities that were seen lit up in flames on television screens last week. It is evident that the threats to health, and in particular to mental health, for people living in these deprived areas are to be found in the social, economic, and physical environment in which they live, play, and probably don't work.

In this paper we want to present the model of need assessment that we have developed

197

in Newcastle. This model is based on a community diagnosis approach - the different aspects will be illustrated. Then we will describe five local initiatives which contribute to the promotion of mental health in Newcastle, and offer a critical reflection on those contributions. In conclusion we will discuss the precept that the process of engaging communities and individuals in setting their own priorities is empowering in itself.

A community diagnosis model of need assessment

This model has six defined but not exclusive elements. These are service data, epidemiological data, socio-economic and environmental data, behaviour and lifestyle data, community competence and cultural data, and community perceptions. (Figure 1)

Community Diagnosis Profile

Figure 1

Service data

Service data would include a description of services available from all sectors, preferably presented with maps, and utilisation data. Hospital-based utilisation statistics are our commonest source of data about demand for health care and mental health services are no exception. Hospital admission rates are commonly quoted and compared.

Epidemiological data

Epidemiological data would include demographic data, mortality data, and data on incidence and prevalence of particular conditions. Epidemiological studies can also tell us about causes and should be able to shed light on the natural history of conditions with or without (medical) interventions. Data about the effectiveness of any given intervention would be included here. In the field of mental health the limitations of available data are as constraining as in other areas. Examination of suicide rates and a knowledge of the incidence of, say, schizophrenia in a population will not tell us very much about the burden of morbidity within the same population. We rely on community surveys which have been carried out in different populations and need to test their validity when applied to a local community. The population figures commonly used in this context are derived from Goldberg's work.(2) This suggests that between 250 and 300 persons in a population of 1,000 have what may be described as mental disorders as defined by a score on the General Health Questionnaire. Goldberg and his co-workers found that 230 out 1,000 people attending their general practitioner were classified similarly. The rates of referral to mental health services and admission to psychiatric beds for the same population at risk were around 20 per 1,000 and 4 per 1,000 respectively. Informal data from a local general practice shows that the order of magnitude of people consulting with problems that were categorised as psychological or psychosomatic by the doctor is indeed of the order of 25%.

Socio-economic and environmental data

A variety of variables may be described in this context. These would include geographical presentation of data about facilities and services; data about employment or lack of it; and indicators of socio-economic deprivation. It is not necessary to be to sophisticated in this exercise. Whatever health indicator is matched with socio-economic census-based data in Newcastle, the map looks pretty well the same. There is a correlation between high scores of deprivation and high indices of poor health including psychiatric admission rates. Affected wards are largely along the riverside. Of course the socio-economic data is limited in that it is largely based on 1981 data, and wards are artificial boundaries in terms of neighbourhoods and communities. Some of these limitations will be addressed when the 1991 census data is available.

Behaviour and related data

This is the area of so-called health and lifestyle surveys. We are aware of the debate about the value of such surveys and the strengths and weaknesses of lifestyle data. In a pilot survey carried out in 1989, Newcastle residents reported a very wide range of alcohol consumption. The maximum number of units drunk in a weekend varies from 36 units for 55-64 year old men to 60 units for men aged 16-24. For women the number varies from 12 units for 45-54 years old to 38 units for 16-24 years old.(3) This simple frequency count from the survey raises a number of issues which are relevant to the promotion of mental health. The National Health and Lifestyle Survey produced an interesting set of results. For instance the impact of unemployment is shown in a comparison of answers from people on the same income level about questions to do with psycho-social health. Those who were unemployed scored much higher than those in employment. (4)

All the data described so far is loosely known as 'hard' data. One of our main objectives in developing this model has been to establish qualitative data-bases to complement this 'hard' data. Qualitative data can be gathered through a variety of methodologies largely founded in ethnography. These include structured or semi-structured interviews, participant observation, and the use of focus groups. These methods can be used to develop and test community surveys and then to explore in depth some of the issues raised through such surveys.

Competence and cultural data

Community competencies which might be investigated include language, assertiveness, self-esteem, and practical skills. In one community survey in Newcastle 26% of those surveyed said they would like to learn new skills. Top of the list of skills most desired were dressmaking and cooking followed by D.I.Y and computing. These may seem remote from promoting mental health. In a book describing the experiences of women living on one of the estates in Newcastle one woman describes how learning word processing was part of an evolution which began with involvement as a parent in school affairs. It lifted her self-esteem and changed her life. Cultural data are included here because of their impact on the ability of individuals and communities to exercise skills and control, and because of the importance of peer values. Some very interesting data has been produced by focus group work with children and parents on the subject of crime and vandalism. Here are some of the issues that they raised:

Bullying

'You've got to live against the people who do that to you. And they always wait, every time, you canna even play out. They just start on you. Every time you see them in the street they come for you' (8 year old)

Being out at night

'I'd like a park cause like when you walk the streets I feel frightened, me, when I'm by myself.' (7 year old)

'Sometimes when we're on our own going to the shop, and it's dark, like, then you think 'we'll get picked up'. In the bushes, like, just far down there, a woman got raped.' (8 year old)

Fire

'We light them and hoy them up in the air and catch them. He did it and he burnt his hand.' (8 year old)

'There was a bonfire down the bank, and kids were hoying gas cans on. One exploded - they got gas on them - and nearly blew this kid's face off. He was only about three. They just saved his eye.' (parent)

Being picked-up

'There's this man down the Tyne said 'show us your knickers, show us your knickers'.

I kept screaming and screaming. He was horrible. I was shaking.' (8 year old)

'About two years ago a girl got raped, and she was eight years old. Another girl about five years old got molested.' (9 year old)

Growing-up on the estate

'Cause all the little bairns are just growing up around, smashin windows and all that, they think it's normal.' (14 year old)

'When they play with their cars they play hoisty cars, and it's the glueys driving and doing handbrake turns.' (parent)

'My first two weren't born here, and where we were before they got the chance to meet nicer kids. But my last ones were born here and them two are right little villains. They picked it all up. But I was still the same parent to them. I brought them up the same way. And I knew it wasn't anything different I had done, it was just the society.' (parent)

Community perceptions

In the community survey mentioned above the residents of the estate were asked about their own health. 20% said there was something affecting their mental and physical health. 33% said stress was affecting their health, 20% pointed to fear of crime/harassment, and 17% blamed unemployment or financial problems. Safety and security is a major problem for people living on these estates and must be a major potential cause of mental ill health. 36% of those surveyed had experienced a crime in the last six months (such as assault, threat of violence, burglary or vandalism). 49% of people surveyed felt unsafe in the area depending on where they lived. 63% thought the area had become less safe over the last few years. Some of the commoner reasons given were more crime/burglary; problems of new people moving in; more joy riding; and lack of parental control. One interesting figure is that 9% of respondents said they 'rarely' or 'never leave the house' because of lack of security. (5)

Local initiatives and the promotion of mental health

The five initiatives in Newcastle in mental health promotion are:

   i.   The establishment of a user group, involving users of mental health services;
   ii. A project with two link workers from ethnic minority groups who are investigating the experience of their own communities in regard to mental health;
   iii. The use of focus groups to determine the needs of residents in selected estates in deprived areas of the city;
   iv. Joint planning with general practitioners, psychologists and health education officers to support mental health promotion in primary health care settings;
   v.   The development of an inter-agency group whose specific remit is mental health promotion.

Four criteria have been selected in order to evaluate the impact of these initiatives in health promotion. The criteria reflect the principles that underline health promotion, based on a model of health education that gives priority to social action. Four questions may be asked:

How far does this initiative involve and promote inter-agency work?
Is there genuine community participation in the process, with access to decision making?
Has there been a genuine effort to discover and represent community perceptions?
Whose voice dominates the output?

Table 1. offers a subjective and personal analysis of these five initiatives. The scores in the middle three columns are for an arbitary scale 0-5 where 5 is maximum positive value.

INITIATIVE	INTERAGENCY WORK	COMMUNITY PARTITION	COMMUNITY PERCEPTIONS	DOMINANT VOICE
User group	2	3	3	Facilitator User
Ethnic minorities	2	2	4	Community Worker
Community Survey	3	4	5	Residents
PHC	2	0	1	Professional
Mental Health Promotion Group	4	2	3	Voluntary Sector (Professional)

Evaluating Health Promotion Initiatives

Table 1

The user group

The User group was established as a consumer group at the initiative of Newcastle Health Authority and the Mental Health Trust who share costs and benefits of the group. It consists of fifteen service users and carers, who were brought together by a paid facilitator. It is intended that the group will elect members from a broad constituency of users and it has developed a wide network of contacts in the district. The role of the consumer group in relation to the Health Authority has been in three main areas:

Contributing to need assessment, particularly presented as anecdotal evidence.
Developing and monitoring quality measures for contracted services.
Contributing to strategic planning.

Although the user group has developed networks and an interface with other agencies such as Social Services, it is not primarily an inter-agency group. However because of its constituency, it is not truly representative of communities, however they are defined. In the first year of its existence the dominant voice has been that of the facilitator but more recently the users' own voices have been clearly heard and they have taken on an effective role in advocacy.

Link worker

The link worker project with the minority communities has been working with Newcastle Mind and the Mental Health Trust and is not seen as an inter-agency project. The community workers have examined the attitudes and conditions for patients from ethnic minority communities within the services provided by the Mental Health Trust. They have also given time to articulate the perceptions of their own community in regard to mental health. However, inevitably the dominant voices are those of the two community workers who are both articulate women well used to functioning in a cross-cultural context.

Focus group

The focus group methodology has been employed as part of action research into the life of people living in estates in target areas in Newcastle. This work has been carried out as a collaborative venture between the Department of Social Policy, Newcastle University, Save the Children Fund, and Newcastle City Council. This work concentrated on crime and vandalism in one estate, and was part of a community development approach which has brought residents from four estates together in a unique forum to discuss their common experiences and to plan area strategies for their own estates. This type of approach allows residents' voices to be heard in a coherent way although it is recognised that the residents participating in the group work are self-selected.

Primary health care

The Primary Health Care Initiative aims to establish a network of supporting self-help groups, courses etc. to offer a practical intervention for patients identified through the health promotion clinic. Much of the work of these clinics may be described as case finding, but the issues that emerge are often about mental health rather than merely the identification of risk factors for coronary heart disease. Assertion training, anxiety management, and behavioural change are topics that would be addressed within such a network. Leaders or tutors would be found in adult education or voluntary organisations, as well as among primary health care team members. However this is a professionally led initiative and it is the professional voice which dominates.

Inter-agency

The inter-agency group which makes up Newcastle's Mental Health Promotion Group were brought together as a follow-up to a Regional Mental Health Forum. This group, which consists of representatives from the voluntary sector and statutory organisations, has successfully planned a 'hearts and minds' week which was launched recently. The aim is to raise awareness of the need to promote mental health in a positive sense, and to focus on innovative community-based projects. Although the members of the group represent very distinct constituencies, it has to be said that the major influence on the development of this work has been the perceptions of the professional volunteers.

Conclusions

It is the work with ethnic minority communities and with the residents of some of the neighbourhoods of the city that has allowed community perceptions to be identified and presented to the health promoters. This democratised method of data gathering is an essential part of planning health promotion programmes. An interesting study of mental health education in a Canadian community in 1951 showed that despite careful attitude surveys to study the relationship between the propositions advocated by the educators and assumptions entertained by the public, attitudes towards the mentally ill remained unaltered. The authors pointed to the conclusion that it is 'insufficient to access popular belief in terms of their scientific accuracy; it is also necessary to know the functions they perform for those who hold them.' (6) I think we need to learn this lesson again in 1991. Residents in areas of Newcastle are saying that making streets safer in every sense is their priority for improving health, and that includes promoting mental health.

The use of methods of gathering data that require the participation of communities will enhance community competence. This brings in the concept of empowerment. The relationship of health promotion, empowerment and the psychology of control has been discussed frequently in the literature in recent years. In a discussion of this subject published this year Tones makes the statement - 'empowerment is per se 'healthy'.'(7) Health promotion strategies predicated on community development need to address issues of internal control, life skills or competencies, and external control. The proposition that we are reiterating here is that engaging communities and individuals in the process of identifying their priorities for health is part of a process of empowerment. Studies in developing countries have demonstrated this in many interesting ways.

Our observation in Newcastle is that people living on the targeted estates have come together around the information that they have created and for which they rightly feel a sense of ownership. In the community survey referred to above, 31% said they would probably get involved if local residents got together to get some changes for the better. 19% said they would certainly get involved.(5) This has led to action within the communities and a process to produce area strategies without the input of professionals. It has led to a desire expressed by some individuals to learn communication skills. And significantly it has caused anxiety amongst the policy makers. An essential element of such a health promotion strategy is the need to build in some cultural reorientation for the decision makers so that they do not automatically refute the data and aspirations of the communities.

These concepts are easily discussed in conferences on health promotion, but the practical application requires commitment and is not without risk for communities and individuals. At the beginning of this paper we referred to the factor of intimidation as one element affecting mental health. One resident who had become a key person in this process of community development, and had organised and articulated the resistance of her community to the joy riding craze, was personally targeted during the violence last week. Her feelings of rejection and her fear for her family have brought her into turmoil emotionally and mentally. Suddenly her very priorities have been challenged. All this begs the question - in mental health promotion, whose priorities are we going to address?

References

1. Ashton. J., & Seymour, H. *The new public health*. Milton Keynes: Open University Press, 1988
2. Goldberg, D., Filters to care - A model. In: *Indicators for mental health in the population*. (Ed. Jenkins R, Griffiths S.) Department of Health. London: HMSO, 1991
3. Newcastle Health Authority, Health and Ill health in Newcastle: The first report of the Director of Public Health. Newcastle, 1990
4. Blaxter, M. *Health and lifestyles*. London: Routledge, 1990
5. Wallace, B. Personal Communication
6. Cumming, J. & Cumming, E. Mental Health Education in a Canadian Community. In: *Health culture and community* (Ed. Paul, B.D.) New York: Russell Sage Foundation, 1955
7. Tones, K. Health promotion, empowerment and the psychology of control. *J Inst Health Educ* 1991; 29:17-24

21 Promoting mental health through social support

D. Milne

Introduction

'Social Support' refers to a very wide range of informal, helping relationships, from the more familiar 'close confiding relationship' with a partner (Brown and Harris, 1978), to the conversation with a hairdresser (Cowen, 1982). As these examples suggest, its breadth almost defies definition, leading researchers to regard it as an 'elastic concept' (Barrera and Ainley, 1983; p 133) a 'conceptual morass' (Winefield, 1987; p633); and, slightly more positively, as a 'multi-dimensional construct' (Gottlieb, 1983; p61)! Historically, social support has been known by such related terms as 'social system psychotherapy', 'network therapy', 'ecological therapy', 'general systems therapy' and 'support systems'. These indicate some of the conceptual morass.

This paper begins with an attempt to provide a workable and conceptually clear definition of social support, by contrasting it with psychotherapy. It then goes on to provide illustrations in relation to 3 core issues, indicating how clinicians can promote mental health by social support analyses and interventions. These illustrations are drawn from small local research projects that I have supervised or participated in, and are intended to indicate methodologies and opportunities, rather than being offered as substantive research statements.

Definition

Given the seemingly boundless diversity of social support, how might it most usefully be defined? Table 1 provides a summary of my attempt to 'compare and contrast' social support with psychotherapy, by means of six of their more dominant features. This is based on the social support literature (especially: Caplan and Killilea, 1976; Gottlieb, 1983; Winefield, 1987). It is clearly a very general analysis, since for example, 'psychotherapy' also refers to a diverse range of professional help. However, the analysis does seem to serve its function in delineating the two forms of help and in defining social support.

VARIABLE	COMMON	SOCIAL SUPPORT	PSYCHOTHERAPY
Type of problem	considerable (e.g., child management and health)	Minor practical and emotional problems	More severe emotional problems
Form of help	Considerable overlap of informational and emotional help	Practical; more Q's, advice and information	Client unconditionally valued (cf. 'EE') and more reassurance and explor./interp.
Function of help	Self-esteem enhancement, provide information	Relieve practical difficulties	Enhance adaptive coping
Consequences of help for helpers	Mostly feel good	Reciprocity: more negative reactions?	Employment
Sources of help	Range of people	Mostly family & friend/s but extremely diverse in all social settings? 'Socioculturally similar' important?	Mostly professional in formal settings; socioculturally disimilar
Mechanisms of help	Enhance coping: direct and indirect (buffer and main effects)	Equally buffer and main effect? via practical and emotional strategies	mostly buffer (i.e. stressor related) via specific adaptive coping strategies

Common and distinctive elements of social support and psychotherpy

Table 1

The essential definition that emerges is that, by contrast with psychotherapy, social support is: informal help in coping with routine life stresses. However, all of the terms in this definition differ only in degree rather than kind. Thus, some sources of help within 'social support' are semi-formal (e.g. voluntary sector, such as a carer support scheme run by Age Concern), having paid employees with some degree of formal training and support. Similarly, the term 'help' refers largely to shared problems foci, helping strategies and help outcomes, though it appears that psychotherapists deal with more distressed clients who have more impaired coping strategies in a more structured fashion. The consequences of help also appear to distinguish the two endeavours, for help provider and recipient. Essentially, psychotherapists seem to have personal qualities, professionally-developed skill, and professionally distant relationships which result in less distress with the helping role. Recipients apparently derive more enduring help from psychotherapists, allowing for successful disengagement. The key to this difference lies in the more effective work done by the therapist on the client's personal coping strategies (e.g. systematically training the recipient to think, feel and behave in a more adaptive fashion), although one sometimes wonders whether this difference is more attributable to the respective goals than to helping skills or methods. To illustrate, reviews comparing professional and non-professional helpers fail to show an advantage to the former (e.g. Hattie et all, 1984). It would seem to follow that the social supporter might achieve similar outcomes in adaptive coping if there was less emphasis on reciprocity and continuity in the relationship.

Turning to the presence of 'routine life stresses' in the definition, this is intended to cover everyday stimuli (internal and external to the individual - hence symptoms or life events, etc.) that the individual regards as requiring a response. This would therefore embrace a large range of private and public events, some readily defined by others as stresses, some best judged by the individual concerned. Seeking 'positive social interaction' (e.g. a cup of tea and a chat) may therefore be an individual's response to the stress of loneliness, rather than necessarily a call for help with a specific problem.

In defining social support in this way I am leaving open the possibility that it may act as a 'buffer' to stresses or serve as a 'main effect', bolstering esteem independent of any stress.

These two models of social support have been proposed as alternatives (see, for example, Alloway and Bebbington, 1987), yet there appears to be a place for both in explaining how people cope. For example, positive social interaction in the absence of a stressful event may serve to boost confidence or morale, in turn helping the individual to cope with problems.

Mental Health Promotion through social support work

The history of clinical work shows a clear trend towards the acceptance of more systems-level interventions (Pattison, 1973). Psychotherapy began as a strictly one-to-one affair, leading in the 1920's to the inclusion of parents during child work. Group therapies emerged in the 1930's, though the emphasis gradually moved from treatment of an individual in a group to the idea of therapy for and by all group members. The 1940's and 1950's saw the emergence of family therapy, followed by a move in the 60's by clinicians out of the clinic into people's 'natural environments' (i.e. homes). Gradually relatives, neighbours and 'significant others' became involved. Similarly, in institutions the therapist began to work on the system by influencing those who worked in it (e.g. teachers, nurses). Recent years have seen the advancement of community based parent training technologies (Dangel and Polster, 1984) and current policies of 'community care' which recognise and appeal to social support.

This trend from the clinic to the community has been accompanied by repeated calls to clinicians to alter the emphasis of their work. Surveys show that the overwhelming majority of people do not take their emotional problems to mental health specialists, but rather appeal for help to their social support system (Cowen, 1982; Barker et al, 1990). It follows that to be optimally effective, these specialists need to develop ways of recognising, influencing and bolstering the social support of their actual and potential clients. As a corollary of this kind of logic, there have been repeated calls to clinicians to improve and strengthen social support (Cassel, 1976), including encouragement to co-operate and collaborate with natural support systems (e.g. as referral agent, trainer, consultant or group initiator: Gottlieb, 1983). There now follow some illustrations of this kind of work.

Illustrations

Some core issues emerge from my analysis of social support. They concern the nature of the help provided by psychotherapists and social supporters, the function served by this help, the helpers role, and the impact of help on those giving and receiving social support.

Formal and informal help

Cowen's (1982) summary of the help provided by bartenders, work supervisors, divorce lawyers and hairdressers indicated considerable overlap with the helping strategies used by clinicians. In order to examine the overlap hypothesis in a UK setting Gormly (1989) recorded the speech of two experienced stylists in the hairdressing salon of a large psychiatric hospital, combining it with data from four experienced stylists in a high street salon in the neighbouring town. He used the Helper Behaviour Rating Scale (HBRS, Hardy and Shapiro, 1985), an instrument for coding twelve types of helper speech (e.g. 'reassurance'; 'open question'). The stylists} data (a total of 20 hours) were then compared with published HBRS data on therapists from studies by Milne (1989) and Hardy & Shapiro (1985), amounting to 18 hours.

Analysis of the HBRS data led to a rejection of the 'overlap' hypothesis. Though there was a positive association between stylists and therapists ($r = 0.24$ across all HBRS categories) this was not statistically significant. In contrast, correlations within the therapist and stylist groups were high and significant ($r = 0.78$ and $r = 0.92$, respectively), indicating that the data were representative. In terms of the individual HBRS categories, stylists mostly gave information (25% of speech), asked questions (21%0, gave reassurance (16%), and reflected their clients speech (11%). They made little use of exploration (1%) and interpretation (2%). By contrast, therapists gave roughly three times as much reassurance (48%) and advice (18%), while using more exploration (3%) and interpretation (6%). They gave less information (8%), asked fewer questions (11%) and reflected the clients speech less often (5%) than did the stylists.

The highly significant association between the speech of the hospital and community stylists tends to suggest that differences between clients groups is not an alternative explanation for these findings, leaving one to conclude that there are real differences between the verbal help provided by stylists and therapists. This is in keeping with similar research findings in the USA (Toro, 1986; Tracey & Toro, 1989).

The function of social support

Related to the above focus on the form of help that is provided by social supporters and mental health specialists is the issue of its function. The two do not necessarily coincide, in the sense that the kind of differences outlined above do not allow one to conclude that one kind of help is 'better' than another. This point is evident within the psychotherapy literature, where it can be easy to demonstrate differences in the form of therapy (e.g. psychoanalysis uses more exploration and interpretation than behaviour therapy: see Hardy & Shapiro, 1985) but very difficult to distinguish their relative effectiveness (Stiles et al. 1986).

Again, while comparisons across therapies are common, it is rare to find comparisons between therapists and social supporters. An attempt to conduct this comparison was made by White (1990), who sent out an ad hoc questionnaire to a sample of 80 current clinical psychology out-patients, receiving 40 usable replies. The questionnaire addressed four major types of social support (i.e., practical, informational, emotional and positive social interaction) in relation to four different sources of help (i.e., relatives, friends, hairdresser and psychologist). It also asked about their helpfulness.

Her results indicated that all four agents provided all four forms of help, albeit in different proportions. To illustrate, while relatives, friends and hairdressers were reported to provide similar amounts of informational support (Mean: 36%), the two psychologists assessed gave more of this support (50%) and also more emotional support (32%). Overall the psychologists' help had a significantly different pattern from that of the three social supporters' groups. This therefore corroborated Gormly's (1989) findings of some continuity but little overlap across the help provide by formal and informal agents.

However, the critical functional question concerned the helpfulness of these four groups. This indicated that while other groups provided more frequent help (especially relatives), the clients regarded the psychologists as providing the most adequate help. Therefore, these statistically significant findings led to the conclusion that the form of the formal and informal help were different, at least as judged by a sample of perhaps favourably-biased psychology out-patients.

The social supporters role

What kind of people make the best social supporters? Where does social support take place? With what consequences for the supporter? Three more local studies examined these questions.

Taking the issue of the 'popular helper' first, it has been suggested that this person will share some important characteristics with the person receiving help (Thoits, 1986). These 'sociocultural' characteristics include education, dress, background (social class), values, calmness, ways of talking, points of view and life experiences (especially having experienced the same difficulties as the help recipient). Dibdin (1991) investigated this hypothesis by enlisting a sample of 38 self-help group attenders to complete an ad hoc questionnaire focusing on their sociocultural similarity to those leaders, helpers and peers who attended the groups. He found a significant correlation between the sum of all eight 'similarity' variables and the helpfulness of the group ($r = 0.35$), but no such association with all 3 types of social support (i.e., 'emotional', 'informational' and 'practical'). Also, only two of the eight similarity variables correlated significantly with these social support dimensions. They were 'life experience' and 'dress' both of which had a modest association with 'practical support' ($r = 0.39$ and $r = 0.40$), respectively. In turn, 'emotional support' was the only type of social support to correlate significantly with perceived helpfulness ($r = 0.44$), possibly a consequence of the sample studied.

Thus, only two of 24 correlations coefficients indicated a strong link between 'sociocultural similarity' and social support, while none of the coefficients indicated a strong association between the eight similarity variables and helpfulness. Although sub-group analysis yielded different patterns of association, some of the significant findings countered the Thoits hypothesis (e.g. the least 'calm' helpers were regarded as most helpful). It is therefore not apparent that 'socio-culturally similar' helpers are the most effective.

Turning to the next issue, where does social support take place? According to Cowen (1982), 'help is where you find it', and most frequently in bars, based on his comparison of hairdressers, bartenders, lawyers and work supervisors. Hextall & Hudson-Peacock (1991) attempted a small replication of this finding in the UK, comparing a large urban centre with a small rural town. They found that their four groups of subjects, (hairdressers, florists, ministers and bartenders) did provide social support to their clients, in similarly moderate amounts and in very similar ways. There was also little difference between the rural and urban samples. The only significant difference that they obtained was that rural bartenders reported using significantly more helping strategies. Table 2 sets out their findings for all four groups of helpers, across both settings.

From their study, Hextall & Hudson-Peacock (1991) were able to conclude with Cowen (1982) that help does indeed take place in a wide range of settings, with a strikingly high frequency.

The cost of caring

The next and perhaps most crucial aspect of the helping system concerns the effects on social supports of providing the kind of help summarised in Table 2. As indicated above, in defining social support, reciprocity is seen as the necessary 'currency' governing help. It follows that in 'natural' relationships help-giving should be repaid in kind if it is to be maintained (cf. therapists who represent a contrived form of help which is so unreciprocated that is has to be 'bought').

Two local studies have addressed this issue, labelled the 'reverse buffer' effect in the social support literature (Coyne & Delongis, 1986). One of these again used high street hairdressers as subjects (N = 11) and assessed the effect of their social support role on their personal stress, coping and strain (Milne et al. 1991). Their social support skills had been enhanced by means of a workshop. It was found that their stress, coping and strain remained steady during a baseline period, but that there were significant improvements in their coping skills following the workshop, and a non-significant reduction in their strain. These findings indicated that there were no adverse effects of providing social support, and that a brief course of focused training helped with their coping strategies and strain. (Their social support role remained constant throughout the research period.)

In a second and closely related study ex-clients (N = 6) were trained as anxiety-management group leaders of a series of community-based, self-help groups (Milne et al. 1989). This time the social supporters completed self-report measures of their own anxiety and self-efficacy, but it was again concluded that there was no negative or 'reverse-buffer' effect. Anecdotal comments indicated some benefits as well as costs, as

HELPING STRATEGIES	BARTENDERS	FLORISTS	HAIRDRESSERS	MINISTERS
Offer support and sympathy	3.3	4.3	3.5	4
Try to be lighthearted	3.8	3.5	3	2
Just listen	4.3	3.5	4	4
Present alternatives	2.3	3	3.5	3.5
Tell them to count their blessings	2	1.3	1	1
Share personal experiences	2.3	3.3	2.5	3.5
Try not to get involved	3.8	2.8	2.3	1
Ask questions	3.8	3.8	3.5	4
Try to get the person to talk with someone else	2.5	2	3.3	2.5
Try to change topic	3	1.5	2.5	1
Point out consequences of bad ideas	2.8	2.5	2.5	2
Help clarify feelings	2.8	3	2.5	4.5
Suggest reading	1.5	1.3	1.5	2.5
Get person to come up with alternatives	2.3	2.3	2.8	3.5
Say, 'I'm not the right person to talk with'	2	1.3	1.5	2
mean	2.8	2.6	2.8	2.7

Mean frequency with which four groups of helpers reported providing social support to clients

Table 2

(1= never or very infrequently
5= very frequently or always)

per Cowen's (1982) findings that social supporters may feel positively (e.g. 'gratified' and 'sympathetic') and negatively (e.g. 'puzzled' and 'helpless') about their social exchange.

The recipient of social support

My final 'core issue' concerns the impact on those receiving social support. The very term suggests nothing but wholesome benefit, yet it subsumes the 'reverse buffer' and other negative effects. It is therefore important to examine the range of consequences for the supported persons, just as it is for the helpers. Fascinating and persuasive examples of this kind of 'side-effects' analysis are to be found in the 'behavioural-ecology' literature (see, e.g., Rogers, Warren & Warren, 1977), and we know from the 'expressed emotion' literature that not all close relationships are supportive.

Hairdressers have again helped us to study this question. In the study outlined above (Milne et al. 1991) and in a prior one (Milne & Mullin, 1987) we asked the question posed by Cowen's (1982) review, namely, how effective or helpful is social support? To assess this we asked random samples of clients attending high street salons to complete a brief 'consumer relations survey' form before and after a workshop provided to their stylists (as outlined earlier). The form included questions on the helpfulness, interest, enjoyment and talkativeness of the stylist, rated on a 100 mm visual analogue scale. High ratings were given on all items, with a significant increase in helpfulness in the second of these studies, following a workshop intended to increase social support skills (e.g. counselling and information giving). A non-significant trend in the same direction was obtained in the other study. These findings indicated that the stylists were perceived as helpful by their clients, and that this was increased by the social support training. Table 3 presents the survey data from both studies.

A second dominant criterion for judging the quality of social support is its adequacy. This is usually operationalised in terms of the clients' satisfaction with their support. MacDonald (1991) studied this variable in relation to the carers of elderly people. These people were receiving help from the Age Concern carer support scheme. A questionnaire survey indicated that the carers were highly satisfied with the type and amount of help, the competence of the care attendants, and the overall quality of the service. In terms of its impact, all of the carers felt that the help enabled them to cope more successfully, by relieving the stress and burdens of caring.

However, the main focus of MacDonald's (1991) work was on social support as a possible explanation for this high level of satisfaction. By asking the care attendants to keep ad hoc diaries and by conducting structured interviews with the carers and care attendants she was able to establish that the most frequently occurring and important form of help was emotional support. This was followed by practical, then informational support, as she had predicted from the literature. Her results illustrate once again that helping relationships that may well have an obvious practical focus are actually valued most of all for their more subtle socially supportive function.

A final local example of the impact of social support concerns its role in bolstering an individual's personal coping strategies. These were assessed in relation to the previously mentioned study with ex-clients as anxiety-management group leaders (Milne et al.1989). The effects of their social support efforts were assessed in terms of the clients stress, coping and strain before and after the group. It was found that while stress remained constant (and therefore was unlikely to explain changes in coping or strain) the clients reported significantly more adaptive coping strategies and significantly lower

ITEMS	FIRST BASELINE (n=320)	SECOND BASELINE (n=94)	POST INTERVENTION (n=145)
How enjoyable was your visit to the salon?	78.6	88.8	88.5
How much did the hair dresser talk to you?	94	99.4	86.2
How interested in you was the hairdresser?	73.6	75.3	81.3
How helpful did you find it to talk to the hairdresser?	78.5	82.1	86.4

Customer relations survey data from two salons presented as mean percent scores
(the higher the score the higher the endorsement)

Table 3

strain following the group. These results were maintained at a 6 month follow-up assessment.

Summary

These small-scale, local studies illustrate how a range of related issues in social support can be considered in terms of promoting mental health. The studies suggest that social support overlaps with some aspects of professional therapy, but nonetheless that it can be clearly distinguished from it in terms of both its form and its function. One distinction made in the literature is that, unlike therapists, social supporters achieve their beneficial effects as a result of their sociocultural similarity to the client. However, similarity did not appear to be an important correlate of help in our local study. On the other hand, in keeping with the literature we did find that 'help is where you find it', as indicated by a range of community agents providing moderate frequencies of help in strikingly similar ways. The consequences of this socially supportive role were found to be generally neutral for supporters and positive for the supported - there was no indication of the 'reverse-buffer' effect. Emotional support was the most frequent and important type of social support on all occasions we assessed it.

Discussion

I realise that this paper mirrors Cowen's (1982) review, in that both were based around local studies in order to highlight and explore issues that had generally not attracted large-scale, systematic research. Like Cowen, I must therefore repeat that the studies outlined above are offered with 'no illusions about their technical elegance,' but more in the character of research in the 'community cauldron' (Cowen, 1982; p 392).

This is not to dissuade others from improving on the rigour of these social support studies, should they also find the topic fascinating and worthy of research. There are some straight-forward ways of improving on our local studies, such as gathering larger and more representative samples (as most of the studies were BSc. dissertations, time was limited). These are not necessarily any more challenging than research in other settings. A relative exception seems to be the capacity of respondents to provide reports in an accurate and candid fashion. This follows from the difficulty in delineating social support from the rich variety of ways in which people interact. We sense that people struggle to answer our questions because of a kind of lay 'medical model' which separates health and illness, and which therefore regards words like 'problems' or 'stressors' as either present (and therefore indicative of personal weakness or illness) or absent. This can also be true of clinical samples, but it is more acceptable to probe such groups so as to reach a better understanding of the help they receive (see, for example, the 'significant events' in therapy research; Llewellyn et al. 1988). In the 'community cauldron' there are unusual difficulties in even gaining permission to raise simple questions.

Having gained access, there also appears to be a difficulty in determining the right questions to ask. Cowen (1982; p 393) has argued that we have to gather 'trustworthy data on effectiveness (i.e. actual helpfulness)'. Properly addressed this strikes me as a more profound question than the kind answered by the customer relations survey reported earlier. Clients are not necessarily equipped to say how effective or helpful some social support has been, for the same reasons as psychotherapy clients. Just because it feels good does not mean it helps. Indeed, theory and evidence point the other way: it seems to be necessary for learning and personal change that there is some discomfort (e.g. anxiety; Kolb, 1984): it has been found that those who learn the most are the least satisfied with the learning environment (Parker & Thomas, 1980). This therefore suggests that our questions need to probe beyond clients' expressions of perceived helpfulness or effectiveness, and focus on these in terms of some more objective criterion. This might include the stress - coping - strain analysis at the personal level, as outlined above, supplemented at the interpersonal level by evaluation of the interactions between the individual and the health care system (e.g. use of GP and related services). This would parallel the emphasis in the psychotherapy outcome literature.

In addition to clarifying the context of social support, the above analysis draws attention to the relative contributions of several variables to mental health. In this sense, it would be very useful to try and clarify the extent to which social support can explain mental health for any given sample, in relation to other variables known to have a bearing (e.g. medication, housing and employment, physical health etc.). It is conceivable, for example, that the 'moderate' levels of apparently superficial support noted in the Hextall & Hudson-Peacock survey (1991) are nonetheless adequate to meet the clients' needs and hence to 'buffer' them to the point that they do not experience mental health problems. This represents a different kind of question from the ones addressed above, yet promises far more insight into mental health.

To illustrate, Fondacaro & Moos (1987) considered the interpersonal transaction by which social support influences an individual's coping, as well as vice versa, for a sample of 380 depressed people. They found that support was greater for women in the family context when they used more problem-solving coping and when there was less emotional discharge coping among men. Different patterns of coping and social support were found in the work context. These results led them to posit that such specific variables buffered the depressed individuals against stressors.

Leaving the questions of research to one side, our small studies concur with the larger and more rigorous USA ones, leading to two main suggestions for mental health workers. These can be summarised as follows:

a) The trend towards greater community involvement should continue into the sphere of social support. 'Passive' involvement would subsume the clinicians' attention to their clients' social support system, including in particular their capacity to elicit and reciprocate such support (Winefield, 1984). 'Active' involvement might entail direct work with the support system, as in the hairdresser and ex-client illustrations above. It might also include attempts to manipulate the local specifics of social support (e.g. which behaviours do resettled long-stay clients need to have for successful community tenure in the locale?; which settings and services best match existing client repertoires?). These kinds of involvement need to take into account the dynamic nature of social support, including specific support - elicitation skills and the possibility of harmful, 'reverse-buffer' exchanges. They should be related to existing mental health services, rather than addressed in isolation.

b) For those with an interest in research there is need for more focused, local analysis in order to examine the relevance of theories and findings for local situations and issues. There is also a need for more research so as to develop theories and interventions, as in the larger samples required to assess the generality of the illustrative studies in this paper. In relation to the rest of the literature, there is a need for more naturalistic investigations. It also appears timely to apply the kinds of multiple measure, longitudinal, intervention-based approached dominant in the psychotherapy literature.

References

Alloway, R. & Bebbington, P. (1987). The buffer theory of social support: A review of the literature. *Psychological Medicine* 17, 91-108

Barker, C., Pistrang, N., Shapiro, D. A. & Shaw, I. (1990). Coping and help seeking in the UK adult population. *British Journal of Clinical Psychology* 29, 271-285

Barrera, M. & Ainlay, S. L. (1983). The structure of social support: A conceptual and empirical analysis. *Journal of Community Psychology* 11, 133-143

Brown, G. W. & Harris, T. (1978). *Social origins of depression*. London: Tavistock

Caplan, G. & Killilea, M. (Eds,. 1976). *Support systems and mutual help*. London: Grune and Stratton

Cassel, J. (1976). The contribution of the social environment to host resistance.

American Journal of Epidemiology 104, 107-123

Cowen, E. L. (1982). Help is where you find it. *American Psychologist* 37, 385-395

Dangel, R. F. & Polster, R. A. (Eds. 1984). *Parent training: Foundations of research and practice.* London: Guilford Press

Dibdin, J. A. J. (1991). *In stormy weather: Do birds of a feather flock together?* Unpublished BSc dissertation: Psychology Department, University of Newcastle-upon-Tyne

Fondacaro, M. R. and Moos, R. H. (1987). Social support and coping: A longitudinal analysis. *American Journal of Community Psychology* 15, 653-673

Gottlieb, B. H. (1983). *Social support strategies: Guidelines for mental health practice.* London: Sage Publications

Hattie, J. A., Sharpley, C. F. & Rogers, H. J. (1984). Comparative effectiveness of professional and paraprofessional helpers. *Psychological Bulletin* 95, 534-541

Hextall, V. & Hudson-Peacock, N. (1991). *Social support in urban and rural environments: A comparison.* Unpublished BSc dissertation, Psychology Department, University of Newcastle-upon-Tyne

Kolb, D. A. (1984). *Experiential learning.* Prentice Hall: New Jersey

Llewellyn, S. P., Elliot, R., Shapiro, D. A., Hardy, G. & Firth-Cozens, J. (1988). Client perceptions of significant events in prescriptive and exploratory periods of individual therapy. *British Journal of Clinical Psychology* 27, 105-114

MacDonald, F. (1991). *Process evaluation of a carer support scheme.* Unpublished BSc dissertation. Psychology Department, University of Newcastle-upon-Tyne

Milne, D. L., Cowie, I., Gormly, A., White, C., & Hartley, C. (1991). Social supporters and behaviours therapists: Three studies of the form and function of their help. Under editorial review: available from D. Milne, Psychology Department, St George's Hospital, Morpeth NE61 2NU

Milne, D. L. & Mullin, M. (1987). Is a problem shared a problem shaved?: an evaluation of hairdressers and social support. *British Journal of Clinical Psychology* 26, 69-70

Parker, R. M. & Thomas, K. R. (1980). Fads, flaws, fallacies and foolishness in evaluation of rehabilitation programmes. *Journal of Rehabilitation* 46, 32-34

Rogers-Warren, A. & Warren, S. F. (Eds.) (1977). *Ecological perspectives in behaviour analysis.* Baltimore: University Park Press

Stiles, W. B., Shapiro, D. A. & Elliot, R. K. (1986). Are all psychotherapists equivalent? *American Psychologist* 41, 165-180

Thoits, P. A. (1986). Social support as coping assistance. *Journal of Consulting and Clinical Psychology* 54, 416-423

Toro, P. A. (1986). A comparison of natural and professional help. *American Journal of Community Psychology* 14, 147-159

Tracey, T. J. & Toro, P. A. (1989). Natural and professional help: A process analysis. *American Journal of Community Psychology* 17, 443-458

Winefield, H. R. (1984). The nature and elicitation of social support: some implications for the helping professions. *Behavioural Psychotherapy* 12, 318-330

WinefieldD, H. R. (1987). Psychotherapy and social support: Parallels and differences in the helping process. *Clinical Psychology Review* 7, 631-644

22 Blyth Valley Walk-in Advice and Information Centre

G. Moore and P. McAdoo

Introduction

This paper describes the setting up of a Walk-in Centre in Blyth Valley, Northumberland. There have been several documented cases of successful walk-in mental health clinics especially in the U.S. These clinics have developed against the background of the Community Mental Health movement with its goal of accessible mental health treatment for all.

In the U.S. the first walk-in clinics were developed in the late 1950s and early 1960s and were designed to be easily accessible, crisis orientated, unrestrained by waiting lists and able to make referrals to a wide range of treatment modalities (Lazare et al. 1976). In the U.K. the concept of walk-in clinics has a lower profile and there have been few published studies.

There appears to be general agreement in the literature that more women than men attend, as might be expected from general usage of mental health services. (Heller et al. 1985, Hersch et al. 1985). The age group most likely to use such services are those in the 20-40 age group (Heller et al. 1985). The main presenting problems found in studies appear to be anxiety, depression and relationship difficulties. Blyth Valley Walk-In Advice and Information Centre is a drop-in evening service established to provide immediate access to mental health professionals for the public of Blyth Valley. It opened in January 1989 in response to the need identified following the release of Northumberland Service aims and objectives.

Development of the centre

The Mental Health Unit's aims and objectives, Part (a), released in June 1988 state: 'The aims of the service are to provide a flexible, accessible, convenient and personalised service to meet local needs and take account of environmental and social factors.'

The community mental health services in Blyth Valley have a good reputation and are therefore well used and grossly overworked. The ideal of meeting people's needs at the point of demand and before breakdown occurs was becoming increasingly difficult to achieve. Our service was thus failing to meet the objective of 'accessibility' and often unable to fulfil its promotive and preventive role, as early intervention was becoming impossible. This identifiable 'gap' in service delivery was accepted at unit level and the objective of developing an out-of-hours stress clinic to help alleviate the problem was allocated to local management within Blyth Valley.

In September 1988 a small working party representing nursing, psychology, occupational therapy and social work, met to discuss the development of the Centre, establish its aims, consider staff recruitment and initiate a step-by-step approach towards the Centre's opening. Financial resources were limited therefore the working party needed to be both inventive and realistic. We decided to site the Centre at the mental health day unit in Blyth Community Hospital. Local managers agreed to supply basic services, such as heating, lighting and refreshments for one evening per week. Our next step was to establish a core team of therapists to work in the Centre, and when recruited this team would accept responsibility for developing aims, introduction of operational policy, evaluative procedures and running the Centre week by week. The democratic style of management was considered vital as the team would need to be mutually supportive. Three fundamental criteria for staff recruitment were decided upon. Firstly, a professional qualification relevant to mental health care was required; secondly, we required experience of one-to one counselling; and thirdly staff had to make a six month commitment to the Centre. The day unit's secretary was appointed as the Centre's receptionist, and a nurse manager, psychologist, social worker, occupational therapist, two community psychiatric nurses and two nurse therapists from the day unit were recruited to work on a rota basis. Each team member worked on a time-back basis, with the agreement of their respective line managers, avoiding additional expense. The professional skill mix and multidisciplinary approach was considered vital as the acute mental health problems presented could be of a wide and varied nature.

The core team was established by October 1988, jointly developed its operational policy and established its functional aims, which are as follows.

To provide immediate access for the public to professional mental health workers.

To provide an assessment interview before determining the next step.

To act as an information resource to the public. Advice would be provided on specialist help, self-help groups, local and national organisations and other helpful bodies.

To provide information to other professionals on the availability of specialist help, interest groups and agencies in the locality.

To run the centre as a 23 week research project and evaluate the demand.

The services of a second psychologist were introduced to help with the 23 week research project. The core team felt that the centre needed to be evaluated according to its effectiveness and quality, as they did not want it seen as 'a temporary arm grafted onto an overworked body to lend a helping hand', but rather an effective preventive service with its own identity, and very much part of the 'whole body' established to help fulfil Northumberland's mission statement.

In November 1988 we decided the Centre would open the following January and we had to inform the local community. A two-month information campaign ran through the Christmas season at a cost of approximately £150.

Drafting an advertisement gave rise to second thoughts in the light of Northumberland's original mission statement, 'to take into account environmental and social factors'. We realised that many members of the local, traditionally mining, community may not enter a stress centre. The title was too specific for the Centre's intended purpose and might be seen as offering a service for 'weaklings'. The title was therefore changed to 'Advice and Information Centre'. References to stress, anxiety, pressure and problems were consigned to the subtext of the advertisement. Placing the advertisement in a local newspaper consumed a portion of our initial budget but a snowball effect of media interest was created. The local press found the service newsworthy and we received wide, free and favourable publicity through feature articles. The Northern based Sunday Sun gave further exposure and interviews on local and national radio followed. We finished our campaign with a public service announcement on the North East's TV network. We had accomplished our goal by using a step-by step approach and in January 1989 the Centre opened.

Running the Centre

It was corporately decided that the Centre would open one night per week from 7.00 to 9.00 pm, this was later changed to 5.00 to 7.00 pm. On duty would be three therapists and one secretary and we would offer a tripartite service to the enquirer.

1. To deal with the identified problem via counselling, advice, information and education.
2. To allow the enquirer two further sessions if more time was necessary.
3. To act as a filtering referral system in which enquirers would be referred to specific agencies best equipped to meet their needs.

During the sessions the secretary dealt with enquiries while therapists met clients' counselling needs. Interviews were limited to 30 minutes. The therapists agreed to meet and formulate a team recommendation to take back to the client. This proved frequently impractical due to the differing times enquirers arrived at the centre, and often team feedback needed to be after the Centre closed.

To preserve the Centre's purpose and to maintain the availability of therapists, it was agreed that no client could attend the Centre more than three times. On arrival each client was welcomed and shown to the lounge where coffee was available. Clients were asked to complete a form for research purposes. It was explained that records were kept of the client's visit and the service offered was confidential. We sought to create a warm, friendly, but confidential professional service.

The numbers visiting the centre were unpredictable. Sometimes just two clients arrived, but on other occasions up to eight enquirers were waiting for the therapist. This was an inevitable consequence of the 'open door' policy at the heart of the Centre's purpose.

Early on it became clear that many people with acute mental health problems were fearful of seeking help through the usual service channels, and a large percentage of those visiting had had no contact with existing mental health services. It was becoming

223

apparent that we were not only aiding existing services but also tapping into a need as yet unmet.

One woman suffered from an obsessive compulsive problem for over five years. She had kept it a secret, convinced she was 'going crazy'. She was deeply distressed, stating it took her up to five hours to shop in a supermarket. She was greatly relieved to be told what she suffered from and that it was treatable by the local behaviour therapist.

One caller in four presented with stress related anxiety as a major concern. A company director described panic attacks she associated with a particular sales area. After two sessions it became clear the symptoms were due to a painful association with the area and a stark imbalance between work and leisure. By reorganising her life style, gaining an understanding of her own reactions, and learning strategies for coping, she effectively became her own therapist. A telephone conversation some time later confirmed that this short interaction had been very successful. Intervention at an early stage had averted what could have proved to be costly in terms of human distress and health service resources.

As the Centre developed, isolation, grief, depression, financial stress, relationship problems and the effects of child abuse were dealt with. It was encouraging to see people in difficulty before they broke down. The Centre was fulfilling a pre-emptive, preventive role that was also highlighting mental health problems in the local community that had not been met.

The evaluation carried out during the Centre's first six months suggested it was a successful and necessary addition to existing services. The Mental Health Unit decided to fund the Centre permanently and agreed to overtime payments for therapists.

Research study

A six month pilot evaluation was undertaken when the Centre opened in January 1989. On arrival at the Centre, all clients were requested to fill in a brief form giving relevant demographic information. Clients were also asked to fill in the General Health Questionnaire (GHQ) in order to obtain a broad measure of their distress. On interview, the therapist filled in a standard interview form which covered details of the presenting problem, duration of the problem, support systems available to the client as well as the client's request and the Centre's response to that request. Following interview, the clients were asked to fill in the Coping Responses Questionnaire (CRQ) in order to obtain a measure of present coping methods and a brief consumer satisfaction rating scale to obtain customer feedback.

Over the course of the six months study period there were 73 recorded visits to the Walk-In Centre of which 62 were first time visits. The remaining 11 visits were return visits. For the purposes of the study, only data on first time visits were analysed. An incomplete set of data is available on some of the variables as form filling was at the discretion of clients, some of whom chose not to fill in forms while others were too distressed to cope with the task.

The majority of clients (60%) were female. This finding concurs with that of Heller, M.B., Kean-Colwell, J.B. & Beeker, J. (1985) who found a similar pattern in a Walk-In Clinic set up by a District Psychology Department in South Tees Health Authority. The main age group using the Walk-In Centre in the present study tended to be adults in the

20 to 40 age group (45% of total numbers). Similarly Heller in her study found that the age group most likely to use such services were young adults. Almost 60% of clients were married with just over 19% divorced or separated and similar percentage were single. Only 31% of the study sample reported themselves as unemployed. However, this may be explained by a high non response rate and a high percentage of housewives. Almost half the sample reported that they were taking some form of psychotropic medication. Over one third of those attending had used other agencies for help while only 40% of attenders stated that they had other sources of support. Most of the study group (89%) who attended the Centre came from the Blyth area. The 11% who travelled from further afield, often travelling long distances, seems to indicate a lack of readily available support systems in these areas. Most clients(69%) heard about the Centre through press notices and word of mouth. The majority of those attending were self-referred as was also the case in the Heller study.

In terms of presenting problems, over 60% of all problems were rated as having existed over six months, with the majority of problems in fact having been present for over one year. Anxiety was the most frequent presenting problem followed by relationship difficulties, depression and family problems, a pattern which again reflects Heller's findings in her study. Similarly Hersch, J.P. and Latham, C. in a review of a Walk-In Clinic in Minneapolis found that the main presenting problems were relationships, anxiety and depression.

		Walk-in Clinic (Mean values)	Psychology Out-patient Clinic (Mean Values)
CRQ (n=35)			
	AC	10.01	1.7
	AB	9.0	1.6
	AV	12.4	1.6
GHQ (n=52)		25.3	21.5

Table 1

A summary of the mean scores obtained by clients attending the Walk-In Clinic and a Psychology Out-Patient Clinic. The Coping Response Questionnaire (CRQ) consists of 'active cognitive' (AC), 'active behavioural' (AB) and 'avoidance' strategies. The General Health Questionnaire (GHQ) is the second instrument.

The results on the General Health Questionnaire (See Table 1) indicate a significantly higher degree of distress among walk-in clients than in an out-patient sample of clients attending a psychologist. These findings seem to dispel the myth that it is mainly 'the wounded well' who attend walk-in clinics. On the contrary, the results indicate that the client group attending the Walk-In Centre during the pilot phase was a group with mainly long term problems, many of whom had no other support system available and many of whom had not sought help elsewhere.

The results on the Coping Response Questionnaire (See Table 1) indicate that clients tended to use maladaptive coping strategies of avoidance more than active coping strategies. Finally in terms of client satisfaction, results indicated that clients were very satisfied with the service received, many commenting particularly on the 'relaxing atmosphere' and 'being listened to'.

A follow-up study analysed attendances at the Centre in a similar six month period (January to June 1990) one year after the original study. A total of 51 clients attended the Centre during this time, 21 male and 30 female. The vast majority of clients were again from the Blyth Valley area. A change was found in the pattern of how people heard about the Centre, with far more people being referred by their GP and in some cases health visitors. The majority (64%) were employed. Almost half of those attending were married. Fourteen clients (27%) reported that they were taking psychotropic medication, The vast majority were not attending other services with over 45% reporting that they had no other system of support available. The pattern of presenting problems indicated that depression, anxiety and relationship difficulties continued to predominate. A huge number of clients (88%) were referred on to other mental health services in the area. This figure includes referrals to members of the Walk-In team itself.

Further developments of the service

The results of the study carried out in 1989 were confirmed by an analysis of data for the same period during the following year. Thus the Walk-In Centre appears to be dealing with a client group who are in a situation of chronic stress often with little other support. The Walk-In Centre team set out to develop a preventive, accessible mental health service but instead uncovered a considerable degree of distress in the community. This seems to imply that a much greater commitment is needed, in terms of resources, to develop primary and secondary services before we begin to tackle problems at a much earlier stage. One of the difficulties with the current situation at the Walk-In Centre is that the level of distress uncovered inevitably places a greater strain on other services, as can be seen by the high numbers who were referred on to other mental health services in the 1990 study. This problem has tremendous resource implications for other staff.

The Walk-In team have considered how to tackle this issue at length and have recently opted to extend the number of sessions that clients can attend from three to six in the hope of containing more problems at the Walk-In Centre without referring on. It is too early to say what effect this will have on other services. To facilitate this change in service, the team has agreed to opt for a 'therapeutic hour' between 4.00 and 5.00 pm in order to avoid a glut of 'sessional' clients during Walk-In time. Therapists can thus see their sessional clients during this time independently of their Walk-In time. The team decided to change the hours of the Centre to 5.00 to 7.00 pm. This decision was taken because there was concern that numbers were beginning to drop. Many clients, particularly women, appeared to favour earlier opening hours. This move has been successful with an almost immediate increase in attendances.

In early 1991 the team refined their policies on confidentiality, particularly in relation to disclosure of sexual abuse. Clients are now informed specifically of the situations in which confidentiality may have to be breached by a therapist. It was felt that it was necessary to make this policy explicit with clients.

Another recent change in procedure arose as a result of the regulations concerning contracting. Following discussion with the Consultant Psychiatrists for the area, the team agreed to refer clients to Consultants through their GPs and not directly as has been done hitherto. This change arose because of the contractual arrangements for psychiatric services. It was felt that the direct referral system had been very useful but every effort was made to ensure that the new system would not be unduly cumbersome.

In conclusion, the Centre continues to grow and develop in its third year of operation. Membership of the team has changed over that time, bringing to the service fresh views on its future development. Within Blyth Valley, it has become an integral part of the mental health services of the area.

References

1. Heller, M., Kean-Colwell, J. & Becker, J. The 'walk-in' clinic for adult psychology services: A pilot project. *BPS Clinical Psychology Forum* , 1985.

2. Hersch, J.P., & Lathan C. The mental health walk-in clinic: The University of Massachuesetts experience. *College Health*, Vol. 34, August 1985.

3. Moore G., McAdoo P. Mental health take-away. *Nursing Times* Vol 86, No 35, 1990.

23 The prevention of domestic violence; skills learning in a group setting

A. Waring and J. Wilson

Abstract

The work of a self-help group for men who batter women is described and evaluated. The group is psycho-educational in nature, seeking to teach men skills in anger management, assertiveness, communication and negotiation. As these skills are acquired and put into practice, men are encouraged to accept responsibility for their violent behaviour and to recognise that they can gain control over it. They are also prompted to change their attitudes from the traditional, exploitive-possessive beliefs concerning women to egalitarian and co-operative attitudes. The group is open ended, with the basic programme being recycled every fifteen weeks. Men can therefore enter the group at any point in the cycle. Established members are used to facilitate the programme and in particular to exemplify and transmit the co-operative attitudes to new members. The style of this group has been argued to avoid the problems caused by the tendency for denial and minimisation of the problem which is inherent in this group of clients. Difficulties surrounding the evaluation of the effectiveness of this group are discussed. Within these limitations it has been found that members who consistently attend the group show much improved control over their violence, with few relapses. Data also suggest that members show less dominant and sexist attitudes towards their partners, use traditional excuses for their violence less frequently and show more positive appreciation of their partners' rights and needs.

Background to the group

In 1985, as the result of a workshop on domestic violence, a self-help group was established for men who had used violence during domestic arguments. The second author had found it helpful in overcoming his own violence but eventually became

229

concerned that it was not providing sufficient practical skills for its members. He therefore sought to establish a similar group in his home town which would offer men some form of practical help rather than being a 'mere talking shop'. After preliminary discussions, the first author agreed to support him in the establishment of this group, now known as MOVE (Bolton).

Broadly the initial aims for the group were to:
provide a telephone contact line for men in crisis;
provide a forum in which men could discuss the basic causes of violence and could come to terms with these;
provide group activities in which men could learn specific skills which would help them to overcome their tendencies towards violent behaviour;
establish an organisational structure through which men who had been successful in relinquishing violence could be trained to help others.

It was decided that while the second author (and others later) would receive the initial telephone contacts and provide support on an individual basis, the first author would normally provide back-up support for this counselling service. He would also offer a series of sessions, within the weekly meetings, each of which would cover a separate, relevant skill. Once the original members were confident that they understood these techniques, he would assist them to teach the skills to new members so that ultimately all of the services would be provided by the volunteers themselves.

General philosophy of the programme

It has been argued that domestic violence arises from a set of attitudes towards women and beliefs about the nature of marital relationships which are, in general, supported by society and even by religious doctrine. Dobash and Dobash (1978, 1984) have argued that men's violence comes from their beliefs that their partners should attend to various domestic needs, such as the provision of food, sexual intercourse and loyalty, without question, at any time the man should require. Men also acquire beliefs in their authority in the home, which they feel should not be challenged, so that decisions in the relationship always go the way they want, irrespective of the needs of their partners. Violence is consequently seen as a form of chastisement to be applied when the partner does not conform to the man's wishes.

A corollary of this is that the man may become fearful if he perceives that his partner might withdraw these services. He may fear that he will be left without means of support, with no one to see that he is fed and clothed. He may fear that he will be seen as a wimp, if his partner resists his demands, does things on her own, or pays too much attention to other men. And he may feel totally threatened at the prospect of her leaving him for another partner. Battering her can therefore be seen as a way of controlling her so that the prospect of these threats being realised can be minimised. The battering is also frequently backed up by the threat that wherever she might try to hide from him he will find her.

Violence is also argued to be precipitated by stress (Gelles 1972), where the man may feel undischarged anger against other people, or his own problems. The violent man has learned, through his socialisation, that it is both acceptable and effective to resolve that frustration by taking it out on his partner.

It may also be considered that violence is a way of controlling the people in one's world, which is adopted in the absence of other more effective and co-operative skills. The man may have learned to use violence in domestic situations, by watching his father's example and observing that such violence usually did bring the immediate rewards that the father sought. Hence, the essential skills needed for negotiation and communication would not be learned because he would perceive no real need for them.

With these propositions in mind, the bases for the interventions in this programme were drawn from a number of sources, including:

attitudes change processes, using peer pressure;

basic techniques for managing anxiety and stress, such as the WASP mnemonic, distraction, etc.;

exercises in awareness of anger signals and processes, using techniques suggested by Sinclair (personal communication) and used in the Maran County programme;

elements of cognitive therapy drawn from the propositions of Ellis and Harper (1971), and from Beck et al (1979). In particular, these strategies are directed at the fears which have been claimed to be uppermost in the violent man's mind - loss of sustenance from his wife;

loss of family pride, etc. (cf Dobash and Dobash 1978, 1984);

problem solving skills, set in the client directed mode developed by Egan (1981);

assertion training techniques, which are relevant in that being dominant is not the same as being assertive, (cf. Smith (1970)).

Each of these general techniques was adapted to the particular setting and illustrative examples were collected from the group, to form a pool of experiences which the volunteers could use in future sessions.

It was also expected that experience within the group would add techniques to this programme and develop more effective devices, as a result of contributions from the members themselves. Amongst the additions obtained in this way was the set of techniques devised for negotiating re-entry into the family or relationship.

Since this client group is well known for its irregularity of attendance (Beckett 1988) the programme, although set out in a time based sequence, was not confined to a rigid progression of topics which would require consistent attendance. It was instead designed as a 'rolling programme', in that each group session covers one of the topics outlined below in such a way that a man attending for the first time can get something from the session, even though he has not attended any previous sessions. The programme recycles every fifteen weeks on a continuous basis and it is assumed that all members will continue to attend subsequent cycles, going through those parts which they have missed. The members who have been through the programme twice or more are encouraged to act as facilitators in later sessions, teaching others the skills which they have acquired.

A mainstay of the programme is the insistence that the man is responsible for his violence, can choose to change and that he can learn skills by which he can control his anger. Alcohol, past history, and other factors may play some causative role but members are encouraged to recognise that it is they who choose to attack their partners in order to maintain control over them. The skills which a man acquires from the programme can be seen as being added on to the set of behaviours he already has, forming additional alternatives which he can use.

The programme uses various techniques of attitude change to replace beliefs about the woman as a servant and a property of her partner and teaches assertiveness and communication techniques to help men to accept their partners as true equals, to negotiate with them and to respect their integrity and rights at all times.

The MOVE programme

The steps of the programme are as follows:

Pre-contact, in which the new member is introduced to the general philosophy of the group and makes a contract accepting the code of practice which governs members attendance at the group.

Session 1 is an introduction, which covers the basic assumptions, outlined above, together with a questionnaire which invites the man to examine his own pattern of beliefs and violence; this session begins to develop an awareness of the beliefs, normally backed up by society, which lead a man to become violent in order to protect what he regards as his position in society, (the notion of women and children as chattels, the assumption of male authority, etc), as a precursor to challenging these beliefs.

Session 2 introduces the WASP mnemonic, strategies for watching for personal anger signals, and some basic ideas about why people get angry; the man also starts his anger diary, through which he will monitor his progress.

Session 3 considers Time Outs which are powerful tools for preventing violent outbursts in the early days of repairing relationships; emphasising the need to break up the escalation of anger and tension in domestic disputes as a means of making the man 'safe' for his partner.

Session 4 considers the difficulties of getting back together after a battering incident and some of the things which the man may expect together with things he should and should not do during this phase; in particular he is encouraged to refrain from 'chasing' his partner.

Session 5 Pekinpah Stills, devised by Sinclair (personal communication), introduces the man, via role play, to the idea that he can slow down the process of anger and can recognise what he is doing during an act of violence; this also demonstrates that he can take the decision not to attack. Through this, the individual can identify the process of chasing the partner both physically and verbally, into the confrontation; recognise the process of depersonalising or 'thingification' in which the partner is reduced to an object which can be abused; and become aware of the decision of attack and of the fact that this is a deliberate decision which can be brought under conscious control. This technique is regarded as being particularly powerful in overcoming the individual's tendency to deny his violence and his responsibility for it.

Sessions 6, 7 & 8 focus on the man's cognitive style and examine the beliefs which lead to anger and show how these can be challenged and replaced by beliefs which are less threatening and which help the man to live better with himself and with others.

Sessions 9 & 10 teach assertiveness so that the man can begin to express his wants in a positive fashion and can enter them into negotiations with mutual respect for his partner; so that he can integrate his activities with those of his partner rather than simply demand that his wants be satisfied.

Session 11 looks at the many ways in which the man might alienate other people, especially his partner and considers a number of ways in which one can avoid doing this and become more positive towards other people.

Session 12. is about building positive self-regard so that the man can nurture himself and confirm his own identity without having to shout other people down.

Session 13 looks at empathy and the various ways in which the man can use a stronger version of himself to understand, help and mesh in with those whom he loves.

Session 14 An overview of the programme and its aims.

Running the group

Group sessions typically ask a man to review the period since his last attendance, with an emphasis on how he has attempted to use the skills discussed in his previous session. There is little emphasis on reliving violent incidents in detail, except where the discussion can centre on how the man might choose a better skill, or employ existing ones better. Each session includes a period in which a new skill is introduced (or for longstanding members, is reviewed), together with examples of how it might be used in practice. At the end of each session, members are given exercises which guide their use of the skill throughout the following week.

Initially, summary handouts were given to members during the session, which they were encouraged to annotate to remind them of those points which were particularly relevant to themselves. Latterly the programme has been presented in book form.

The programme assumes multiple causes of violence and the consequent need for each member to be exposed to a selection of techniques in order to find the right ones for him. Hence, when appropriate, the programme elements can be taken out of order. Evening meetings are preferred because most potential members were in employment.

In the early days, attendance at groups was often insufficient to establish a regular routine. In particular no-one was attending for long enough to become involved in assisting others, as was the original intention. Some detailed examination of this problem revealed a number of possible causes. In the first place, it seemed possible that the acquisition of a few techniques may have been sufficient for the potential members to feel more in control of their lives, such that they believed that they did not need to come again, especially if their partners had returned to them.

Secondly, the second author was then handling the telephone enquiries by talking the client through the various principles endorsed by the group and suggesting, where appropriate, the techniques presented at the group meetings. In some case, he would agree to make home visits, where the same kind of intervention would be practised.

In order to reduce wastage from the group, it was subsequently resolved that:

clients would be encouraged to attend the group, with extended telephone contacts and home visits being discouraged;

strong suggestions would be made at the group meetings that there were many techniques to be acquired over a long period of time and the handouts were numbered to indicate that there were many to collect;

follow up calls were to be made to those who had attended occasionally to encourage them to rejoin the group.

The final programme, as amended with the aid of the men who attended the early groups, has now been published in the form of a self-help manual ('Be Safe', Waring and Wilson 1990). Although it is normally expected that the group would be all male, success has been obtained by two satellite groups which are facilitated by women.

Assessment

This was initially quite difficult. During early cycles of the group, too few members attended for conventional assessment of the programme. However, the indications were that after completion of one or more cycles of the programme, those men who had stayed the course had been non-violent for a significant length of time and had developed a confidence that they would remain so. In general, these members considered that they had fewer relapses than likely if left on their own and in each case the nature of the relapse was much less violent than previously. (In one case, the individual spat at rather than struck his partner and then left immediately without prolonging the incident). Members reported that relationships which were threatened had been preserved and that they valued the support which they received from other offenders who were eager to change.

Later in the development of the programme, more conventional monitoring of a man's progress was made through the use of the self-evaluation questionnaire which he is asked to fill in at the start of the programme and again at the completion of each cycle of attendance. This indicates the extent of his violence and the nature of his beliefs in terms of five factors;

use of aggressive language and attitude, to control partner (VERB);
use of physical and other overt violence (PHYS);
beliefs which support violent behaviour (BELIEF);
excuses used for being violent (EXCUSE);
presence of positive social and empathetic skills (SKILLS).

This is somewhat parallel to an initial assessment interview, which could, as indicated below, alienate the individual. However, the results of this questionnaire are for the man himself. He is primarily asked to judge himself. There is no comment on the score by the group leaders. If a man has concealed his violence or fudged issues, he knows about that himself. Next time he looks at the questionnaire, he is able to see the extent of that fudging and to see that it is neither necessary nor productive. Typically, when he first attends, the man's scores are high for the first four factors (which indicate undesirable behaviour and beliefs) and low for the last (which indicates positive, co-operative behaviour).

At the end of each cycle, the man is asked to complete the questionnaire again, partly to enable him to gauge how far he has changed and partly to provide data through which to monitor the effectiveness of the group. Because there is a capacity for self-deception in these questionnaire scores, both on the occasion of first administration and when they are repeated at the end of the programme, any data so collected needs to be treated with care. Also, much data is missed because the results of the questionnaire are necessarily treated as confidential to the member, so the authors did not have access to all such records. However, the data collected from these sources and listed in Table 1 do show a robust difference in the scores after a completion of one cycle of the programme. When this is repeated into the second cycle, the scores continue to move in the preferred direction.

(Maximum)	1 Verb 20	2 Phys 30	3 Belief 18	4 Excuse 16	5 Skills 32
Pretest (n=16)	10.4	12.3	3.5	5.0	20.8
First (n=9)	4.0	2.6	2.1	1.2	25.1
Second (n=5)	2.4	2.2	1.4	0.3	30.8

Members self-reported mean violence scores

Table 1

These initial data show that all of the scores on the questionnaires do move in the preferred direction at the end of each cycle. The changes brought about in the first and last sections are believed to result from the acquisition of new skills, as alternatives to existing ways of behaving. The changes in beliefs and attitudes are considered to be brought about through the group discussion, which are largely facilitated by men whose own beliefs have changed through their own work in the group.

After the group had been in progress for two years, 50 ex-members were contacted, together with their partners and asked to complete follow up materials. The men were asked to complete a version of the original questionnaire, modified to relate to their current status. Their partners were asked to complete a parallel version, intended to indicate the extent and direction of change shown by their partners since completing the sessions with MOVE. Unfortunately, only around 10 per cent of the materials were returned.

Such information as was collected indicated that the men who replied were claiming still to use and find valuable various of the techniques which they had acquired. They were also confident that they had achieved positive changes in their relationships.

Forms returned by partners, who were coincidentally not always the partners of the men above, were less encouraging. While three out of five respondents felt that their men had

235

shown less verbal and physical violence, one reported little change and a fifth reported that things had become much worse. In the latter case it appears that the man had been using his attendance at the group as a device to reassure his partner and draw her into marriage, without any real intention of changing his way of life. Such a misuse of this kind of group is unfortunately difficult to avoid. In all cases, the partners were much less confident of the changes in their men's positive attitudes and skills than were the men themselves.

Clearly, the number of respondents in this follow-up data are too few to draw clear conclusions. But it does seem likely that there are some changes which are retained after the men leave the group and that the improvement in positive skills, as opposed to the avoidance of violence is slower to emerge or be seen by their partners.

After evaluating the group processes themselves, it was realised that the style of the group had helped to avoid the barrier to progress in work with these men which arises from their well-documented tendency to deny the occurrence or the severity of their actions.

Some workers have claimed that it is important to make the men acknowledge in full their actions and their responsibility for them, (eg. Jukes 1990). However, when confronted with this demand during initial assessment, we felt that many men will choose to withdraw from the group and any potential gains will be lost. Elsewhere, we have argued, (Waring and Wilson 1991) that in the context of this group the difficulties caused by the process of denial are minimal for the following reasons:

1. There is less confrontation because the men who attend MOVE sessions are not required to 'confess their sins' either publicly or individually. Miller (1983) has pointed out that denial is a product of the interaction between the therapist and the client in which insistence by the therapist that the client should admit that he has done something wrong, induces the client to deny the behaviour or explain it away. The review of homework encourages men to concentrate on the essential process of learning to control their violent behaviour and does not dwell on details of what the man did, and thus minimises the amount of denial which could otherwise be induced.

2. The group does not adopt an overt political position. While it is clearly its function to promote positive attitudes to women's rights, we feel that if potential members came to believe that one of the functions of the group was to make them 'feminists', they would be likely to reject that demand and with it the group. MOVE therefore retained the approach which seeks to alter behaviour, on the grounds that changes in attitude will follow, rather than vice versa.

3. The batterer is encouraged to acknowledge his responsibility for his violence through indirect means. Thus, if a man sees that he can learn to avoid the use of violence, it can be made obvious to him that he has chosen a non-violent solution this time, and that by comparison, he has clearly made violent choices in the past. We feel that he can more readily accept his responsibility for such choices, through means which do not immediately challenge his convenient beliefs and which thus does not invite denial of his past acts.

4. Control. When he comes to a group, the batterer has learned that an efficient way of running his life is to threaten his partner with violence whenever things do

not go his way. To deprive him of that well learned and effective piece of behaviour, is highly threatening. He may feel very anxious, unless he is reassured that there are alternative behaviours through which he can maintain his relationship and thus, again, tend to deny his problem. This programme relieves this anxiety by promoting the positive aspects of the alternative skills through the experienced members demonstrating to new members that co-operation and negotiation do work.

Hence we believe that the style of the programme substantially reduces wastage due to denial, believing that later changes in the batterer's behaviour would render it less necessary to him as a defence mechanism.

Comments

Central to the group's operation is the idea that men can be encouraged to change their attitudes towards women, mainly through the use of peer pressure from members of the group who have previously been through the programme. It is possible that this process makes positive use of the 'male bonding' mechanism to provide support for men who recognise the value of abandoning traditional sex-stereotyped behaviour. Particular care is taken to ensure that these group processes are not used by the members to justify or excuse their violence towards women. Expressions of traditional, dominating attitudes towards women are also avoided.

Problems are experienced with self-referrals to groups such as this. It is often assumed that men will only attend such programmes as part of a legal requirement from the courts, such as occurs in California. In our experience, a few men do self-refer when they become frightened by their own actions or when prompted by their partners. Mostly, they tend only to self-refer when their partners have finally suffered too much; or when the divorce papers or the injunctions appear. It may require much more in the way of attitude change in society before this resistance disperses and men self-refer because they see their battering as socially unacceptable.

For obvious reasons, not many women's movements are in agreement with men's groups such as MOVE. However, good relationships have been established with some women's refuges. In such cases the group takes on men as referrals from the refuges and always works towards improving the safety of the woman concerned. The MOVE group welcomes contact with partners where they actively seek information but it never acts as a 'go-between' on behalf of the group member, to put pressure on his partner to return to him. Currently it is seeking to establish a partner's group which would focus on the attempts which the men are making to change and the consequences of these attempts for their partners.

The overall philosophy of the group is psycho-educational, rather than assuming a 'therapy' model. Thus, the emphasis is upon acquiring new skills which the man can develop and add to those ways which are already part of his style of life. It therefore does not regard the violent man as either sick or not responsible for his actions but places the onus for change firmly with the man himself.

References

Beck, A., Rush, S., Hollow, S., & Shaw, B. (1979). *Cognitive therapy of depression..* Guildford Press.

Beckett, R. (1988). Violent behaviour. Paper presented to *Northern BABP.*

Dobash, R.E., & Dobash, R.P. (1978). Wives: The appropriate victims of marital violence. *Victimolgy, 2,* 426-442,

Dobash, R.E., & Dobash, R.P. (1984). The nature of antecedents of violent events. *Br. J. Criminology, 24,* 269-288,

Egan, G. (1981). *The skilled helper: A systematic approach to helping.* Brooks & Cole.

Ellis, A., & Harper, R.A. (1971). *A new guide to rational living..* Wilshire.

Gelles.(1972). *The violent home: A study of physical aggression between husbands and wives.* Sage.

Jukes, A. (1990). Working with men who are violent to women. *Counselling, 1(4),* 124-126,

Miller, W.R (1983). Motivational interviewing with problem drinkers. *Behavioural Psychotherapy, 11,* 147-172.

Smith, M.S. (1970). *When I say no I feel guilty.* Bantam.

Waring, A.J.G., & Wilson, J.(1990). *Be safe: A self-help manual for domestic violence.* Bolton, MOVE.

Waring, A.J.G., & Wilson, J.P.(1991). The management of denial in a group programme for domestic violence. *Counselling.*

SECTION FOUR
PROGRAMMES

24 Psychic hygiene in mental health promotion

A. Chwedorowicz

Introduction

The present paper is a short presentation of some Polish experience in mental health promotion with special emphasis on how it is determined culturally and how it benefits from attachment to spontaneous social movements. The author's experience results from work for the Centre of Psychic Hygiene in Lodz which is a Mental Health Service unit, and recent work for a Local Government Training Centre which helps people find their way in the new situation in Poland, also from participation in numerous informal mental health promotion and compatible programmes.

The cultural dimension in mental health

Even a short review both of current concepts of mental health and of programmes undertaken in two different countries for promotion of mental health shows big differences which seem to point to the fact, that the mental health issue is determined culturally. If it really is, efficient work for the promotion of mental health should consider numerous cultural factors, both at the stage of defining the very concept of mental health - deciding which of the many definitions of mental health, is the most suitable for the given society, and at the stage of designing mental health promotion programmes. Every definition of mental health has inherent cultural assumptions and it is important to make them clear. If we want a society to understand, accept, and use to its benefit the concept of mental health we introduce, or to participate in and benefit from a mental health promotion programme, we must elaborate or choose them for this very society, at the given stage of its historical development, considering its cultural, social, economic and even political situation.

Of course, this is not to say that people living in different cultures have different psychological needs. The culturally bound nature of mental health promotion is due to the fact that different cultures tend to each meet different needs while suppressing or ignoring different other ones. Frustration of individuals' psychological needs in different societies results from different constellations of mainly cultural factors. For this reason the nature of mental health problems and the proportion of factors that need particular attention in mental health promotion will vary from society to society.

It is important to bear in mind that what mental health promotion is about is, at least in the long run, cultural change. What large scale mental health promotion programmes are expected to result in is considerable change in what people think, understand and do - in their beliefs, habits and behaviours. Cultural change does not take place overnight. It is a long and gradual process. As it seems, it is much easier to regulate than to initiate a process that is to result in cultural change. For this reason it is probably worth while considering a possibility of attaching mental health promotion to whatever compatible bottom up, spontaneous process can be found in a given society, thus to endow mental health promotion with the natural social dynamics, and to provide it with definite social roots.

The Polish background and the questions it raised

Before outlining the programme, a few words are needed to present the cultural and political background of the mental health issue in Poland for the recent 10 years. Introduction of martial law in Poland in 1981 resulted in general frustration and loss of hope. Yet again Polish people were deprived of dignity and personal freedom . The values, self-identity and integration of the people were in danger, which resulted on the one hand in greater passivity, helplessness, and a lot more emotional disorders than before, and on the other hand in greater sensitivity to the needs which could not be met. The disillusionment was general and very many suffered, and admitted suffering from depression or other mental disorders. Inability to cope with the abnormal situation did not surprise anybody. Many people 'opted out of life' or gave up their efforts to control their situation or environment. All that could be done was to try to become more aware of one's identity and one's needs, to be more autonomous in one's values and wants, whether it was possible to realize them or not, and to be more ingenious and creative. In this 'internal resistance' to the situation the society was integrated better than ever before. People wanted to be together and to find out together who they were and what they needed, which resulted in a great surge of informal group meetings. With time they tended to become more and more of encounter and training groups sponsored by various organizations. People of various professions - psychologists, sociologists, priests, artists etc., began acting as group leaders. Whatever were the overt goals of the groups, and there were many different ones, the real one was to 'resist internally' the system, to meet some frustrated needs and to create as strong and dense a network of interpersonal bonds as possible, thus to make the society stronger.

In order to address the mental health issue in this situation three questions were asked. The first one was about the needs. Which needs could not be met in our society? What frustration of what needs prevented our people from enjoying life, from enjoying good mental health?

The second one concerned the definition of mental health. What is mental health? Which definition of mental health to use and whether to use the concept which is not popular and not very likely to become popular, considering the fact that many people associate it with mental illness?

The third question was how to meet those needs, how to help people make sure that their psychological needs are met within the already existent encounter and training movement which was a spontaneous, natural reaction to the abnormal unfavourable situation?

The growth of a strategy

The analysis of the psychological situation of Polish Society showed that the question of how a person's needs can be met cannot be separated from considering a wide range of environmental factors that can make it easier or more difficult, or even quite impossible for a person to have his or her psychological needs met. For this reason it seemed reasonable to distinguish two stages of work devoted to the improvement of people's ability to have their psychological needs met; development of awareness - self-awareness of what is going on around, and development of skills, attitudes, mental programmes or habits.

Being aware of one's needs is not enough. It is not enough even to be able to communicate one's own needs. The necessity of being aware, understanding and communicating one's own needs always goes together with the necessity of acquiring skills and developing habits that would enable him or her to control or create a psychologically favourable environment conducive to his or her health. It was assumed that the main method of work in mental health promotion should be training, as only training can result in real development of self awareness and development of positive attitudes and skills. Publishing and informing should lead directly to training.

As for the choice of definition of mental health, it was defined as capability of personal growth and development. As it seemed, realisation of one's creative potential appealed to Polish society much better than any other concept defining mental health, and it was associated with well being and happiness. Personal growth proved to be more meaningful and thus more acceptable than mental health itself, which was due to the fact that it has already been used, or could have been used in the context of the above mentioned movement of internal resistance. Using the terms personal growth and mental health interchangeably with more emphasis on personal growth, it was possible immediately to find eager and cooperative participants in mental health promotion programmes, and to avoid misunderstanding the programmes as designed for the mentally ill.

Exchanging personal growth for mental health made it easier to attach mental health promotion to the spontaneous social process, and to root the attitude of care for mental health of the people in the mainstream of social goals and desires. It was simple: one of many not very clear concepts to be found within the movement was chosen to be made the key concept. Ever present with more and more meaning fed into it, personal growth became a more and more popular concept, and as such it was a really attractive and powerful substitute for mental health.

One more concept was introduced to supplement the concept of personal growth in mental health promotion. It was 'psychic hygiene'. The need of hygienic life was presented as the way to personal growth. The concept of psychic or emotional hygiene is similar to that of physical hygiene. The basic assumption is the ability of an organism to maintain or restore mental health if the satisfaction of basic psychological needs is maintained on a given level. Psychic hygiene is concerned with practical ways of controlling emotional, physical and environmental factors which determine the level of satisfaction of psychological needs and thus affect the individual's mental health.

Psychic hygiene and motivation

The most emphasized recommendation of physical hygiene is the demand for systematic intensive physical activity which is expressed in the formula $3 \times 30 + 130$, recommending 3 times a week 30 minutes of intensive physical activity raising the pulse rate to 130 beats per minute. During such activity the organism gets rid of toxic products, regulates tonus of the muscles and relaxes tensions. Hygienic exercises raise the level of the organism's effort to the upper boundary of the individual physiological norm, thus forcing each organ to maintain high efficiency. Analogously, maintaining psychic activity on the high level, appropriate for the individual psychic constitution, is the main condition of the individual's mental health. A high level of energetic emotional involvement is necessary to maintain mental health, just as it is probably necessary to enjoy life. Only people deeply involved, people truly alive energetically, are capable of the realisation of their creative potential; only such people act rather than respond, enjoy acting, and actively influence people around them - their environment. Hygienic means energized. This is why the main question in the process of elaborating the recommendations of psychic hygiene was how to motivate a person to high energetic involvement.

It is well known that people who have substantial motivation to life, are needed, and have a positive vision of their future - people who love and are loved, have better resistance to disease, and in case of illness more quickly come back to health, and have a greater chance of surviving when their lives are in danger. Developing the concept of psychic hygiene on the analogy between the mental and the physical it is possible to claim that similar conditions are conducive to mental health. Vital, deep relationships with other people, goals and tasks consistent with one's individual system of values and compatible with one's actual abilities, definite, clear-cut as opposed to unclear, general visions of the future - they all motivate not only to physical but also to mental life. Relationships, tasks and actions which, so to say, 'have a future' and give hope, involve energetically the entire person. Hope and motivation to life which result in highly energized mental activity contribute to mental health. (It is important here not to mistake involvement, energisation, and activity highly involved energetically, with being busy without energetic involvement, which is very common in our culture. Any activity which is forced by the environment, which is response rather than free action is harmful. The best distinguishing criterion is the amount of experienced pleasure and satisfaction, while acting).

The programmes and their effects

These presented theoretical assumptions determined the shape and the nature of mental health promotion programmes developed in Lodz. As has been already stated, they were training programmes and were offered as psychic hygiene for personal growth. The training offered within the programmes developed emotional literacy and life skills, positive attitudes and motivational skills such as vision building, goal - setting and positive thinking. At the end of the programme participants were expected to know themselves better, to know what they liked and what they did not like, what they missed or longed for and what they were afraid of, to have a new understanding of their situation and greater awareness of their creative potential, talents and skills, as well as of their shortcomings. The programme was to allow for a realistic overview of participants' relationships with other people - their needs, failures and desires in that respect, and to teach them how to handle successfully their future interpersonal relations. It was to give participants insight into their interpersonal behaviours and habits and to develop their communication skills. It was also to give participants a better understanding of their values as opposed to values imposed on them by other people. They learnt to set realistic goals compatible with their values, to split the long term goals into short term goals and to transform them into tasks. They practiced visualizing their goals and creating positive visions of their future, as well as planning and visualizing the following day. Positive flexible and open attitudes were trained, as well as participants' ability to concentrate, integrate information, make decisions, manage their time, be here and now and meditate.

The training process evolved from general integrating exercises gradually opening, stimulating and involving the entire person of each participant, to more specific ones - intellectual, emotional, intuitive, physical and spiritual. All the time participants learnt by practice. First they were finding out about themselves, their emotions, mental habits, attitudes, abilities and difficulties. Then the training tasks encouraged them to experiment and test in several directions which allowed them gradually to learn more, and by trial and error to master desirable skills. The only incentive to do so was curiosity and pleasure. Time was given to share self-observations and re-evaluations, and the process went on a step further - the participants decided themselves how far they wanted to go. They were encouraged, and only progress, as opposed to failures, was discussed and celebrated. The diversity and multidimensionality of exercises allowed different participants equally to benefit from the training. Parallel, repetitive arrangement of exercises allowed everybody systematic improvement in performance.

The length and frequency of training (each group met several times) varied from group to group and all that can be said is that the longer the training blocks the better the results. It may be interesting, however, that there was a natural tendency to maintain the interpersonal bonds of friendship after the training in the groups, where no criticism was allowed and the emphasis was on the positive. Those groups tended to survive very long as tiny environments for the participants, conducive to their further growth. Rooted in their groups people tended to use what they had learnt in them while training, to a much greater extent than others, who lost touch with their groups. Prolonged informal group participation determined the permanence of personal progressive changes due to the training.

245

25 'Look after your mental health': A mental health roadshow

K. Childs

Abstract

In 1990 a health roadshow focusing on mental health was held in Southern Derbyshire Health Authority. This project was initiated by the Health Promotion Department and Mental Health Unit and executed in collaboration with a range of other agencies including social services, voluntary groups and user groups.

This activity was a contribution to an overall mental health promotion programme within the Health Promotion Strategy. Its aims were to raise awareness about mental health and the factors that contribute to it, provide an introduction to some coping skills and deal positively with the change from hospital to community care.

The evaluation was of process rather than outcomes. The collaboration achieved between agencies was its greatest success. Its limiting factor was the attitude of some community mental health staff to mental health promotion. This area of work needs to be validated among managers and staff of the Mental Health Services in order to ensure the continuation of any such ventures.

Introduction

In 1990 a health roadshow focusing on the promotion of mental health was held in Southern Derbyshire Health Authority. This activity was initiated by the Health Promotion Department and the Mental Health Unit and executed in collaboration with other agencies in the community.

This paper will examine the roadshow in terms of its

Background/rationale.
Methodology.
Evaluation.
Future events.

Background/rationale

In recent years physical health has become high profile within the media and among the general public. There is a ready acceptance to discuss our levels of physical exercise, eating patterns, etc., mental health, however, has enjoyed no such favour.

Fear of mental illness appears still to lead people to put it 'out of mind' just as psychiatrically distressed people were themselves 'put away'.

That poor mental health affects more people either directly or indirectly than any other type of health problem still remains a quiet fact.[1] An informed public therefore seems to be one of the most important priorities for action. Against a background of increased awareness we can begin to challenge those attitudes which lack an understanding of mental health problems and the care and service which they require.

The Health Promotion Department in writing its strategy document[2] for 1989 began to identify the absence of any programme specifically to promote good mental health. As a result a programme was devised which had as its main aim the need to place mental health promotion on the agenda of health professionals and public alike.

The mental health services in their Strategic Plan[3] also recognised the need for education on mental health among the general public and stated that:
'a process of mental health education within the community at large will aim to ensure that individuals' (returning from hospital) 'will not be frustrated in leading an appropriate lifestyle'.

This shared interest i.e. to undertake a programme of mental health education within the community led to the formation of a joint working group between Health Promotion and the Mental Health Unit.

The motivations for activity were however different. For the Health Promotion Department the activity was seen in the context of an awareness raising campaign which would provide the springboard for future mental health promotion work. Its concern was to educate about mental health and the many and varied factors which can affect it. Through our approach we hoped to bring mental health into the mainstream alongside other health promotion activities.

The mental health unit however saw the exercise as being valid only in terms of its link with the closure of institutions and the resettlement of clients within the community. This focus on service delivery led to a fear that increased awareness on mental health issues would lead to an increased demand on services and that by 'popularising' mental health we may in fact 'trivialise' the problems of those suffering from long term mental illness.

These two perspectives are illustrated in Figure 1. Although at times divergent in approach the working group did agree a set of aims for a programme of mental health education within the community. These were:

> to raise awareness about mental health/illness and the factors that contribute to it;
> to challenge attitudes towards mental illness;
> to introduce strategies to reduce the 'risk' factors associated with poor mental health;
> to inform the general public of the change from hospital to community care for the mental illness service.

An important 'hidden' aim would also be:

> to develop intersectoral collaboration between the many agencies involved in this

248

field, particularly health service, local authorities and voluntary groups.

An area was chosen in which to pilot our activity, on the basis that it would be the first community to receive clients due to the gradual closure of the local psychiatric hospital and consequently was already seeing the developments of a changed service in terms of a housing development for people with mental health problems.

In order to fulfil our last aim the planning group was broadened to include representatives from the community mental health services, social services, user groups, community groups and the voluntary sector. These representatives were all working or involved in the area chosen for the pilot activity.

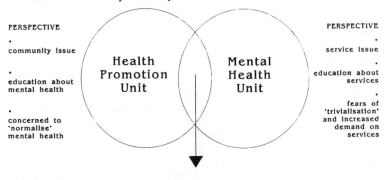

PERSPECTIVE

• community issue

• education about mental health

• concerned to 'normalise' mental health

Health Promotion Unit

Mental Health Unit

PERSPECTIVE

• service issue

• education about services

• fears of 'trivialisation' and increased demand on services

Mental Health Education

Figure 1

Methodology - Why a roadshow?

There is a growing confidence in the field of health promotion about the promotion of physical health. There is clear evidence of the scope for improvement and a growing understanding of a range of interventions both societal and individual. There is much less activity towards the promotion of mental health and mental wellbeing.

The Mental Health Foundation has recently pointed out that only six percent of the United Kingdom total available (public and private) research funds are channelled into mental health topics[4]. The field of health promotion appears similarly to have marginalised work on mental health promotion.

However, research available in the field of physical health promotion has identified skills and practices for successful intervention. This led us to attempt to transfer these skills and practices in the field of physical health promotion to that of mental health promotion.

In Southern Derbyshire the Health Promotion Department had recently been involved in a successful educational activity relating to Coronary Heart Disease. This had involved the use of health roadshows - activity based exhibitions which encouraged dialogue between staff and participants. These roadshows had received a great deal of publicity in the local press, a high profile within the community and exceptional attendance at events.

It was felt that a similar format could be appropriate to the mental health field. The use of a similar format would not only allow us to use existing skills within the authority in organising such an event but also contribute to the process of 'normalisation' of mental health issues because of the popular appeal of this approach.

The challenge was to develop publicity, activities and resources that would have a popular appeal. Attracting the public to the event meant an acceptance by them that mental health is relevant to their lifestyles. The planning group agreed that 'stress' is the one aspect of mental health with which the general public feels comfortable. This would therefore be used as a 'handle' into other dimensions of mental health, and be a dominant feature in the publicity. The range of activities developed is illustrated in Figure 2.

Two of these, information needs and the use of computer quizzes, will be discussed in greater detail.

Information needs

One aim of the roadshow was to raise awareness about mental health issues. Many leaflets and posters were available to us from local and national groups, but two 'gaps' in our information system were identified. These were the need for a general leaflet on mental health as opposed to mental illness, and a need to collate information available on the support services available in the community.

Leaflets covering both of these areas were designed and produced by the planning group. The leaflet on services in the community is now being given out to patients on leaving hospital therefore bridging the gap between hospital and community services.

Use of computer quizzes

Two computer questionnaires were used at the roadshow. One, a Stress Questionnaire based on the work of psychologists Miller and Smith, had been used previously at Coronary Heart Disease roadshows, and continues to be a useful tool to promote dialogue with participants. The other questionnaire aimed to explore knowledge and attitudes to mental illness. It was adapted from one being used at Park Prewitt Hospital in Basingstoke Health Authority[5]. In the latter context it was used pre and post a ten week training course for volunteer befrienders.

The questionnaire required simplification for use in our context and development of the computer programme allowed us to design a programme which stored the replies of the participants.

Results

Some twelve months from its inception the Look After Your Mental Health roadshow was ready. The title was chosen with 'mental' written as an omission to highlight the forgotten nature of mental health when thinking about health issues. The roadshow was held for two days (Friday and Saturday) at a leisure centre in the pilot area.

A wide range of agencies and groups participated including Community Education, Health Promotion, The Mental Health Association, Social Services, the Schizophrenia Fellowship, the Alzheimers Disease Society, DAPAS (Derby Alcohol Problems Advi-

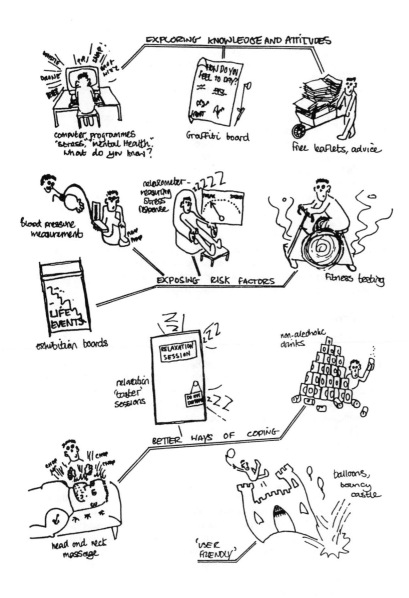

Figure 2

sory Service) and a Befrienders group.

Media coverage for the event was patchy. The provincial media did not cover the event at all, but the Derby Evening Telegraph and BBC Radio Derby both expressed interest and carried features. The Health Telegraph (a monthly insert into the Derby Evening Telegraph) carried a centre page spread on mental health issues including the roadshow.

An estimated 150-200 people attended the event over the two days of whom 71 completed the computer quiz on knowledge and attitudes to mental illness. The responses to the statements asked are shown in table 1.

The results show a confusion among the respondents in terms of their attitudes to mentally ill people. For example 85% of respondents believe that mentally ill people have a right to have their needs met in the same way as those who are physically ill, yet 75% believe that they should be kept quite separate from the rest of the community.

In terms of knowledge, the misconceptions centred mainly around cause, incidence and treatment. The majority of respondents (56%) believed that mental illness is inherited from a parent with just over half as many (27%) believing it to be due to inadequacies in the people themselves. When looking at incidence only 18% of respondents correctly estimated the extent of the problem in women compared to 51% being correct for men. With regard to treatment the majority of respondents (86%) believed that sufferers from mental illness are treated in hospital with 38% believing that padded cells and straight jackets are still used in the treatment of mental illness.

Discussion

The lessons learnt from this activity which need to be addressed if this work is to be repeated successfully in the future, fall into three categories.

The first concerns practical issues such as the publicity, venue, timing and use of the roadshow itself as a medium for mental health promotion, the second concerns the messages we are trying to convey. Are the messages about health or illness or services, and how are we to use the information collected on the misconceptions held by the general public about mental illness. The third is much more fundamental and concerns the future of mental health promotion itself.

Practical issues

Experience of health roadshows for coronary heart disease demonstrates that they have popular appeal. Attendances at the Look After Your Mental Health roadshow was poor in comparison. The obvious difference between the two was the extent of the media coverage. For coronary heart disease the media had been prepared to fully sponsor the event and had carried full page centre spreads each night for a week using competitions and local celebrities. The net gain for the newspaper was the potential for increased circulation. In comparison the coverage for mental health was scant. The climate is however changing and with a growing interest in a more holistic approach to health, this attitude may change.

Without wide scale media coverage the venue itself becomes more crucial. Our experience in using a leisure centre, which required the public to make a positive intention to attend, suggests that any future events should consider the use of venues such as

Percentage of Responses to Statements from all Respondents (N=71)

Statement	Agree	Disagree
Mental illness is contagious, 'catching'	18	82
Mental illness is always a lifelong condition	20	80
Mentally ill people always behave abnormally	11	89
Mentally ill people are usually violent or aggresive	14	86
Keeping a close eye and a tight rein on all patients in psychiatric hospitals is a necessary part of their treatment	13	87
The best way in which we can help mentally ill people is to allow them to tell us what they need	86	14
90% of people suffering from mental illness are inpatients in hospital	86	14
Mentally ill patients are generally kept in locked wards	79	21
In Pastures hospital, padded cells and straight jackets are used for the more severely ill	38	62
It is cheaper to treat mental illness in the community than in a psychiatric hospital	24	76
The mentally ill should be kept quite separate from the rest of the community	75	25
I believe that the community within which I live would accept the mentally ill as part of the community	66	34
I would be displeased if a person suffering a mental illness came to live next door to me	69	31
Mentally ill people have the right to have their needs met in the same way as those who are physically ill	85	15
The only effective thing to do with large psychiatric hospitals is to close them down	65	35
We need to allocate more resources into the effort to prevent mental illness	59	41
I believe the number of women who experience mental illness to be: 1 in 14 1 in 42 1 in 7 1 in 70	35 39 18 7	
I believe the number of men who experience mental illness to be: 1 in 10 1 in 50 1 in 100 1 in 20	51 28 7 13	
All people suffering from mental illness do so: ..because they inherited from a parent ..because they are inadequate ..because of their social class ..none of these	56 27 9 9	

Levels of Health Knowledge and Attitudes to Mental Illness

Table 1

shopping centres where there is a 'passing trade'.

In terms of timing always consult the football league calendar and try to avoid FA Cup Final!

Health or illness?

There is much complex academic debate on the definitions of mental illness and mental health. There is however, a danger that too much emphasis on this can undermine the already limited public (and even professional) comprehension of mental health issues.

The roadshow attempted to address the whole spectrum of mental health issues from health to illness. This may have caused some confusion in the messages that we are trying to give but it presented the opportunity to develop collaboration between the many agencies involved and this was one of the most positive and sustaining aspects of the roadshow.

The data from the computer programme is a valuable source of information on misconceptions currently held by the general public and can be used to inform future practice. The underestimation of the extent of mental health problems confirms its 'hidden' nature within the community, and underlines the needs for more openness on these issues. That so many people believe that the majority of mental illness is treated in hospital, suggests the need to increase the profile and image of the community mental health services. The knowledge that the majority of mental illness is treated in the community already may help to dispel much of the fear associated with the closure of hospitals. The lack of understanding of the factors that can affect our mental health is evidence of the need for more work in the field.

The future of mental health promotion

One of the most disappointing aspects of the project was the lack of involvement and in some cases antipathy from some community mental health service staff. The main objections stemmed from a view that we were trivialising mental health problems by our approach, and that much mental illness cannot be prevented.

This highlights the need for more dialogue between health promotion and the community mental health services. There is a need to design a model of mental health promotion within the service that has validity with its staff. It may be that the disease model of mental health promotion sits more comfortably with them than one from a health perspective[6]. However, for those staff who feel happy with both they need to have their work legitimised and recognised by managers.

The dialogue between health promotion and the mental health services has now begun and the roadshow certainly was one of the factors which nudged it onto the agenda. 'Political' pressure such as Regional interests and the potential contracting of mental health promotion services will help to keep it on the agenda. But it is now time that, like community care itself, mental health promotion stopped being 'everybody's distant relative but nobody's baby[7]'.

References

1. The Mental Health Foundation. (1990). *Mental illness - the fundamental facts*.

2. The Health Education Department Strategy. (1989 - 1991).

3. Southern Derbyshire Health Authority/Derbyshire County Council. (1988). *Strategic plan for mental health services.*

4. Office of Health Economics. (1989). *Mental health in the 1990s - from custody to care*

5. Doyle, R., (1989 November 16th). *Health Service Journal.* Pg 1407.

6. Newton, T., (1988). *Preventing mental illness.* London: Routledge & Kegan Paul.

7. Griffith, R., (1988). *Community care: Agenda for action.* Pg IV HMSO.

26 The Shrewsbury Mental Health Promotion Project

R. Davies, H. Baily, G. MacDonald and
F. Mooniaruch

Introduction

The purpose of this paper is to give an account of a project which was developed in Shrewsbury to promote mental health. The scheme involved a number of individuals, including the four authors of this paper. We shall describe the ideas that guided the project, its chronology, and its practical outcomes. We have included various appendices in order to give a better idea of what the project was trying to achieve.

The Shrewsbury Mental Health Promotion Project had its origins in discussion which took place in late 1989 between two of the authors of this paper, who shared their perception of mental health provision from respective standpoints of health promotion and social work. In terms of mental health promotion, it was 'starting from scratch'.

Defining the problem was the first task; in fact this became defining the *problems* and seeing their interrelatedness. We identified four main areas of concern:

Social stigma

Public perception of mental health problems in our society is still characterised by anxiety, fear and distaste. Ignorance of the nature of mental disorder is wide spread and this is associated with the use of pejorative language to describe people who are ill. One factor which promotes this ignorance is the low priority that mental health education has within school curricula. One result of this is that mental illness can be seen as something shameful.

Media treatment of mental health problems adds to this situation. At worst it promotes insulting stereotypes. At its more serious end, media debate about mental health issues is narrowly focused. Most media comment concerns the wisdom of policies for people with chronic mental health problems, along the lines of the 'hospital v's community care' debate. More general discussion of mental health issues is largely absent.

Service provision

It is true of most services provided by Health Authorities or Social Services Departments that they are reactive: '....the dominant model within the National Health Service is one of illness repair rather than health promotion. Prevention is an implicit, rather than an explicit function of most primary care roles', (Newton, 1989). Thus it is normally not until an individual has a defined or diagnosed mental illness that s/he can expect to have help or treatment. In addition, many Social Services Departments have been re-organising along specialist lines with the attendant risk that individuals' problems will have to be explicitly defined before they know which door to knock on.

Within agencies specifically asked to promote health, mental health promotion tends to fall a long way behind the more prevalent concerns of heart disease, AIDS, etc. Yet it might be argued that how we view ourselves - a fundamental question in mental health - is a determinant of our attitude to our physical health as a whole. There seems no rational explanation for this omission. The personal cost to those suffering mental illness, and their families, is clear. There is also a significant loss to the economy through days lost. Yet fatalistic attitudes prevail; mental illness, like the poor, is always with us. It is as if we are confronting a blind spot in social attitudes.

Individual inhibition

We must also consider the feelings and beliefs of individuals suffering from mental distress. In particular we should consider the prevalent mental disorders of depression and anxiety. Their very ubiquity might make us underestimate their serious, sometimes disabling, effects. Certain aspects of these conditions - lack of confidence and power, the tendency to blame oneself, feelings of shame, helplessness and hopelessness - militate strongly against the individual seeking help. 'I must pull myself together', 'its's all my fault', 'I'm not worth bothering with' are all typical beliefs.

Inhibition plays an important role in determining whether individuals seek help. Such inhibition - based on shame and self-doubt - is likely to be strengthened by disparaging and uncaring attitudes within society.

Interpersonal problems

There is evidence that confiding in another individual can be protective for those vulnerable to depressive disorder. The experience of some of our clients is that disclosure of anxieties is sometimes responded to in an unhelpful manner. Individuals may rush to offer solutions instead of simply listening. They might want to help, but feel unqualified, and so seek to pass the problem on to someone more 'professional'. The point at which disclosure of personal difficulties is made can be crucial; if thwarted, the individual may become wary of taking that step again.

Our early discussions about these issues concluded that all these factors interacted in ways which strengthened their negative effects. A result of this is that individuals with potential mental problems (in particular depression and anxiety) are deterred from seeking help, and this has repercussions for the development of coping skills and longer-term protection from mental disorder.

We judged that a mental health promotion initiative should address itself to these issues. We were concerned with the stigma that surrounds the subject of mental ill health and felt that it would be important to deal with the subject as ordinary and commonplace, and to challenge the stigma and myth by debating these issues in a very open and public way.

In order to find out if our ideas were matched by other mental health professionals and volunteers, we invited over 100 of these to a meeting held in Shrewsbury, of whom 30 attended. Following this, invitations were sent for a follow up planning meeting, which 8 people attended.

Looking back, this was a fairly confusing, even depressing time for us. The open meeting was well attended and produced a great deal of interest. On the other hand, many who attended gave an impression that little could be done, or that their main concern was to find out who they could refer people on to. From some people and professional groups, there seemed to be resistance to the idea that there was anything they could do themselves to help. When it cam to forming a planning group, only a few people felt they could contribute to a project that was only at an exploratory stage.

Thus, although our original ideas met with some recognition, there was considerable scepticism about the whole concept of promoting mental health.

At this point, we began to look more closely at the concept of stress. The word has wide, commonsense usage, has no pejorative connotations and is recognised by both professionals and sufferers as contributing towards depression, anxiety and 'mental breakdown'. Could we not give our ideas a focus by producing a leaflet which would suggest practical ideas for people who felt they were under stress or were becoming anxious or depressed? Once we had decided upon this task we set out once more to get people on board. We now found that people were more willing to commit their time and energy as there was something concrete to work on.

A working group was formed. This group remained largely unchanged over the succeeding 12 months. It comprised individuals from health promotion, MIND, social work and health visiting. Loose in structure, it depended more on individual commitment than an elaborate organisation. Essential to its functioning, however, were the effective secretarial skills of one of its members. The group was responsible for raising money, organising events, commissioning artwork, and agency liaison; it drove the Project towards its climax.

The working group set about reviewing a variety of material on stress and found a leaflet produced by Bristol and Western Health Authority to be particularly useful. We spent long hours refining and adapting this to our own purpose, testing the results on colleagues, friends and clients.

The ideas in the leaflet (see Appendix 1) break no new ground. Ideas of dealing with one thing at a time, allowing time for oneself, not having to be perfect, etc., are familiar hallmarks of stress management. We wanted to keep our '10 tips' simple, direct and expressed in commonplace language. We emphasised that individuals have rights - to be listened to, to say 'no', to express their feelings, and so on.

At intervals we discussed the merits of producing an information booklet on local services. However, we felt that merging this information with the '10 tips' leaflet would cloud the issue. We were setting out to emphasise informal sharing, for example talking

259

to a friend or family member. However, we concluded the leaflet by making reference to the family doctor as a source of help, and identified the local Citizens Advice Bureau as an information source for more specialised agencies.

The working group never envisaged the '10 tips' leaflet as being an end in itself, simply adding to others of its ilk. On the other hand, we decided that it should have the widest possible distribution within Shrewsbury. Also, its launch could be used as a pretext for broader public discussion about mental health issues.

As work progressed throughout 1990, we decided to coincide the launch of the leaflet with MIND week (6th - 11th May, 1991), thus cementing the relationship we had developed with the local branch of that organisation.

We now needed to make another attempt to encourage wider involvement. We convened a meeting of local voluntary groups and interested people. The purpose of this was to publicise our plans for Mental Health Week, enlist practical support, and enable local groups to give presentations on the sort of services they offer. This meeting was successful on all counts and from it were formed smaller working groups which are able to carry the work of the project forward (e.g. media liaison, leaflet distribution), as well as branch off in a new direction (a 'listening skills' group was formed).

The climax, but not the conclusion, of the Shrewsbury Mental Health Promotion Project came during MIND week, 6th - 11th May, 1991. It is worthwhile to catalogue the activities which took place at that time:

1. The '10 tips' leaflet was distributed so that it was available from the beginning of the week. 7,000 were printed, and were displayed in a variety of venues to which the public have access, including the Housing Department, Community Charge Office, Public Libraries, Supermarkets, Petrol Stations, Solicitors' Offices, etc. In three venues they were accompanied by poster exhibits displaying the same basic information as the leaflet. In addition, leaflets were sent to Shrewsbury's major employers for workplace display and, in one case, inclusion with wage slips.

2. We had aimed for press coverage, of events and issues, but the results were disappointing. An individual's personal story was offered for publication, but failed to find favour with the local weekly paper. Response from local radio was better; two members of our group took part in a daytime radio discussion programme which explored the issues raised in the leaflet.

3. The Project worked hand in hand with Shropshire MIND, who organised an Arts and Mental Health Day. This was open to all, and included workshops on painting, voice movement and music, and reminiscence.

4. A video of a TV programme about mental health was shown at a local youth centre and watched by school students during their lunch break, with ensuing discussion.

5. One day during the week was devoted to meeting the public. We had booked a place in a Shrewsbury shopping precinct. On display were posters, leaflets and other information. A relaxation tape played at intervals and copies of it were on sale. We had also produced a questionnaire (see Appendix 2) whose main function was not so much statistical as a means of engaging members of the public. There were stickers to be given out with the Project logo and slogan

contact with people with young children.

6. At the shopping centre, invitations were issued to a free taster session on stress management which took place the following week at a National Health Centre.

7. Shortly following MIND week two members of our group gave talks at local women's clubs about the Project. The discussions at these meeting indicate that people are willing, even keen, to discuss questions of stress and illness in a non clinical environment.

One factor missing from the Project, which its members somewhat regret, is an independent evaluation. The following tally of positive outcomes arises, therefore, only from our own perspective;

1. In both structural and personal terms the Project has helped to break down some of the barriers that exist between and within statutory and voluntary agencies as well as between professions. Members worked closely together, each recognising that the other had a contribution to make to the overall plan.

2. A body of new experience and skills has been built up amongst the group. In addition, resources have been established for future use (e.g. posters, tapes).

3. The meeting of voluntary groups, and their subsequent collaborations, brought together a variety of people who were able to share information and problems and to highlight their common need for training. Relationships between the voluntary groups and the Psychiatric Services have now been put on a firmer footing.

4. The Project has helped to put mental health promotion on the agendas of Health, Social and Voluntary Agencies. Many staff are involved daily in promoting mental health but do not readily recognise this role. Perhaps the Project has helped people think more consciously and explicitly about their work in this area.

5. Although the Project was task-centred, its work is not at an end: it just keeps setting itself new tasks! In particular, it is producing a leaflet about listening skills and plans workshops in this area to visit local clubs in Shropshire. Indicators for future work have become clear through the contacts we have made so far. Discussions with personnel officers and youth workers have highlighted workplace stress and problems of young people as areas which may benefit from the collaborative approach that has been established. &The Project now seeks to establish itself on a more permanent, possibly more formal footing, and will look towards sponsoring and supporting schemes around Shropshire.

6. The most important outcome is that which is the most difficult to evaluate: the impact on the public. Our evidence here can only be anecdotal. The leaflets were rapidly taken up; when we did 'bin checks' in the town centre, we found few had been thrown away. Returns in our questionnaire revealed both a desire for information on mental health issues and a generally favourable response to the displays and leaflets. Most strikingly we found a willingness amongst members of the public to share problems - their own and others'. Although, therefore, we cannot claim anything quantifiable in terms of results, we do feel that we have revealed a demand - that problems of stress and ill-health be discussed and dealt with in a more open and adult way.

261

Reference

Newton, J. (1989). *Preventing mental illness*. Routledge.

10 tips ......

on how to cope with everyday tensions and anxieties.

1 Talk over your worry.

Everyone needs to do this at different times in their life.

Choose a friend, relative or professional helper you can trust

Some results : You will have a relief from strain and be more able to see what you can do about your problem

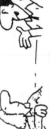

2 Deal with one thing at a time.

Forget the rest for the time being. Tension and worry make even an ordinary day seem unbearable. This need not be a permanent state.

Some results : This will help you achieve something and the other tasks will seem less daunting when you get round to them.

3 Escape from your problem – even if only for a while.

Lose yourself for a while in a change of scene, or an interest. There is no merit in 'sticking it out' and suffering.

Some results: Afterwards, you will be more clear – headed to come back and tackle your problem.

4 You don't have to be perfect.

If you expect too much of yourself you will create a constant state of worry and anxiety. So, decide which things you do well and put your major effort into these.

Some results : You will avoid setting yourself up to fail, and make life easier for yourself - and others.

5 Try not to be too critical of others – or yourself.

Concentrate on other people's and your own good points and learn to understand and develop these.

Some results : You will probably feel less frustrated and let - down by yourself and others, and begin to concentrate on the real causes of your problems.

6 Develop co – operation with others.

Give other people a chance to meet you half way. Find out what they want rather than be suspicious of their motives.

Some results : You will have less emotional and physical tension in reaching your goals.

263

7 Allow time for yourself, however short.

You have the right to put yourself first sometimes. Let other people know that this is what you want.

Some results : You will return to your work, or your problem with a fresh outlook.

8 Try out some form of relaxation

There are a variety of techniques you can learn. Join a class or borrow books or tapes.

Some results : You will find that relaxation helps reduce tension and gives you a better feeling about your life.

9 Physical activity can help.

Find something that you enjoy doing - walking, cycling, swimming or gardening, for example.

Some results : Regular exercise will keep you healthy. You'll feel better about yourself and gain a sense of achievement for your efforts.

10 Make the first move sometimes

Don't let fear of rejection hold you back or lock others out. Even a smile or a kind word can work wonders

Some results : At least you will know you've made an effort and this will build your confidence. Others will appreciate you and respond.

....and remember,

You have rights too !

You have the right :
- o to be listened to
- o to be taken seriously
- o to your own privacy and space
- o to ask for what you want
- o to say 'no', and not feel guilty
- o to have feelings and express them
- o to respect yourself

Produced by :
Shropshire Social Services Department.
Shropshire Health Authority.
Shropshire MIND.
Published by :
Shropshire Centre
for Health Promotion

Adapted, with kind permission from a leaflet produced by Bristol & Western Health Authority.

Everyone has stress in their lives – relationships, moving house, changing your job and even everyday living can cause tensions and anxiety. But letting it build up can lead to larger problems. If you do find yourself becoming anxious or depressed, don't let things go too far. Do talk to someone, like a friend or a member of your family. You may need to talk to someone who can offer further help, such as your family doctor.

There are other more specialist agencies or voluntary bodies who can help, for example with bereavement or marital difficulties. The Citizens Advice Bureau has details of these organisations, or may themselves be able to help.

In Shrewsbury, the Citizens Advice Bureau can be contacted at :

Sidney House, School Court, School Gardens, Shrewsbury (near the main Library.)
☎ Shrewsbury 357855

Appendix 1 (Cont.)

Mental Health and you..........
Some Help for us

Q1. Would you or anyone you know like more information or help (if it were available) about thses mental health problems? Please tick the ones that apply.

Stress	☐	Adult sleep problems	☐
Bereavement	☐	Dealing with anger	☐
Depression	☐	Being overweight	☐
Smoking	☐	General life changes	☐
Constant thoughts	☐	Problems with alcohol	☐
Memory Problems	☐	Everyday coping	☐

Q2. If you had a problem like stress or depression, who would you choose to talk to?
(Please write '1' in the box for the person you would choose to talk to first; a '2' in the box for the person you would choose second, etc. Put an 'X' for anyone you would choose not to talk to about a problem like stress of depression.)

A friend	☐	A health Visitor	☐
Your partner	☐	A District Nurse	☐
Someone at work	☐	A Neighbour	☐
A Social Worker	☐	Citizens Advice Bureau	☐
The Samaritans	☐	A Volunteer Counsellor *e.g. Relate, Confide	☐
Your Doctor	☐		

Q3. What do you think of our Mental Health Promotion? Please write your comments:

The Display ....
The '10 Tips....' Leaflet ....

Q4. How often do you feel stressed or tense? Please tick one box:
Very often ☐   Quite often ☐   Sometimes ☐   Never ☐   **Appendix 2**

27 Early intervention for stress problems: Experience of 3 service delivery models

P. Gordon

Introduction

Mental health is often defined as much by an absence of mental ill-health as by the presence of positive attributes (1,2). Whatever the merits of this approach, it implies that any intervention to reduce stress disorders must constitute a legitimate way to improve 'mental health'. Stress programmes may also perform a more genuinely preventative function, by enhancing personal coping skills and thus the sense of control or self-efficacy which is known to mitigate against future problems. Unfortunately, stress seems to be on the increase, and finding ways to intervene quickly, effectively and with all those who require help is not easy.

Reviews of surveys conducted at the primary care level suggest prevalence rates of 15% or more for psychiatric disorder in the general community (3,4), and many more people might be expected to feel stressed to some lesser degree. By way of a pilot study, I recently carried out a surgery of all attenders at a general practice in our District over one day, which detected 15 patients who rated themselves as needing help for stress and were similarly perceived by their doctor. This figure was actually lower than expected from the surveys cited above, but still suggests that across our Health District, over 200 people could be seeking help for stress-related problems on a single day.

How do we deal with such numbers? It is helpful initially to argue that stress disorders are not a psychiatric illness, but rather a normal response to some common features of modern life. As well as being de-stigmatising, this view leads to the idea that reducing stress is an educational process with 'life skills' as the subject, rather than a form of therapy. Such a 'psycho-educational' model (5) is attractive as a potentially highly efficient approach to health care. The work reported here is therefore based on this view. In Winchester, we have been seeking to develop a method of service delivery which can address the scale of stress problems positively, through the mobilisation of individuals' self-help resources. This paper focuses specifically on how best to provide such programmes.

I will be discussing three new styles of service, though there is an implied fourth method which we have sought to replace, namely the system of referral of individuals by their family doctors to a Clinical Psychology outpatient service. As I have implied already, this is unsatisfactory as a preventative service because of the numbers who can be served by it, but it also fails because of the inevitable need to refer the 'most ill' to any limited treatment service, so that late rather than early intervention becomes the norm. Lastly this form of specialised intervention is impractical on grounds of cost, particularly in current climate of business approaches to management of health care. It has, however, been a continuing element of our District Services, and one which has allowed us to develop expertise in design of stress management group protocols, information booklets and self-help materials. These have formed the basis for the new models described below.

The first of these consisted of classes held in Adult Education settings on the theme of 'Coping with Stress', the second, provision of an extensive library of self-help books and materials, and the third a project to train primary care staff to present advice on stress as part of their role in general health screening and promotion, for example through well-person clinics.

Although little hard evidence is available to date on the efficacy of each approach, they do provide an illustration of some of the organisational and systemic features which have to be considered in planning any community approach, and indeed that these considerations may at times outweigh the technical niceties. I have argued elsewhere (4) that crisis services are shaped more by aspects of the community in which they are sited than by their planned role, and much the same argument applies here: projects must be congruent with other local services, client requirements, and funding systems.

Adult education classes

Let me start with some detail of the Adult Education class on stress, which was set up in 1985. At that time, a number of pioneering projects were being reported which linked health and education services in positive ways. Butcher and de Clive Lowe (7) describe an evening class with the broad title of 'Strategies for Living', which aimed to offer a wide range of self-management strategies as a single package. The authors covered self-awareness, relationships, anxiety, depression and adjustment to life changes over their 8-week course, and present uncontrolled questionnaire data to suggest some positive change in locus of control resulted. Other workers at the Maudsley Hospital (8) had reported on a scheme to offer the skills programmes which characterise psychiatric rehabilitation through a local college, and thus overcome stigmatisation and encourage their clients to socialise in the community. Rowan and Eyres (9) more specifically describe a class on *Coping with Anxiety* and present data from 8 subjects which suggest significant reductions in anxiety symptoms were achieved.

The Winchester project was similarly held at an Adult Education Institute in the evenings, and was based on well-established psychological interventions, adapted for a group educational format. These were cognitive-behavioral in style, presented in 10 weekly sessions which each lasted one and a half hours, and were geared to experiential learning, with periods of discussion, workshop activities and homework assignments.

Table 1 summarises the course content.

Week Number	Topic
1	The nature of stress
2	Personal coping styles: stress diary
3	Progressive relaxation skills: thoughts diary
4	Modifying negative thought patterns
5	Stress-producing beliefs and assumptions
6	Applied relaxation
7	Assertion skills
8	Other relationship difficulties
9	Analysis of general lifestyle patterns
10	Revision / feedback / discussion

Syllabus for coping with stress group

Table 1

The course had been advertised in the local press, together with other general educational courses, and attracted 15 attenders, of whom 13 enrolled formally. Attendance was good, averaging 8 out of 10 sessions per student.

The group completed the SCL-90, a well standardised check-list of common psychiatric symptoms (10), which gives an overall score indicating general distress. For comparative proposes, their scores were contrasted with those of an (unmatched) group of 24 people referred by General Practioners to health service treatment groups for anxiety during the same period. Mean total scores were 64.5 and 123.1 respectively for the two groups, a significant difference, and one which suggests that we had targeted a less symptomatic group at the evening class. Despite this, a follow-up questionnaire completed by 8 students revealed that 75% had consulted a doctor about stress problems, and most viewed the group as a way of learning to cope better, rather than merely gaining knowledge about stress. At follow-up, all but one reported gains from the course, with most aspects being rated highly, particularly relaxation, information on stress, and the homework assignments.

Thus the group seemed to be helpful, and drew in people with significant but currently sub-acute difficulties. Interestingly, all but two students reported they would not have attended the course if it had been held in medical premises. It therefore seems that the course was meeting its health promotion target. It gave more effective coping skills to people vulnerable to stress but who did not currently require formal treatment, and who would not have approached medical services at that time.

Unfortunately, our survey also revealed that only two students would have been prepared to pay the full Adult Education fee for the class, rather than the nominal fee charged during the pilot scheme (the reduced fee being a feature common to the other classes described earlier). This seems to imply that people do not greatly value health education. It became of more practical significance as we sought to extend the project, because we were unable to attract scarce Health Service funds to support its continuation on a subsidised basis and in fact, the project subsequently folded. Since then, the local Adult Education system has however again begun to offer classes on related topics such as relaxation, so the classroom approach may remain viable.

The self-help library

I will now move on to briefly mention a second project initiated by my colleague, Lorraine Bell, which attempted to move the focus further away from 'expert' helpers. This consisted of the provision of an extensive self-help library containing over 250 books concerned with stress and psychological problems. Such manuals have proliferated over recent years, and appear to be highly popular. Disquiet has been expressed that the language in self-help books is too difficult for many of the vulnerable population to comprehend (11), and that they are rarely evaluated. The latter criticism is now beginning to be addressed by development of behavioural self-help manuals linked to research projects (12,13,14). In the case of Marks' 'Living with Fear' for example, a trial on an outpatient sample showed that provision of the text reduced anxiety levels significantly, and there was no improvement in effectiveness when brief psychiatric counselling was added (15). Kiely and McPherson (16) showed that leaflets on stress could reduce symptomatology in primary care patients over a three-month trial. As a means of cheaply broadening the scope of mental health care, self-help libraries are therefore an obvious choice.

Our self-help collection has been in existence for 4 years. It is administered by the Hospital Library Service, but sited within a community mental health centre, and books are loaned by a voluntary worker and other staff members. The library has been consistently used, with about 200 loans being made per year. Particular books are clearly favoured, and now held in multiple copies, whilst across categories, those on anxiety are the most popular. One unfortunate sign of a book's usefulness is the tendency for it to go missing, and funds are needed to replace these books, as well as for keeping the collection up to date. We have also added cassette tapes on a number of subjects, though these seem to be less popular. Finally, short leaflets are available on a number of topics.

Our attempts to evaluate the service have centred on a simple feedback system. Each book contains a slip with space for the reader to rate its helpfulness and make general comments. In practice, the majority of loans are returned without a completed rating, despite the simplicity of the system. However those comments which have been received are largely positive, with ratings ranging from slightly to extremely helpful and remarks such as 'after reading the book I didn't feel such a freak' and 'useful and rewarding in combatting my problems'.

Impressions of the self-help library to date are that it is a promising scheme, and useful adjunct to other projects and to direct therapy. However, as a community health promotion project it seems limited by its siting in a mental health facility. Increasing the availability of this type of book at local libraries, health centres and advice centres seems an obvious next stop.

I therefore undertook a brief comparison of loan rated for 1990/91 for certain self-help manuals which are held in both our library and the County Library in the City centre. For the same 10 popular books on stress, the mean number of loans at the self-help library was 1.2, whilst at the City library it totalled 5.4. This seems to favour the central location. However, not all of the books I looked at were favoured by our team and therefore would not often have been recommended, so another indicator was needed. Looking instead at the most poplar 10 self-help manuals for stress in each library, the comparison is closer, with annual loan rates of 4.9 and 6.9 respectively. There is some distortion due to differing loan periods (which are shorter, and this produce more renewals at the City library) and the number of alternative books from which to choose) (larger at our library), so the final picture is of little real difference in uptake of books at the two sites. The case for housing self-help manuals in generic public collections seems, to date, unproven.

Stress clinics in primary care

Currently, our third project is under way. This tries to find a middle way between the pure self-help of the library and the expert tuition of the evening class. The idea is to 'cascade' psychological skills to generic health worker. The approach follows the 'triadic' model, where a mediator offers direct help to the client, but themselves receives training and supervision. There is encouraging evidence that this type of work by para-professionals can be effective for delivering circumscribed behavioural therapy intervention, given adequate supervision (see review by Milne (17)). Specifically, in our project, training is being offered to a range of staff working in primary care settings, to enable them to offer better support and advice to people with stress problems. Back-up in the form of consultation and supervision is available from the clinical psychologist.

The focus is on Health Visitors and Practice Nurses. Whilst health visiting is traditionally associated with preventative medicine, Practice Nurses are now also becoming involved in health promotion as Doctors increasingly employ a nurse to run health screening programmes for major preventable illness, such as coronary disease. Within our District, major programmes in this area have been under way for several years, but the nurses involved have begun to identify stress as a major health problem amongst their clients, and one to which they feel they have a limited response. In a recent survey of all practice nurses employed in our District, replies were received from 38 nurses (or 63% of the total). Of these, 58% felt they needed additional training on stress issues. Amongst potential group work topics, 'Coping with Stress' was most often chosen (by 42% of nurses) as being needed in their locality.

271

At the same time, central government has started to recognise that stress is a legitimate area to target through the system of Health Promotion Clinics. A financial incentive is therefore available to general practices which develop programmes to combat stress. These developments have coincided with a recognition that Clinical Psychologists should place greater emphasis on skills transmission and supervision (18). Thus a coincidence of factors make a stress programme led by Clinical Psychologists, but delivered within primary care, timely at present.

The Winchester project began earlier this year. It centres on a policy of (a) providing specialised training on dealing with stress disorders to a range of primary care staff (b) joint working and supervision to ensure effective stress clinics are developed, and (c) evaluation of certain pilot clinics against a background of data on needs within that centre.

Initial 2-day workshops on stress management have already been held for about 30 primary care staff. These were designed mainly to help nurses and doctors work more effectively with stressed clients on their normal case load. A second level of more intensive training is now placed, which will cover the skills required to set up specialised stress clinics or groups. At the same time, we have been investigating the perceived extent and types of stress problems in particular General Practices, using both structured interviews with staff and direct questionnaires to a sample of patients. This data will allow us to design the health promotion clinics which will next be run as a pilot scheme, and should form the basis for an evaluation of whether they have met needs within the practice. Depending on the outcome of this trial, the package of training and supervision will be modified or extended. Although it is early days, the project seems to have created widespread interest and enthusiasm, with a waiting list of further training courses. It had already significantly increased the skills available around our District for managing stress.

Comment and discussion

I have now described three care systems, each of which sought to offer earlier help for stress problems than can be achieved through conventional treatment structures. Table 2 (below) presents four key aspects of each of these projects. It can be seen that they differ on each of these factors, and other permutations would therefore be possible, and perhaps desirable.

What lessons can be learnt? In discussing the projects, I will look at each key factor in turn, starting with the service setting, the aspect which relates to how accessible the project was. The use of education premises seems to draw in people who would not have sought medical help at the time, so it clearly widens the net of any programme. By comparison, primary care seems rather a compromise as a location. However, both settings pre-suppose some limitations. Attendance at a Health Centre group may depend upon whether people see their distress as a 'medical' issue, but to attend an evening class, people must still identify themselves as having a 'problem', which may not always be obvious at an early stage. They must also want to try to deal with it themselves, and thus have some sense of competence or self-efficacy, yet we know this is reduced in mental health disorders. A group or class will not therefore meet all needs for intervention in the population, wherever its location.

Setting	Therapist	Method	Funding
Education	Psychologist	Classes	D.H.A. / Education
Mental health	Self	Reading	D.H.A.
Primary care	Nurse	Individual / Group work	F.H.S.A.

Note: DHA = District Health Authority   FHSA = Family Health Services Authority

Aspects of the three projects

Table 2

Providing self-help reading materials is a possible adjunct, and people might more easily browse through a book than enrol for a formal series of meetings, but there are still limitations regarding access, such as whether the target population are all people who have the habit of using libraries and written text. Siting of such book collections in generic or specialised libraries is an unresolved question. I suspect the' browsing' role occurs in a public library setting, whilst the texts act more as treatment manuals when in a mental health centre. The issue of access remains crucial, and more work needs to be done on finding ways to get across positive health ideas to those who most need them, rather than to those who already recognise their value.

As to therapist, there is a trade-off between the range of people who can be targeted and the expertise which can be delivered (and thus, presumably, the effectiveness of the intervention). There are also implications for the provision of adequate supervision. In our primary care project, the use of therapists with a general nursing training promises to ensure that quality of support and advice can be maintained, and though staffing costs remain relatively high, they are less than those of the specialist therapists sometimes advocated (19). Through the link to their wider health promotion role, the nurse may also help people consider change who would not have been sufficiently conscious of a stress problem to seek out self-help groups or literature independently. In that sense, using Practice Nurses may actually improve access as well as maintaining expertise, and this argues strongly in favour of such primary care projects.

Moving on to methods, I have mentioned some doubts or limitations about the value of reading material alone, and for this reason again I would advocate direct contact by a trained counsellor to advise on stress, though I suggest this should normally be in a group setting, for economic reasons. The length of such contact needed to produce useful gains is at present an open question, though our work has all been based around series of 6 to 10 group sessions, which is typical for effective anxiety management projects (20,21) and much greater than the minimal contact of the self-help study of Marks' book cited earlier (15).

Having mentioned economics, the aspect of funding seems in our experience to have great practical influence on the style of health promotion which can be offered. Simply put, no project will survive long unless it has very modest demands on other funds of statutory bodies, and/or reduces their other financial commitments. Self-help groups are particularly attractive in this sense, though as most of us know, they rarely arise spontaneously, and so again, we are back to at least some commitment of professional time. It is no coincidence that our current work developed at a time when funds were being directed into health promotion at the primary care level, and future innovations may need the same sort of encouragement if they are to take root.

Of course, the ideal system would not put undue reliance on any one tactic for reducing stress disorders, but instead aim for a network of facilities. This would include self-help materials and groups, educational classes, and low-level, easy access advice within the primary health system, and lead on to a full back-up of professional referral and consultancy. As this may never be realistic, we are left in a dilemma about priorities. The only way to resolve that will be through evaluation of more projects like our own, and particularly by finding more exact methods to assist the impact on the population of the numerous factors I have discussed. I believe that will be a long and difficult task, but in the end, a worthwhile enterprise.

Reference

1. Veit, C.T. & Ware, J.E. Jnr. The structure of psychological distress and well-being in general populations. *J Consult Clin Psychol* 1983;51(5):730-741

2. Eysenck, M. *Happiness*. London: Lawrence Erlbaum, 11991.

3. Goldberg, D.P. & Huxley, P.H. *Mental Illness in the Community*. London: Travistock, 1980.

4. Reeler, A.P. Psychological disorder in primary care and the development of clinical services: an African perspective. *Psychologist* 1991;14(8):349-353.

5. Authier, J, Gustafson, K,, Guerney, B., & Kasdorf, J.A. The psychological practioner as a teacher: A theoretical, historical and practical view. *Counselling Psychol.* 1975;5:31-50

6. Gordon, P.K. Client characteristics at two psychiatric emerency services. Paper presented at the Annual Conference of the British Psychological Society, Bournemouth 1991.

7. Butcher, P. & de Clive-Lowe, S. Strategies for living: teaching psychological self-help as adult education. *Br J Med Psychol* 1985;58(3):275-284.

8. Rose, J. The 'Choices Course' Paper presented to MIND Annual Conference, London, 1984.

9. Rowan, D. & Eayrs, C.B. Coping with Anxiety: An adult education Evening Class.

Paper presented to the Annual Conference of the British Association of Behavioural Psychotherapy, Sussex, 1982.

10. Derogatis, L.R. SCL90(R): Manual of administration, scoring and procedure. Towson, *Clinical Psychometric Research*, 1977.

11. O'Farrell, T.J. & Keithen, N.J. Readability of behaviour therapy self-help manuals. *Behav Ther.* 1983;14(3):449-454.

12. Northumberland Health Authority. *Coping with anxiety.* Durham, Northumberland Health Authority, 1986.

13. Marks, I.M. *Living with fear.* New York, McGraw Hill, 1978]

14. Mattheews, A.M., Gelder, M.G. & Johnston, D.W. *Programmed practice for agrophobia.* London, Tavistock,1981.

15. Ghosh, A., Marks, I.M. & Carr, A.C. Therapist contact and outcome of self-exposure treatment for phobias. *Br J Psychiat.* 1988;152:234-238.

16. Kiely, B.G. & McPherson, I.G. Stress self-help packages in primary care: a controlled trial evaluation. *J R Coll Gen Pract* 1986;36:307-309.

17. Milne, D. *Training behaviour therapists: methods, evalution and implementation with parents, nurses and teachers.* London, Croom Helm, 1986.

18. Manpower Planning Advisory Group. *Clinical psychology project: full report.* London, Department of Health, 1990.

19. Barker, P.J. & Fraser, D. The nurse therapist in a primary care setting. In: Barker, P.J. & Fraser, D. *The nurse therapist: a behavioral model.* London, Croom Helm, 1985: 92-114.

20. Jannoun, L., Oppenheimer, C. & Gelder, M. A self-help treatment programme for anxiety state patients. *Behav Ther* 1982;13:103-111.

21. Powell, T.J. Anxiety management groups in clinical practice: a preliminary report. *Behav Psychotherapy* 1987;15:181-187.

28 Working in partnership with depressed parents and their children

A. Jenkins

Introduction

All references in this paper will be to young mothers and their children. It does not exclude those men who are becoming main carers of their children nor those who are now being referred into New Parent and Infant Network (Newpin). It is to acknowledge that in Newpin's ten years of existence the main carer has predominantly been the mother. Working in the area where the first Newpin centre is, I became increasingly aware of the degree of depression there was in young mothers. This area in which I work is considered to be deprived. Indeed all the characteristics of inner city deprivation are evident. Along with such associated problems, there is a high degree of single parenting and family breakdown. For many of the people referred to Newpin where extended family kinship still exists, relationships are largely destructive and not supportive.

The picture painted here is one which many people working with parents and their children in urban areas will be familiar with but I do not wish to convey the notion that depression in young mothers is necessarily more likely to occur with the economic/social disadvantage that I have mentioned, than in situations which conventionally appear more conducive and favourable to child rearing. Whether the aforementioned indices contribute to the depressed state in young mothers is not for this paper but almost without exception the words 'depressed and isolated' feature in the description of the majority of those referred to the project by multi-disciplinary professional workers. My belief, based on the experience gained through the fifteen years of working directly with mothers and their children is that the base line for the occurrence of depression is when a necessary and fundamental positive emotional relationship between mothers and their children cannot develop because enough personal value has not been able to be transmitted to the mother in her own formative years. This resulted in a fragile sense of affinity in attachment, a lack of emotional maturity, and an inability on the part of the adult to wholly recognise the vulnerability and dependence of her child upon her. This influences her capacity to cope with the birth experiences and the subsequent responsibilities of child caring. In depressed parenting there is what I would describe as a 'void'. Instead of a dynamic psychic inter-relationship between mother and her child, fundamental for healthy psychic growth, there is an emptiness or an unoccupied space. It is as if this space is a fracture in early bonding. Linked to the depressed state of many people who come to Newpin, is an inability to cope with their children's emotional needs, the children appearing not to be valued or protected, especially in times of adult distress. It is as if personal resources are so slender only the minimum of involvement with the child, which is usually practical such as nappy changing or feeding, can be tolerated. An infant or child can be seen to be severely unhappy yet apparently unnoticed by the mother who seems unable to respond and may even appear indifferent to the child's crying. Many of the women who come to Newpin are very dependent on others around them to produce the action for them. This helpless dependency, so often initially a feature of those referred into the project, can often mask feelings of impotent rage which spills over into the way their children are erratically and often harshly controlled. The responses of the children are varied. Some will react apathetically as if they have learned quickly to mirror the maternal state, others in what seems to be a frantic attempt to engage a reaction from their mothers, will behave with intensifying vigour either as an infant by crying or an older toddler by destructive behaviour, which may elicit some response from the parent, but not usually a helpful one. Some children in their passivity behave as if they have learned to be 'good' early in life. I believe that this unhealthy symbiotic emotional affect has long term damaging consequences on the parent child relationship. Therefore with the focus on the adult's distress and their own early emotional deprivation and the child's right to autonomy and happiness in a loving, secure, nurturing environment, an attempt to prevent cyclical destructive patterning from occurring and to improve the mental health of the adult is Newpin's aim. The recognition that this can only be achieved by helping the adult to empower themselves in order to change is implicit to Newpin's ethos.

The pre-Newpin chat

From the first meeting arranged at home the notion of choice to personally control one's circumstances and mental well being is reinforced. Although some reference will be made to the problems which the mother may be experiencing and which usually would be known to the Co-ordinator at the point of referral, the approach will concentrate on the whole person and not the problem centred focus which is common today. The raison d' être for involvement is that from the beginning Newpin views 'the problem' as being only a part of the whole human make up, and there are many more facets to an individual to counterbalance the negativity of being labelled as having some malfunction. The meeting is the first step toward a process of change, and begins always at home unless otherwise indicated, and at a time which is arranged at the convenience of the mother. The Newpin Co-ordinator, who herself has been through the initial training programme and in most instances was originally a referral herself into Newpin, is the person who visits. The 'Newpin chat,' as assessment is called, is of vital importance when needing to gauge how a person sees themselves and how Newpin could be of use to them. Respecting the individuality and unique contribution each person can make, with emphasis on their inherent strengths, is its main purpose. This is particularly important when people register a diagnosis such as depression, and as a result, are more inclined to see themselves as ill and vulnerable and unable to identify with their wellness and strength.

This home visit is divided into two distinct parts, the first of which is a comprehensive description of Newpin and its activities. Emphasis is placed on giving an all round picture of the project, including what could be difficult to tolerate such as areas of conflict, adult to adult, parent to child, and the problems which can arise from such situations. If these matters are not mentioned, people may idealise Newpin then find it does not live up to expectations, and could drop out before a secure attachment has been formed. This is particularly important for those who are depressed, as the tendency is to view their life without hope or confidence, leaving them unable to cope with adversity, however minor, and this subsequently adds to despair. As there is a link between the depression and early adverse life experiences it is vital that the Newpin activities are understood, since for many people, running away from problems has been a long standing situation. In particular, the development training and the therapeutic work must be carefully discussed. To ensure that this comprehensive overview is clear, the mother is asked to 'play back' what she believes she has heard, and it is only when an accurate picture of Newpin has been drawn, and one which satisfies the Co-ordinator that she sufficiently understands Newpin and welcomes involvement, that the second part of the meeting, concerned with personal disclosures, begins. This involves the sensitive drawing of intimate experiences tracing back throughout childhood, schooling, working life, their perception of relationships with their family of origin, past and present relationships, and if there are personal changes they would like to make. A discussion of how they view and interact with their own children, and their expectations of them, makes up the rest of the visit.

The Co-ordinator will be looking at where the mother may be able to make the most use of the Newpin structure, her potential for change, and to some extent making her aware of what change means, and its effect on current personal relationships.

This very individual approach ensures that there is no mould into which people have to fit, no prescribed formula or treatment, and no timescale. In other words they have their own mould, which is themselves. Change and development is a very individual process, although Newpin has found that, in an atmosphere geared to self worth and respect, positive changes such as the lessening of and recovery from depression can be swift.

Acceptance of Newpin

Working on the basis that acceptance must primarily be in the hands of the mother, it is crucial to start the energising process of self empowerment through choice, regardless of how small at the time of referral that may be. What Newpin can offer will be tailored to the mother's individual requirements. However, as the main aim is to get her attached in some way to the project, one of the women who has been involved in Newpin for some time, and has undertaken a Newpin training programme, would be empathetically matched with her. There is a significant point to the empathetic matching. Some women will say they will come in by themselves but Newpin has found that without some form of attachment they are more likely to have a poor outcome and subsequent drop-out. This is particularly important with people who are depressed, as the lack of motivation and drive, the listlessness and loss of persona make it difficult to sustain involvement without this initial holding. How long or short this attachment is depends on the individual needs and degree of damaged self worth. It is the first step to enable her to begin to gain in confidence, to mix with others and slowly begin the process of relationship building between members within the Newpin living room. Any circumstance which arises and provokes anxiety is more easily contained if some attachment has been arranged. The fact that the woman knows someone who will be with her in the early stages of her involvement seems to have a greater positive effect. There is no particular task expected, apart from encouraging attendance, though strong bonds are formed which are supportive in many ways both in and out of the project. However, for most people referred to Newpin the establishing of relationships may take a long time, as trust in others has little foundation and is therefore viewed suspiciously.

At this first visit the mother will be given a list of everyone involved in the project including the visiting Co-ordinator. Although this may appear meaningless initially, it has proved to be a vital link in creating a feeling of belonging for many women in the beginning stages. One very depressed woman remarked to me that she kept the list by the telephone for the whole of the weekend, for although she did not at that stage know the people, seeing it made her feel less isolated and she felt that ringing any of those numbers would bring a response even though she did not have the courage to actually do it. This very important connection, which has never in the whole of Newpin's history been abused, is part of the Newpin philosophy which believes that emotional networking reduces the impact of a depressed state. It is the first sense of attachment that the women may feel, and it is from this early awareness of one's own importance in a chain through the 24 hour, round the year, communication that positive relationships can begin to grow. The widening of her social network, the chance to view herself through the eyes of others all helps to reduce the mother's negative attitude of poor self image. Through the same channel, she will have the opportunity to see in the Newpin living room how other mothers are themselves, and how they behave with their own children.

This plays a part in diminishing her sense of isolation and guilty feelings associated with disabled mothering. The interactive relationships with other adults and their children is also facilitated through the use of the crèche where she will be encouraged to focus on her relationship with her child, in a way that is non-punishing and non-judgemental. Starting the training programme is often the beginning of healthy relationship forming. For others, just actually discovering Newpin seems to help them flower, and in these instances the change can be very dramatic and speedy. Apathy is then replaced by frustrated energy with a desire to start the training programme as soon as possible.

The initial training programme

Newpin currently runs two, one day a week for 38 weeks, training programmes a year. These programmes cover a wide range of issues which are pertinent to human development and social behaviour and are concerned with the attitudes prevalent in society which influence us all. A substantial section is devoted to both the adult's own childhood hurts and the situation for the children they have, and is concerned with the emotional needs of children, developing constructive relationships, child abuse, and play, to name just a few topics. The aim is to enlighten rather than teach didactically, to raise consciousness, and to be mentally stimulating. Because the topics are concerned with life situations they can be emotionally disturbing. Speakers are from both academic and non-academic backgrounds yet must be experts in their field. (Some Newpin women run these sessions). All will have the ability to engage active participation from the group. Apart from these two hour sessions, one and a half hour group therapy, conducted by a trained group analyst, runs for the same duration as this initial training programme.

The programme is open to anybody referred to the project, but as the course is very intense and many of the women have experienced multiple negative childhood experiences, it is essential that the time is absolutely personally right for them to begin. The Co-ordinator will take time to talk through with each person the merits of starting at the right point. It is fundamental that they start at a time when they are secure enough in the Newpin environment and are at a time able to get maximum value from the training and the therapy. Particularly as the therapy will inevitably bring up the not inconsiderable pain of past experiences. Participation in the sessions may take time for some individuals but the main aim is to help them maintain continuity. Again, the pride in sustaining attendance is another element in the precess of developing emotional well-being. The programme certainly contributes greatly to increased self esteem. This is helped by the fact that the group is a closed group from the time it begins. It is in this milieu of the sharing of one's personal life circumstances with each other during the therapy sessions, a closer bonding can begin. Not only do the mothers share this time together but they are cared for by having a sustaining meal prepared for them which they eat together. This simple but effective way of nurture helps to underpin the belief in oneself as being worthy of attention and respect. Increased esteem can only come from within oneself, and Newpin merely attempts to reinforce this message by its structure. There is no corrective training, only opportunities to be taken for oneself, with encouragement.

During the training time, the children are being cared for by the crèche staff, who themselves will have been part of a previous training and therapy programme. This has the added advantage of increased understanding by the crèche workers of the situation for the mothers, and also respite for the women from their children, and special time for themselves, often for many for the first time. The children gain from this too. They also have respite from their mothers, and sociability and less chaotic behaviour starts in the crèche and the Newpin living room where the interaction with other children and adults reinforces the child's sense of its own identity.

The Newpin living room

The more the living room is used, the more all round improvement of self esteem and consideration for ones child's needs is likely. People are encouraged to come as much as possible. Co-ordinators are aware that some individuals will take a long time before they can feel comfortable and own Newpin as their place. Many women in their depression come to Newpin with ambivalent feelings towards their children, and yet their parental self esteem depends upon approbation from others to their children. The conflict of emotion that the depressed mother experiences when her child hurts another child, or is perceived by her as to behave 'badly', usually ends in harsh punishment for her child. Even if restrained physically, emotional withdrawal from the child by the parent causes unhappiness for the child long after the event. Newpin encourages the notion that if a child is hurtful toward another there must be a reason, and tries to help the mother recognise other ways of handling the situation by detaching herself from her own hurt and rejected feelings toward her child, and by this means she has the capability of keeping her child's self esteem intact. Depressed adults may not be able to recognise their children's emotional needs when their own are not met. This is understood and considered. Self recognition of the need to be a mature adult for one's child's healthy maturing is learned slowly but is a persistent message throughout Newpin.

Children in Newpin

Although Newpin's concentration may appear to be on the adult's development, this is not entirely true. There is no doubt that there is an improvement in mother child relationships when the attention is on the hurt child within the adult, but is it fair to the child to wait beyond the adult time scale of self fulfilment? Newpin believes that many of the children who come to Newpin are also depressed. How can they be otherwise if they have not experienced a sense of their own value, for whatever reason, through the withholding of consistent emotional nurture? Therefore, it is all the more important that quality care in the crèche has a high priority. Newpin looks to the crèche staff not merely to mind children but to be therapeutic agents between the mother and her child, to encourage mothers to come into the crèche with their children and learn to play themselves. Many of the depressed women who come have little notion of play, or how to enjoy their children, and there is a lot of resistance to going into the crèche. The more depressed a woman is, the more intolerable she will find the level of noise. The crèche is adjacent to the living room and always remains open, apart from training or therapy group times. This is necessary for the emotional security of the children as it gives access to the mother whenever the child wants it. Particularly so when the fear of separation is noticeably high. In Newpin this acknowledgement of the child's timescale as being different from the adult's is constant. Newpin looks to stable adults to work in the crèche. Rapid turnover of staff is damaging to children, particularly if they have an insecure attachment with their mother. Newpin endeavours to seek crèche managers who can commit themselves to stay. Although undoubtedly there is value in qualifications for the care of children, Newpin believes that not enough attention is paid in formal training to understanding the complexities of the inter-personal relationships between the adults and their children. Neither does Newpin believe that, overall, the care of children in society is valued, and therefore intentionally seeks to enhance the role of crèche workers in the Newpin structure. In-service training for the crèche staff, concentrating on the emotional needs of the children who come and also the needs of the mothers, has been found to be necessary to help strengthen the attachments. Any parent who feels that she needs further help understanding how to cope with her child can have individual help over a period of time, with one to one counselling, usually with the Co-ordinator, who has had training in this field. Newpin is currently devising a scheme which should ensure that whilst the self development of the mothers is ongoing, the children's well-being is kept in focus with some specialist group work. This will be open to those parents who have themselves not enjoyed good enough care as children and who are repeating these destructive patterns in their own infant and child caring. Newpin, through its work with young mothers and their children, would like to raise the profile of parenting and by doing so gain the affirmation from society that the importance of loving respect for children comes from being loved, respected, and valued for oneself.

In this way young parental depression and its cyclical effects might begin to be reduced.

29 Emotional well being: A Samaritan perspective

N. Keir

Introduction

Reading the World Health Organisation's definition of health as 'a state of complete physical, mental, social and moral well-being' brings to mind one of the aphorisms of the Eighteenth Century German scientist and philosopher, Georg Christoph Lichtenberg:

'I have looked at the register of illnesses and did not find anxieties and gloomy thoughts among them: this is very wrong.'

Were Lichtenberg alive today he would surely welcome the importance that is attached to emotional well-being, the recognition that anxieties and gloomy thoughts impoverish and even endanger life. So, too, would Shakespeare's Macbeth. Remember how he asked the doctor:

'Canst thou not minister to a mind diseas'd, pluck from the memory a rooted sorrow, raze out the written troubles of the brain, and with some sweet oblivious antidote cleanse the stuff'd bosom of that perilous stuff which weighs upon the heart?'

There was much truth in the doctor's reply:

'Therein the patient must minister to himself.'

But left to minister to themselves, those burdened with anxieties and gloomy thoughts can become overwhelmed by them and reach the conclusion that only suicide can bring relief.

The Samaritans are volunteers whose prime purpose is to be available at any hour of the day or night to befriend those passing through personal crises and in imminent danger of taking their own lives. A crisis organisation? Yes, but as one Samaritan advertising poster says, 'You don't have to be suicidal to talk to the Samaritans.' The importance is recognised of providing a listening ear to those whose despair has not yet led them seriously to contemplate taking their own lives, that is before their thinking has become so constricted that suicide may be perceived as the only remaining option.

The Samaritans were formed in 1953. Their founder was Chad Varah, who described them thus:

> 'The Samaritans are listeners. Whatever their human failings in the world outside,
> when they come on duty they leave behind their self-regard and self-concern in
> order to be as far as possible what callers wish them to be, need them to be.'

Samaritans are ordinary men and women, no doubt afflicted in their everyday lives with
the disease of which Falstaff complained:

> 'It is the disease of not listening, the malady of not marking, that I am troubled
> withal.'

But, on duty, they are empathising listeners, a role in which they occupy a privileged
position. As anonymous strangers, they find their clients, or callers, as they prefer to call
them, sharing feelings with an intimacy probably shown to no-one else. The Samaritans
are anonymous confidants, and those who confide in them can retain the security of their
own anonymity.

In short, Samaritans offer what the Unidentified Guest at T. S. Eliot's Cocktail Party
called:

> 'The luxury of an intimate disclosure to a stranger.'

Though, for those in despair, it may be much more than a mere luxury: it may be a matter
of life or death.

All Samaritans know that talking about their deepest feelings is helpful to those in
despair. Experience has shown that the listening therapy Samaritans offer can contribute
to the recovery of emotional well-being, without which life can become intolerable.
Samaritans cannot pluck out a rooted sorrow; they have no sweet oblivious antidote to
offer. But by helping their callers to articulate their feelings, by offering emotional
support through a period of crisis, they enable the callers to cope with that perilous stuff
which weighs upon the heart.

There are some 23,000 Samaritan volunteers in more than 180 branches located
throughout these islands. And beyond these shores, in branches scattered round the
world, there are thousands more, all following Samaritan principles and practices, and
linked to each other through common membership of Befrienders International.

No-one can expect to go through life without some emotional disturbance, whether it
be through stress, trauma, illness or bereavement. Most people weather episodes of this
kind, but many are driven to thoughts of self-destruction. The statistics of suicide give
no real indication of the incidence of such thoughts. Not only are the figures published
for suicide undoubtedly lower than the true level, but there are many people who have
suicidal thoughts and impulses without succumbing to them. The figures for parasuicide,
that is non-fatal acts of self-injury, are equally misleading. Perhaps some indication of
the incidence of suicidal thoughts and hence of serious loss of emotional well-being can
be gained from the number of calls received each year in the Samaritan branches in the
United Kingdom and the Republic of Ireland. Last year there were some two and a half
million and about two thirds of these included references to suicidal thoughts.

There are so many experiences which disturb people's emotional well-being. Eric
Sevareid said:

> 'The biggest business in America is not steel, automobiles, or television. It is the
> manufacture, refinement, and distribution of anxiety.'

Samaritans are told about anxieties caused by work and by the lack of it, by relationships and by the absence of them, anxieties which have clearly understood causes and those which apparently have none. They listen to expressions of unhappiness that have arisen from, and given rise to, drug and alcohol abuse. Above all, they listen to people who, though often surrounded by friends and colleagues, feel isolated. They listen to children who are being abused, adults who have been abused and adults who abuse others. They listen to the battered and those who batter. They listen to callers on the telephone, they meet those who wish to talk face to face and they read and respond to the letters of those who wish to unburden themselves in writing. They do so round the clock, morning, noon and night, year in, year out. The task is endless.

Reference has already been made to Samaritan principles and practices. One of these states quite clearly that:

'the fact that a person has asked the help of The Samaritans, together with everything he or she has said, is completely confidential within the organisation...'

Confidentiality is fundamental to the work of the Samaritans. Before a caller will make an intimate disclosure to a Samaritan there has to be trust. The sacrosanctity of confidentiality and the desire to preserve anonymity produced, in the early days of the organisation, a fairly low-key image. Samaritans were willing to sit in their centres and await calls. They did not have to wait long. The number of calls received by Samaritan branches has grown steadily throughout the thirty-seven years the organisation has been in existence. But Samaritans recognise that it takes courage and desperation for a caller to initiate contact. It is also clear that if Samaritans are to be available to those who need them, people have to know that they are there. As Chad Varah observed many years ago, publicity is their life blood. Thus there has been a growing recognition of the need to reach out to those who need help. The word 'outreach' is now firmly placed in the Samaritan vocabulary.

For fifteen years it has been Samaritan policy to follow up third-party referrals. Thus

'Samaritans listen to those concerned about the welfare of another person, and, if satisfied that the third person is despairing, depressed or suicidal, may discreetly offer befriending.'

Experience has shown that the incidence of suicidal thoughts among those contacted in this way is somewhat higher than it is among callers in general.

Consideration of suicide statistics has spotlighted areas where outreach is especially relevant: the young, the elderly, those in prison, those living in isolated rural locations. Ways of increasing contact with these and other groups have been sought. For many years members of the Samaritans' Festival Branch have set up their tent or caravan at pop festivals to be available for young people who may be in distress. Samaritans visit prisons. In many areas they make regular appearances at hospitals. Publicity is targeted at rural communities. Talks are given in schools.

Samaritans have recognised that they have a role to play on occasions when people have been subjected to traumatic events. Thus they have been involved in the aftermath of most of the major disasters that have occurred in the last few years: Kegworth, Lockerbie, Zeebrugge and many others. Experience has shown that after such tragic events Samaritan empathy can be helpful to the relatives and friends of the victims, to those awaiting news and to members of the public services. Asked by a TV interviewer what she most needed after the Clapham rail crash, one of the nurses involved in the treatment of the injured said, 'someone to talk to.' Often in such circumstances Samaritans find that, as well as disclosures of current anguish, they encounter deep-rooted sorrows. At Lockerbie, Samaritan volunteers listened not only to the horrendous experiences of those who had to scour the moors for human remains, but also to the stored-up memories of earlier traumas, such as the Falklands War.

Traumatic events are just one of the factors that can adversely affect emotional well-being. But at the bottom of everyone's personal pit is suicide. It is important to remember that suicide is itself a traumatic event which can gravely undermine the emotional well-being of all involved, directly or indirectly: family, friends, colleagues, even bystanders. Think of the feelings of the engine driver whose train has become a means of suicide. Consider the fact that the suicide rate of young people can be influenced by the suicide of a pop idol. Reflect upon the recent observation of a welfare officer on the suicide of an employee of the organisation for which she, too, worked: none of his colleagues would venture into the victim's office to clear out his desk and the task had been left to her; even weeks after the event she spoke of the feeling of unease it had caused her. Such feelings can become the rooted sorrows, the written troubles of the brain of Macbeth's speech. It is likely that for every suicide that has occurred in the last few years there will be at least a handful of people whose emotional well-being has been impaired.

Samaritans do not make moral judgements about suicide. They believe that:
> 'A caller does not lose the freedom to make his or her own decisions, including the decision to take his or her own life.'

There have always been those who argued that suicide is the right of the individual. Not least was the ever-logical and previously quoted Lichtenberg:
> '...if one day you should find suicide beneficial, if that is to say all your reasons do not suffice to restrain you, then for you suicide too is - permitted.'

Samaritans would not argue with that. But - it is a very big 'but' - no-one wants to be suicidal. As George Borrow's Lavengro said,
> 'There's night and day, brother, both sweet things; sun, moon and stars, brother, all sweet things; there's likewise a wind on the heath. Life is very sweet, brother; who would wish to die?'

People do not choose to be suicidal; they feel they are compelled to be so, compelled by unendurable psychological pain, by intolerable deprivation of emotional well-being.

One of the contributions that Samaritans can make, and have to some degree already made, is to publicise the possibility and prevalence of suicide and to inform the public about the clues people give of suicidal intent. How very often we find that, although the signs had been there for all to see, suicide comes as an unexpected shock to family, friends and colleagues. With more awareness, might it not have been possible to respond sensitively to the victim's feelings of isolation and to help him or her to find a way out of that lethal, suicide-is-the-only-way, constricted pattern of thought? To give this response, this help, is the business of the Samaritans. But suicide prevention and the promotion of emotional well-being are everybody's business.

So far, we have been looking at the direct contribution that Samaritans can make, and indeed have made, to emotional well-being. But there is another aspect that should not be forgotten.

Every year some six thousand Samaritans retire from the Movement and have to be replaced. Thus, each year several thousand people receive Samaritan training and so there must be many thousands of people in the community who know when and how to listen. And, of course, the Samaritans do not have a monopoly on listening. Many other organisations have sprung up in recent years to help people with special problems. Many of them have adopted training methods similar to those developed by the Samaritans. More and more people are practising the gentle art of listening. More and more people are recognising that helping those with difficulties does not have to be paternalistic, but that the most effective way to help may simply be to listen.

The listening approach to helping has been taken up by many commercial organisations, and people are being trained and paid to listen to those whose job performance is impaired by stress and anxiety. Thus the society which, in Eric Sevareid's words, has as its biggest business the manufacture, refinement and distribution of anxiety, is also beginning to adopt ways of helping people to overcome their anxieties.

Some years ago, the writer, Monica Dickens, herself an experienced Samaritan volunteer, encapsulated the Samaritan listening approach in two words: 'Tell me.' These two simple words are among the kindest in our language. They are the words the friendly general practitioner says to the worried patient. They are the words a parent says to the child who comes home in tears from school or play. And they are the words spoken or implied by a Samaritan to the distressed caller. And responding to these words is often the first step the caller takes towards the recovery of emotional well-being.

30 Promoting a mixed economy of care through use of specific grants for mental health projects

R. Roulston and G. Kappler

Introduction

Early in 1990 the Government indicated that specific grants for Mental Health Projects would be available in the first instance of the financial year 1991/92 (1). In Scotland the sum of 3 million for Mental Health Projects was identified by the Scottish Office from the revenue support grant. The Scottish Office made an allocation to each Regional and Island Authority and each authority had to guarantee a 30% contribution towards the sum identified by the Scottish Office. The grant criteria demanded that developments were based on partnerships, thus giving direction towards a mixed economy of care for people suffering from mental ill health or dementia. The concept of a mixed economy of care was not new in itself. In Fife, partnerships with the voluntary sector were a regular feature of the social work department. Grant aid had been made available to voluntary organisations and self help groups, thereby giving users access to the non-statutory service provision.

The population of Fife is 345,000 approximately. The Region has within it a variety of cultural backgrounds which had been linked to the major industries of coal mining, farming and fishing. These industries have changed significantly and in the case of coal mining, there was a serious decline which led the Regional Council to promote economic developments to provide alternative employment within the Region. The area therefore has known considerable change in recent years.

The policies of the Social Work Department had been amended during 1986/87 for all client groups and it was clearly understood that people should take control of their own lives where possible and where practical, with decreasing reliance on institutional care.

The annual award of grants to the non-statutory sector and partnerships with other agencies including Housing Associations were important factors in the implementation of policy into practice. In this way, people were supported without necessarily becoming or remaining clients of the Department. Such decisions were of course always based on assessment of the needs of the individual and the support available from other services.

Mixed economy of care - planning

There was therefore experience of a mixed economy of care in Fife which had had positive outcomes for consumers. The experience had highlighted the problems which can be associated with Partnerships, e.g., deadlines not met, perhaps too much reliance on informal contracts resulting in damaged relationships which always take time to repair. It is vitally important to ensure adequate planning with relevant recording. The time-scale for the application from the receipt of the final Circular to the submission of the application for the grant for 1991/92 was too short to accommodate comprehensive financial and strategic planning. Some preliminary work had been done in anticipation of receiving the final documentation. The preparation in Fife included the creation of a new post of Principal Officer, Mental Health, the development of a Service Plan for people with Mental Illness, the review of findings from Mental Health Officers' reports and the annual reports of the Mental Welfare Commission (2) and the views of Practitioners leading to the targeting on quite specific areas of identified need. A small number of young mentally ill adults who experienced homelessness demanded a resource which could respond when a need occurred and offer respite to the ill person and the carer and perhaps prevent an unnecessary admission to hospital.

The major target group remained the dementia sufferer which had been rated as a first priority in the joint planning process by the Fife Regional Council and Fife Health Board.

The principles underpinning the service policy statements adhered to in the development of the Projects were that there should be*Choice* which will be *Local, Accessible, Non-discriminatory* and meet required*Standards* (CLANS).

CLANS principles, together with Scottish Office criteria, set the parameters for the partnerships.

Significant progress had been made and experience gained throughout the first 4 years of the discharge programme of mentally handicapped people from long stay hospitals. This programme had involved social work, in the lead role, Health Board and a number of voluntary agencies. A parallel programme had not progressed for people with a mental illness, although the need for such a programme had been identified. Strong links had already been forged, partnerships were operational and the initiative by the Scottish Office was welcomed. There were established relationships even though in some instances the level of trust had been uneven at times and it was decided to move forward within the short time-scale in collaboration with agencies currently operating within the Regional boundary.

The Principal Officer was in post to take the lead role in co-ordinating the development, screening and prioritising of Specific Grant Project proposals.

Specific grant criteria

The Scottish Office issued certain criteria for projects which would be eligible for funding. The grants are confined to new projects or extensions of existing projects aimed at either 1) assisting in supporting patients discharged from hospital; 2) reducing the number of people with mental health problems requiring admission; or 3) improving the quality of life for persons for whom institutional care is not necessarily in question, or for their carers.

In addition Local Authorities are to enter into full consultation with the Health Board and relevant voluntary organisations (including those representing service users and carers) in drawing up applications. The applications are also to be based on an assessment of need for the area and must be integrated into Community Care plans when they are prepared.

New opportunities

These grants must be viewed in their proper perspective, i.e. seed money to stimulate the development of new projects, not mechanisms for funding a Community Care infrastructure for people with mental health problems. As such they present the opportunity in a period of stagnant growth for exploring new ideas, developing new networks and partnerships and jointly clarifying the views of the various participants as to service priorities and objectives.

All seven of the projects which were approved clearly met The Scottish Office criteria, while addressing the service priorities of the Local Authority and the Health Board. Some of these projects were also identified as needed by service users. Bield Housing, for example, had conducted a survey of residents in their Sheltered Housing units which strongly supported the development of their project, while local groups of service users such as the NSF and the Express Group (a user led group) supported the development of crisis and respite beds for people with mental health problems.

Promoting a mixed economy

At least as important is the fact that these grants actually meet the government's objective in promoting a mixed economy of care and in doing so are able to maximise the use of existing resources. Services were created which it would not have been possible to create independently by the Local Authority, voluntary organisations or Health Board. The sharing of material, financial and staffing resources was essential to the success of many of these projects.

In the Barony project two beds are reserved in a new residential facility for people with mental health problems. The varying patterns of demand and the difficulty in accessing DSS benefits make separate provision of a respite and emergency care facility unrealistic financially. The additional staff person funded in this project extends the support available to the other seven residents in the home. The other available staff supporting the seven permanent residents make possible the provision of a workable duty and on-call system for the respite and crisis care project.

The Bield project makes use of under-utilised Sheltered Housing communal areas to provide a base for both on-site day care and respite care while increasing the peripatetic home support staff for elderly tenants of Sheltered Housing who might otherwise have required institutional care. The project would not have been possible without the resources provided by Bield. Bield alone, however, did not have the financial resources available to make this project a reality.

Difficulties and lessons learned

It became apparent in organising the grant application for 1991/92 and liaising with the various organisations over the starting up of the projects that the complexity of this task is directly related to how well the statutory and voluntary bodies have been communicating. Luckily we had the mechanisms in place which had led the Local Authority to draw up a service development plan which was shared at an early point with the Health Board. However, no resources were available from the Health Board to facilitate the development of the Projects in 1991/92.

Liaison with voluntary bodies was a great deal more time consuming as a mental health forum for voluntary agencies had not at that point been established. Voluntary organisations were invited to place applications for grants through the Department and many were advised of service areas we felt were in need of development. Consultation, however, proceeded mostly on a one to one basis. Ultimately over 25 applications were submitted to the Department out of which seven were chosen. Our experience has taught us the following lessons and potential danger areas:

1. The time-scale for consultation and preparation of applications in the first year was much too short to do the job as the Government intended. It is essential that these grants be brought into the mainstream of Community Care planning and make use of existing forums to minimise the delay which can be brought about by the different administrative and budgetary structures of individual statutory and voluntary agencies.
2. Good communication is extremely important. Respective expectations must be clarified and details agreed before the project starts up. Financial arrangements, availability of essential property, recruiting strategies and deadlines for completing certain tasks must be stipulated prior to the start of the project to avoid unnecessary delay.
3. Statutory bodies must pay close attention to the voluntary agencies' administrative and managerial infrastructure to determine whether they are in a position to handle the additional growth.
4. There is the potential danger that such grants favour established organisations with a proven track record and 'off the rack' projects which have been well utilised elsewhere. If a project fails to meet its stated objectives future funding might be withheld and there is a danger that this money will be lost to the community mental health system. This could bias Local Authorities against innovative schemes more geared towards local need or against organisations with whom they have not worked previously.
5. Such a system of grants can create tension with and between some voluntary organisations who are unsuccessful with their applications.
6. Trying to distribute limited funds equitably amongst a variety of organisations, client groups and geographical areas can seriously dilute the effectiveness of the grant scheme as a whole.
7. There is always the danger that in competing for scarce resources voluntary organisations might make their bids financially attractive and that this might be at the expense of the quality of service delivered.

Quality of service

The Scottish Office has built in a system of monitoring of these projects which it is hoped will have some impact on the quality of service. This monitoring, however, is geared more to ensuring that services are delivered as intended in the application and that the grants and projects represent good value for money. The question of Quality Assurance, i.e. the standards of the service delivered, is not directly addressed in the Specific Grant guidelines as it is taken up in both the National Health Service and Community Care Act 1990 (3) and, in Scotland, The Scottish Office discussion paper 'Improving Quality Assurance in Community Care' (4) as well as in other guidance.

The process of consultation and planning can go some distance in determining the quality of the service to be delivered. Most important, however, is the voluntary organisations' own systems of quality assurance, and how these systems are owned by those staff charged with implementing them as well as understood by those people using the service. It is for the Local Authority to assure itself that these systems are in place in voluntary organisations, and to assist in their development where not, before entering into agreements on specific projects.

The future of specific grants

Once again it has to be stressed that these grants must be placed in their proper context. The money available, 3 million last year in Scotland, an anticipated additional 2 million this year, and a similar sum, one would hope, next year is a small percentage of what is required. Thirty percent of this funding has to be found by Local Authorities at a time of severe financial constraints. The additional monies available through Bridging Finance in Scotland will not help provide any significant services to those people who are already living in the community. The Scottish Association for Mental Health has estimated that at least 50 million is needed to provide Community Care projects in Scotland for people who have mental health problems (5). Administratively these grants have also been extremely cumbersome and time consuming. Nevertheless, these grants and the processes entailed in consulting, screening and implementing these projects have undeniably helped move Community Care Planning forward even if the pace is less than thrilling. The networks and partnerships which have been created and renewed, the exploration of new patterns of services, and the lessons learned in trying to incorporate users of services into the planning process are all valuable spinoffs of the Specific Grant system. When and if proper funding of a community-based mental health service comes about we will be much better placed to draw upon the models and systems necessary to develop the services needed.

There is no doubt that such a development requires an identified lead person who can devote time, take the initiative throughout the stages of development, demonstrate a commitment, and establish standards in the development of project applications.

Implications for relationship with voluntary organisations

The provision of grant aid to non-statutory agencies and the quality of the services provided by the agency/organisation was rather loosely 'controlled' through an annual report, the presence of a staff member in an advisory capacity on the relevant Committee and contact with a named person. It had become increasingly obvious in joint projects that there required to be clarity of objectives, time scale, resource availability, commitment, reporting and standard of service delivery within a formal joint agreement.

Quality will be more clearly demonstrable within a newly agreed formal contract system ,as will value for money. In addition, the Scottish Office will carry an inspection function, and the Inspection Unit of the Social Work Department will carry out inspection in registered establishments. The user has access through the Department's formal complaint procedure (6) which is now in its third year of operation. In summary a fixed economy of care is not new, a more formal system replaces previous informal agreements. Significant factors are:

    a) identification of need through discussion with staff, consumers and other groupings

    b) establishing of priority

    c) forward planning

    d) regular liaison with all participants

    e) clear objectives, which will contain quality within them, flexibility to enable growth rather than control which might stifle development

    f) work within broad policy parameters.

The introduction of the Specific Grant requires a demonstration of mutuality of profitable partnership and taken alongside the preparatory work for the introduction of Care in the Community has enabled this Social Work Department to pursue the establishment of more formal systems which have within them the ability to oversee the quality of the service delivered, meeting the quality assurance perspectives which must be a basic right for all users of a social work service.

References

1. Scottish Office Circular No. SW10/1990. National Health Service and Community Care Act 1990 Specific Grant for Revenue Expenditure on New Community Projects in the Mental Illness Field.

2. Mental Welfare Commission, Scotland. Annual Report.

3. National Health Service and Community Care Act 1990.

4. *Improving Quality Assurance in Community Care*, Social Work Services Group, Scottish Office 1991.

5. Scottish Association for Mental Health 1991.

6. *Open to Complaint,* Social Work Department, Fife Regional Council.

31 Promoting mental health in the workplace: The staff care concept

J. Sloboda and J. Hopkins

Introduction

It has long been recognised that work and the working environment is a major determinant of mental health. Characteristics of the experienced working environment have been shown to directly affect physical and mental health (e.g. Cooper and Marshall, 1976; Parkes, 1982) as well as such general psychological characteristics as work motivation and satisfaction (e.g. Hackman and Oldham, 1980).

When considering individual mental health many people have used 'stress' as an organising concept. While this has been a useful way of making the discussion of mental health issues acceptable within the workplace, the concept carries with it a strong presupposition that stress comes about through an individual's perceptions of, and responses to, a situation. This leads to the further presupposition that the primary method of dealing with stress is at an individual level: the stressed individual needs to learn to change his or her perceptions and responses.

The vast majority of documented responses to stress within workplaces are based upon this presupposition. Organisations arrange for individuals to receive training or therapy, either delivered through 'stress management' courses of various kinds, or through individual counselling (see, for instance Murphy, 1984; Matteson and Ivancevich, 1987).

Whilst individuals can undoubtedly be helped with mental health problems in this way, several commentators have pointed out that such an approach can leave the basic organisational causes of stress unchallenged and unchanged (Orlans, 1991). If an organisation is malfunctioning in some way then stress can only be dealt with effectively by making organisational changes at an appropriate level.

In this paper, we outline some of the insights and advances that have been achieved through work within a particular occupational setting, that of the personal social services in the UK. In the first section we summarise some of the major perceived causes of individual stress and distress as distilled from our experience with individuals and groups over several years. In the second section we briefly describe the process of consultation which led to the formalisation of the 'staff care' concept in a Code of Practice now endorsed by major employers' organisations. In the third section we describe three different case studies in staff care.

Sources of stress and distress at work

In the course of a wide variety of conversations, meetings and workshops with social services staff at all levels, the following list of sources has been developed and refined. It represents categories that staff in these organisation routinely recognise.

Personal problems: People at work, and their families or partners, experience problems of bereavement, divorce, serious physical illnesses, alcohol and drug abuse, mental illness and debt. This category includes any of the other misfortunes which befall individuals.

Organisational change: Living with change is now part of the way of life at work for most people. The process of change may be experienced as a burden. Moreover, if individuals feel discounted or discarded, and their skills rendered meaningless, the goodwill necessary to implement change successfully may be lost.

Dangerour and threatening situations: People at work may face dangerous or threatening situations. The effects of these is, in some cases, traumatic. This is distressing not only for the individual and his or her family, but also for colleagues.

Discrimination and harassment: People at work may be subject to discrimination on grounds of race, gender, age, sexual orientation, disability, religion or rank. Intimidation and harassment happen in the workplace as in other areas of life. Victims may need help as might the perpetrators.

Damaging and dangerous practices: Staff who are aware of practices which are damaging or dangerous may find themselves in a conflict between loyalty to their colleagues and their own personal or professional integrity. Those who choose to report such practices tend to be identified as 'trouble makers' and isolated within the organisation.

Staff teams in disarray: In some work situations, mutual support and assistance is essential. Sometimes the intensity of life together can echo the bitterness of a family quarrel. At other times indifference breeds indifference. If we feel that we have no place in the life of those around us, this can lead to disaffection with the workplace itself.

Disciplinary procedures: Disciplinary procedures can create their own distress: for the person subjected to them; for the manager who is obliged to prosecute and is seen as a persecutor; and for colleagues whose loyalty may be divided between the two; and for their partners and families.

Work related stress: Each workplace has its own characteristic stresses and risks. These arise from the nature of the job. The work needs to be stimulating in order to involve those engaged to do it. However, in a climate of uncertainty, an unending stream of decision making can be as stressful as continuous physical strain, or the fear of being left exposed when things go dreadfully wrong. Over a period of time stress will lead to detachment and cynicism.

Staff in social services organisations strongly believe that the sources of stress described have profoundly damaging consequences both for individuals and the organisation. The level of sickness absence is high. Every organisation routinely has several staff (including very senior staff) on long-term sickness absence. Many staff leave this type of work after only a few years, taking the results of investment in training and expertise out of the system for good. Other individuals function indifferently or poorly for long periods of time.

The staff care concept

Most organisations in the UK do not have any meaningful strategy for addressing the mental health of their employees. Those that do usually follow a 'medical' model. A range of services are provided for employees ranging from personal counselling through to health education, but the providers of the care are outside the core management process. They are expected to 'get people back to work' rather than contribute to development of organisational practice and policy. Care is also seen as something provided for employees by experts rather than as something which needs to be an aspect of how all employees relate to one another.

The 'Staff Care' concept we have helped to develop is different from the prevailing model in a number of respects:

1. All employees have a role to play in enhancing mental health in the work-place, and require organisational policies, training, and support to fulfil this role.
2. Specialist workers need to be multi-skilled. The usual counselling skills must be supplemented by skills in training and group work, formulation and dissemination of policy and procedures, as well as knowledge of management issues and processes.
3. The staff care function needs to be represented at senior management level so that staff care experience can inform management decision-making. This is doubly important when planning change, so that the staff care procedures to help employees deal with the change are in place prior to the commencement of the change process.

These, and other consequences of the 'staff care' approach are formalised in a recently published Code Of Practice for Staff Care in the Health and Social Services (Keele University, 1991). Our experience suggests that this approach is perceived as effective in both enhancing individual mental health and improving organisational climate. We are beginning to accumulate both practice wisdom and research evidence about the processes involved.

Case studies in staff care

The remainder of this paper will be concerned to illustrate the practice of staff care. The examples we draw on are from the personal social services. Firstly we describe two examples of the use of the concept of staff care to address a particular experience of stress encountered within a child protection service and within a Residential Children's Centre. We then describe an example of an in-house staff care service.

(a) Child protection

Two workshops on staff care were organised for Senior Managers in part of an Authority. As external consultants we advised on the format and assisted with the presentations. In between the two workshops, managers from each workplace undertook their own projects. The seminars legitimated the well-being of staff as a corporate management responsibility as well as the responsibility of individuals. We presented a view of the organisation as a social system in which performance is affected by the nature of the life that they lead together in the workplace. Our method was to encourage staff to acknowledge the work related stress, to recognise it as a shared problem and to find ways of limiting its effect. We described the organisation as a community of people creating a life together at work. We asked the managers in each workplace to share their personal experience of work-related stress and to reach agreement amongst themselves as to the one that they felt should be tackled first.

We then gave them the task of finding ways of mitigating the effects of the underlying tensions and reporting back on their project. We offered consultancy on demand to assist the process. In effect we gave them permission to acknowledge their stress, to put into words their fears. to make them concrete, to have those fears acknowledged by their colleagues and to begin to get control of the situation by a process of mutual concern and support. There is a traditional saying that if you name the Devil, the Devil will leave. We found it to be a bit more complicated than that.

In the child protection team it was agreed to confront the fear that any one person could be left carrying the blame for the death of a child on the child protection register. Once this fear was acknowledged it became possible to confront it. This was done in two ways. The first mitigated the effect of the underlying anxiety on work performance, and the second anticipated what would happen if the fear was realised.

The underlying fear of those involved was that if they admitted to a mistake or concern, recriminations would follow, and their manager would disassociate themselves from the individual in order to protect their own position. The first move was therefore to reframe the perception that staff had of managers as not caring, into one of managers not knowing. If managers were made aware of fears and doubts about the work, they were beholden to do something about them. They could then put boundaries around individual responsibilities. A structure of reporting and decision making was devised that ensured responsibility was not left with any one individual. it was also made explicit that advice and guidance could be sought from anyone outside line management. Disseminating experience amongst colleagues was encouraged. A work pattern was established in which concerns were shared and the likelihood of human error in a high stress job was acknowledged.

It was recognised that, however vigilant staff were, it was likely that at sometime a child on the register would die in suspicious circumstances. When a child dies the preoccupation is with the decision taken rather than the distress generated. Emergency procedures were therefore set in place. These supplemented the formal arrangements for inquiries by assigning roles to support the families and staff involved, and to ensure that people were properly informed and that the publicity was handled in the least distressing way. Once the arrangements for underwriting responsibility, and for the standby 'emergency care service' were in place. it became obvious that any informal inquiry would be able to conduct an examination of the processes of the case, without staff fearing that they would be thrown to the wolves.

(b) Residential Children's Centre

The second example of this approach comes from the project undertaken by managers of a Residential Children's Centre. They agreed to use the staff care approach to tackle the problem of low morale. They identified a number of contributory factors and broke down the work to be done into specific tasks, and then shared responsibility for addressing the different tasks amongst themselves. We describe below two of the steps taken.

One of the most significant factors affecting morale was the low public image of the Centre that was held by local residents and the wider community. The local press in particular perpetuated the image of the Centre as a source of trouble and all the young people at the Centre were tarnished with the image of troublemakers. With the support of the staff, the young people made a video and invited the press in and presented their side of the story. This was very successful in changing the attitude of the reporters. A part-time community worker was appointed who organised a liaison group of local residents and key members of the community, as well as involving young people in positive work outside the Centre. The processes set in train by these two interventions have become institutionalised, through the issue of regular press briefings, and by placing the meetings of the liaison group into the calendar of regular meetings.

Sometimes the young people behaved in a violent or threatening way towards staff. There was a concern to address the debilitating effects of this. It was decided to take a more proactive approach that acknowledged the threat of violence as an inherent feature of life at work. It was therefore decided that when violence occurred, the member of staff would be assigned a Senior Manager who was not their own line manager and who did not conduct an investigation into the incident. The staff member was encouraged to express his or her feelings about the incident and to talk about what they needed. The line manager was then free to establish what had happened and how to get the staff member, the young person, the shift team, and the group of young people functioning again. The result was that the managers established a strategic model for dealing with such incidents. This model separated management issues from personal issues; led to the construction of action plans which put the pieces back together, and fed what had been learned from the experience directly into the policy making of the Centre.

(c) A service-wide staff care service

A medium-sized social services department in an ethnically mixed urban area decided to invest in a service-wide staff care programme. We acted as consultants to the senior management team, and have also arranged an evaluation of the service over a three year period.

The first task was to assist key individuals in the organisation, who saw the need for staff care, to turn unfocussed management support into a definite action plan. It was decided to establish a staff-care management group chaired by a senior manager of the service. This group is responsible to, and reports regularly to, the senior management team.

The group decided that the major investment should be in full-time staff positions, and two Staff Care Officers were appointed. Although the postholders are trained counsellors, their job descriptions specify that no more than 50% of their time should be spent in personal counselling. The rest of the time is shared between a number of activities. There is a rolling programme of visits to staff teams to ensure a high profile for the service. The officers respond to specific team requests for e.g. team building, assertiveness training etc. In line-management terms the officers are located within the training department, and the overall training programme is planned in the light of staff care needs.

It was decided that the service should be formally evaluated. The ongoing evaluation takes two forms. First is a service-wide survey of employee stress. If the staff care service is having a major impact on the organisation then this should be reflected in reduced absenteeism and turnover and reduced levels of reported stress. A randomly selected sample of the workforce was surveyed in 1989. The same sample will be surveyed again in 1992. Although the study is incomplete, the first survey revealed useful information. It was discovered that reported stress levels and sources of stress were very different in different parts of the organisation. Although some of these differences could be attributed to the nature of the work (for instance direct work with children and families is inherently more stressful than clerical work in the administrative headquarters), others pointed to different practices of staff support within work units. This brought the realisation that models of good practice already existed, albeit patchily, within the organisation, and that these could be built upon. Key issues for the organisation turned out to be the quality of mutual support within work-teams, and the balance between positive and negative feedback for work performance.

The second strand of the evaluation is a more fine-grained study of the outcomes of individual counselling. Staff Care Officers complete a confidential and anonymous report on each staff member who receives counselling. This report combines statistical data (on age, type of work, presenting problem category) with brief qualitative data on the process and outcome of the counselling. Recipients of counselling are also encouraged to complete a feedback form, asking them to evaluate the degree to which the counselling helped them, and returning it confidentially and anonymously to the external evaluator.

Preliminary data from this study reveal a number of pertinent facts:

1. For the majority of clients, work problems and out-of-work problems are intimately connected. Help with something which seems a purely domestic problem can actually have profoundly positive effects on work performance.
2. Few clients need large amounts of counselling. Many clients seemed significantly helped by one session, and most did not ask for more than three. This meant that the Staff Care Officers could see a very substantial percentage of the workforce in the space of a year (over 5%).
3. Workers in particular categories (for instance, ethnic minorities) often found it easier to contemplate receiving personal counselling after having got to know the Staff Care Officer in safe and familiar group settings. Trust needs to be established in ways appropriate to each culture, highlighting the need for relevant diversity in the skills and backgrounds of a staff care team.

4. Many recipients of counselling experienced the support of the staff care officers as a lifeline, emphasising the empowering effects of being accepted and valued without condition.

Feedback from these evaluations is useful to the staff care service in targeting under-represented groups and specifying problem areas for the targeting of training. It also allows counsellors to reflect on the implications of outcomes for their practice in a more systematic and objective way than is normally possible.

Conclusion

We began our work in the personal social services because we appreciated that unless staff felt themselves to be cared for they were not in a position to care for others, especially their clients. However, we believe that this experience holds true for all people at work and the quality of the services and products that they provide. However much managers agree with this approach, most organisations will spend more on maintaining one building than on maintaining their entire workforce.

It is our experience that unless Staff Care is continually on the agenda, it gets buried in the economic and task oriented demands of the organisation. Moreover, the experiences of stress and distress change through time. A work community is a loosely structured social organisation, something of a shifting sand on which only a flexible and changing structure will survive. The shelter that we build for each other at work must therefore reflect the need to be watchful and to respond imaginatively.

Thirty one years ago, Isobel Menzies (1960) showed that institutions can develop in organisations which act as defence mechanisms against tasks in a work system that arouse anxiety. What happened in the case of both the Child Protection Service and the Residential Children's Centre, was that routines were deliberately devised which had as their prime purpose the containment of anxiety in a high stress situation. It is our argument that unless staff working in the high stress fields, such as child protection, feel safe in their work environment, their performance will be undermined by a continual concern for their personal and occupational survival. We would further argue that the construction of procedures to protect the emotional well-being of staff is as legitimate as the physical safety procedures in work carrying risk of physical danger.

References

Cooper, C.L. & Marshall, J.(1976) Occupational sources of stress: a review of the literature relating to coronary heart disease and mental ill health. *Journal of Occupational Psychology, 49*, 11-28.

Hackman, J.R. & Oldham, G.R. (1980) *Word redesign*. Reading, MA.: Addison-Wesley.

Keele University Centre of Occupational Studies (1991). *Code of Practice for Staff Care in the Health and Social Services*. Newcastle, Staffordshire, UK: Keele University.

Matteson, M.T. & Ivancevich, J.M. (1987) Individual stress management interventions: evaluation of techniques. *Journal of Managerial Psychology, 2*, 24-30.

Menzies, I.E.P. (1960) A case study in the functioning of social systems as a defence against anxiety: A report of a study of the nursing services of a general hospital, *Human Relations*, <u>13</u>, 95-121.

Murphy, L.R. (1984) Occupations stress management: a review and appraisal. *Journal of Occupational Psychology*, <u>57</u>, 1-15.

Orlans, V. (1991) Stress interventions with trade unions. *Personnel Review*, <u>20</u>, 11-17.

Parkes, K. (1982) Occupational stress among student nurses: a natural experiment. *Journal of Applied Psychology*, <u>67</u>, 784-796.

32 Breakthrough '91: Promoting mental health

J. Such and J. Robinson

Introduction

This paper outlines a mental health promotion event, Breakthrough '91, that is taking place during the period 23 September to 5 October 1991.

Breakthrough is being held in the East Suffolk Health Authority area. It is a multi-agency, multi-disciplinary event that is being organised by representatives of Suffolk Social Services Department, the Local Health Services Unit of the Health Authority and two local MIND associations - East and Mid Suffolk.

This paper outlines how the idea for Breakthrough originated, the activities being organised, the problems encountered in planning the whole event and plans for evaluation.

Background to Breakthrough '91

The idea for Breakthrough '91 originated from the locality planning structure that exists in mental health services in East Suffolk. The Locality Planning Teams that form this structure are part of the Joint Planning system for mental health services for adults (18 - 65 years). Figure 1 shows how these Locality Planning Teams fit into the overall joint planning system as established under the Joint Consultative Committee.

Locality Planning Teams are groups of professional workers, users of mental health services, carers and representatives of voluntary organisations. They were set up in 1988 to replace a system of sub-committees on specific subjects such as day care.

Ten Locality Planning Teams were established. These were not based on genuine localities, or communities, as such. Rather the artificial boundaries of the Social Services area teams were chosen for administrative convenience. However, this did mean that the Locality Planning Team boundaries were relatively well understood by those in the statutory authorities.

The Locality Planning Teams were given a daunting range of objectives that were, with hindsight, too ambitious, and not explicit enough. Professional workers, and others, from the health and social services were asked to take part in this new system without adequate training and backup. This led to frustration and disappointments with the new planning system. However, the locality has produced new resources in the community through putting forward projects for joint financing and seeing these projects developed.

The system has involved many professionals from different agencies who had not routinely been involved in mental health issues. Thus it created new informal networks that have helped to raise awareness about mental health, and improved local communication between the professional workers involved. It has also helped to build better networks and improve communications between the mental health professionals from the different agencies. However, it has not been as successful in getting users of services or carers involved in spite of the hard work of many of the Teams.

There has recently been a review of the whole locality planning system. This came about because of the experience of continuing problems and the changes that are being made in the local joint planning structures. The outcome of this review is that the structure of the Locality Planning Teams will be retained but with much simpler aims. The new aims are:

> To share knowledge, identify gaps in services and resolve local communication issues where possible. To develop existing networks.
>
> To advise on methods to monitor the quality of local services and the extent to which they reflect user choice.
>
> To encourage local communities, including service users, to express views on the development of local services.
>
> To advise/seek approval for improvements to local area services which involve change of use of existing services as well as extra resources.
>
> To advise the locality planning co-ordinating groups of gaps in services in the area and recommend solutions.

Breakthrough '91 emerged from this structure when one of the Locality Planning Teams discussed ways of carrying out some local mental health education. The Locality Planning Team concerned wished to do some education work aimed at the general public, to combat the prejudice and ignorance about mental health problems and to raise awareness about mental health issues. They put forward the suggestion of running a one week local campaign in Ipswich. Through discussion within the Locality Planning Teams this was translated into running a campaign for a fortnight across the whole District Health Authority area. A meeting of representatives from the Locality Planning Teams was called to establish a co-ordinating group. The co-ordinating group represented a range of Locality Planning Teams, agencies and disciplines. It was perhaps more through coincidence than design that major game players, such as the health education unit, were represented. This is an issue explored further in this paper.

Breakthrough '91

From this background the details of the then 'mental health fortnight' were worked out, including a great deal of brainstorming for a suitable name for the event. The co-ordinating group established a number of sub-committees on the different aspects of the draft programme of events for Breakthrough '91. These sub-committees drew in a variety of different professional workers, users of the services and representatives of organisations in order to plan the event in more detail. It took some months for the general aims of Breakthrough '91 to be worked out properly. Initially some general aims were drafted but tended to get adapted and changed by different people. The initial aims were full of jargon and were not easily understood.

Therefore the co-ordinating group agreed on three simple aims which could be easily publicised.

The primary aims of Breakthrough '91 are to educate the public about;

Current ideas on what makes for healthy minds.

Help that is available to people who experience mental and emotional distress.

Challenging the myths and fears surrounding mental health.

It was also agreed to highlight the needs of adults aged 18-65 years rather than running an event that projected needs from childhood to elderly people.

The co-ordinating group wished to build on the initial idea from the Locality Planning Teams of a time limited campaign which was trying to raise awareness and combat prejudice. Through creating a network of people interested in mental health promotion there was hope that the whole concept could be translated into a concerted campaign to be carried forward into future years. The co-ordinating group also wanted to learn from the experience of Breakthrough by evaluating its perceived usefulness with a view to develop a better formulated strategy of mental health promotion in the future.

With this strategy we hoped to influence the District Health Authority Health Promotion strategy, and the attitude of other Authorities to the whole concept of mental health promotion.

Breakthrough '91 activities

The following programme of activities outlines the current state of planning at the time of writing. Plans are reasonably firm for all of these events, and funding has been secured. However, new ideas and initiatives are emerging every day. These will be acted on if funding can be obtained.

High media profile

Local radio, TV and press are all being contacted to cover the event from the news angle. Press releases went out early to all types of local newsletters, and magazines to ensure we met publication deadlines. The main approach to press, etc., came later. The co-ordinating group are also talking to the local media about feature articles and programmes on mental health. The whole event will have a high profile media launch involving a celebrity who will be Jane Lapotaire, the actress.

Exhibition

An exhibition will tour the district for the fortnight. This will consist of display material, photographs and creative materials to illustrate the aims of Breakthrough. The creative material will be poems, paintings, etc., by people who have experience of mental health problems.

Mental health festivals

There will be a series of mental health festivals around the District. These are intended to be on the theme of 'holistic' approaches to mental health. They will highlight the complementary approaches available to combat mental health problems, in addition to traditional psychiatric services. The aim is to illustrate the range of approaches available. The biggest festival is a two day event in the major town of Ipswich. However, there will be five smaller one day events in local market towns around the district. These festivals will have stands and stalls carrying information, goods and services from the traditional mental health services, voluntary organisations and complementary practitioners.

Workshops/lectures

In association with the festivals outlined above there will be a series of workshops/ lectures on different themes throughout the fortnight. For example the Mental Health Media Council will be holding a series of video workshops, which include discussions about their work. The Mental After Care Association and a local carers project are running a workshop on carers. Other topics for workshops and lectures include stress management, counselling and topics such as 'Does Mental Illness Exist?'

Season of films

One of the local cinemas has agreed to run a season of films with mental health themes during the first week of Breakthrough '91.

Information

An information pack is being published. This will contain information on positive mental health, and the services available. The Health Authority and Social Services Department will be publishing a Directory of services for local professionals, users of services and voluntary organisations.

Conference on philosophies of mental health

A conference with the title 'Viewpoints - Perspectives of Mental Health' is being held. This is aiming to examine the different philosophies and perspectives on mental health and their effects on the professional and users of services.

Problems encountered in planning

The problems we have encountered in planning Breakthrough '91 are numerous. In this paper we can only touch on those that seem most problematic. Also at the time of writing problems are still being encountered. Therefore, in the final analysis the problems highlighted may change.

Setting the agenda

The first problem encountered was trying to get agreement on the aims of Breakthrough '91 and who the target group should be. The Locality Planning Teams originally thought of it as positive action that would help raise the profile of Locality Planning Teams, as well as helping to combat prejudice and ignorance in the public about mental health issues. Therefore, it was not initially explicit that a particular health promotion strategy was being adopted for a specific target group.

The various representatives of the Locality Planning Teams had their own agendas, whether they were from statutory organisations or voluntary organisations. This obviously meant there were many different viewpoints. Some people involved wished to include a wide spectrum of mental health problems. That is to try and cover everything from the diagnosed condition of schizophrenia, stress and anxiety, emotional distress, to drug and alcohol problems. Other people wished to just concentrate on 'mental illness.'

Through a great deal of discussion it was agreed that the campaign should include all conditions that could reasonably be attributed to a mental health service. However, issues of alcohol and drug problems were specifically excluded. It was felt that issues of substance misuse needed their own focus, and had their own particular needs.

Another issue was what age range should the target group relate to. The Locality Planning Teams involved were part of the joint planning structure for mental health services for adults. Therefore, should this campaign cover the needs of elderly people and children and adolescents? Whilst many of the issues are common to all these people, many are also different. Therefore, to include the needs of elderly people, or children and adolescents would have involved co-ordination and involvement with different joint planning groups, as well as trying to cover a wider spectrum of need.

The decision was made to concentrate on the needs of adults aged 18-65 years. It was recognised at an early stage that the whole event would be a complex one to co-ordinate and work with. As the initiative arose from the joint planning structures for adult mental health services it was decided to stay within that structure, without wishing to be too parochial. There was no advantage in trying to be too ambitious setting ourselves up to fail by widening the scope of Breakthrough '91. If the event proved to be successful then lessons learned could be translated into a wider event in future years.

It should be said that these discussions took place in the co-ordinating group with no particular reference to any other group of interests. In retrospect it may have been better to take these discussions to a wider audience in order to achieve better understanding and agreement, also it might have been helpful to ensure a wider representation of major game players in the co-ordinating group. In other words, the health education unit and others should have been deliberately brought in at an early stage. The issues of the scope of the event and the target group kept surfacing in different ways, possibly due to the fact that this wider debate had not taken place.

Range of information

In the co-ordinating group there was a great deal of interest in complementary approaches to mental health. It was agreed that part of Breakthrough '91 would be events highlighting these alternative approaches. Debate then took place as to whether these events should be separate from events highlighting mainstream psychiatric services. Also what was alternative or complementary? Should this only extend to 'recognised' alternatives such as homeopathy, or could it include astrology and spiritual healing?

The approach adopted was that Breakthrough '91 should be about making a greater range of information available. Therefore, complementary approaches should be included alongside the traditional psychiatric services, thus highlighting the spectrum of services available. However, it was recognised that some alternative approaches could cause problems for some vulnerable people. Therefore, it was agreed that certain approaches such as astrology should be excluded, as would anything with a religious context.

However, there continued to be disagreement about the inclusion of the complementary practices in Breakthrough '91. The opposition came from the mainstream psychiatric services. Their feeling was that the inclusion of complementary approaches, alongside the statutory services, implied that they (the complementary services) were endorsed by the statutory services. Rather than taking the attitude that it was making information available. This particular disagreement was never really fully resolved. Again it probably largely sprang from not ensuring that all the major groups were properly represented from day one.

The other issues for debate over the complementary approaches was that these services are all provided through private practice in East Suffolk. Public funding was being sought to run Breakthrough '91. Therefore, should public funding subsidise what could be regarded as private health and social care? At the same time if we wished to involve organisations from the voluntary sector could they afford to pay for their involvement if charges were made for facilities at the mental health festivals? Indeed should they pay at all? These issues expressed in this way may not seem very topical. However, for workers in the statutory services faced with trying to provide an adequate service on slim resources they could pose ethical problems. The issue was overcome by agreeing to charge private practitioners for stands at the festivals that are being held. However, no charges were to be made for voluntary organisations or the statutory services.

Funding

Seeking funding for Breakthrough '91 has been a problem since its inception. One aspect has been trying to get some funding from the statutory authorities at a time when they are all very stretched for resources to provide basic services. It was felt that we needed some core funding from statutory sources in order to pay for basic printing and publicity materials. Thus we needed to convince senior management of the Health Authority and Social Services Department that Breakthrough was a worthwhile event, and that it needed some priority. In the end we managed to obtain a few thousand pounds from mainstream budgets, and £5,000 from Joint Finance. This has allowed us to plan the event in the knowledge that there is a minimum level of resources to run Breakthrough '91.

We have been attempting to obtain sponsorship form local businesses. These attempts have confirmed what we already knew - that mental health is not sexy. It does not have the emotional appeal of children or cancer, and businesses do not seem to feel it would enhance their public image like sponsorship of the arts. We have been successful in getting some small scale sponsorship, and attempts to obtain money from local firms is still going on at the time of writing.

There was also a moral problem with seeking sponsorship - should we approach the pharmaceutical companies? We know that the drug manufacturers do spend large amounts of cash promoting their products. However, would it be right to obtain this sponsorship for Breakthrough '91? Would it be like getting the cigarette companies to sponsor the Olympics? Initially the decision was made that we should not seek this form of sponsorship. Many members of the co-ordinating committee were outrightly opposed to such sponsorship. Others felt much more ambivalent. In the end it was agreed to try and seek sponsorship.

The reasoning behind the change in decision was two fold - we needed the money and the co-ordinating group's original thinking genuinely shifted. The basis of seeking sponsorship from the pharmaceutical companies is that we will only agree to use the company name. Breakthrough '91 will not highlight any one particular drug. As we already have the name British Telecom on literature - what is the difference to having another company name on leaflets etc? Whatever one's view of drugs, properly prescribed, they do help many people with a whole range of mental health problems. Provided of course that people are given adequate information on their side effects etc. The fault lies not with the medication, but with those who prescribe. Therefore, should we not use some of the money that drug companies are willing to spend in promoting their products in a more constructive manner, that is promoting mental health on a wider basis? The view of users of the mental health services, on this proposal, were sought from the local Patients Forum. The co-ordinating group would not have gone ahead with seeking this sponsorship if the Patients Forum had been opposed.

Time

Another major problem for all of those involved in planning Breakthrough '91 has been time. As the actual fortnight gets nearer the time spent on Breakthrough '91 activities has escalated. Everyone involved has their own normal busy workload. Therefore time spent on Breakthrough '91 is an extra burden. Originally there had been an idea to try and seek funding for a paid co-ordinator for the event. However, because of the problems in trying to raise money it became clear that money spent on a salary would leave nothing left over for the actual expenses of the event. This idea was, therefore, dropped.

Co-ordination and communication

As there is not a paid co-ordinator, no one person has been able to take on the whole of the day-to-day organising of the event. This has lead to a dozen different people organising different parts of the whole event. This has made communications very complex and time consuming. The structure of the co-ordinating committee, sub-committees, Locality Planning Teams and individual agency management made communications slow and difficult - internally and externally.

The co-ordinating group have been keen to involve as many people as possible to give ownership of the whole event. However, this complex structure has meant misunderstandings, problems of information flow and lack of involvement from many areas.

Some of these problems are currently being tackled by issuing a newsletter, active attempts to involve some key players, and larger information meetings. One of the real problems of communications are that plans have changed, almost on a daily basis, as circumstances, finance or other factors play their part.

311

Despite the problems outlined the co-ordinating group is confident that the event will be a success. It has generated a tremendous amount of enthusiasm from many grassroots workers, managers, voluntary organisations and some users of services. By positively directing this energy we can start to build a properly co-ordinated continuing strategy for mental health promotion.

Evaluation

Evaluating the effectiveness of the range of activities and events of Breakthrough '91 presents a variety of problems. Not only does it need to explore some of the less visible measurable aspects of the programme, it also aims to address potentially sensitive areas such as participants' prior contact with mental health services. The evaluation needs not only to say something about individual events, but also to give an overview of the value of the total enterprise.

A relatively small amount of the total conference budget was allocated to evaluation with the hope that additional funds could be sought from outside agencies.

Evaluation was seen from the outset as an integral part of the implementation process. The results of evaluation could then be used to inform future initiatives and provide strong arguments for further funding should this initiative show some success in achieving its goal.

Evaluation strategy

The main questions which the evaluation aims to address are:
a) to what extent are events reaching the target group?
b) to what extent do events give new information to those who attend?
c) how useful is the information in helping to meet attenders' own needs be they potential or ex-service users, carers or workers?
d) what were the experiences of organisers and contributors of the whole process of implementation?

Many methods were considered by the co-ordinating group. It was felt that although mail shots and polls would give best information about how many people had been reached by the events and media activities, the cost would be prohibitive.

It was decided that questionnaires would be developed using scaled, checklist and open questions to explore a range of issues relating to the aims of the initiative. These questionnaires would be supported, where possible, by in-depth interview with volunteers to give a more detailed picture of people's experiences of the event.

Planners were aware of the need to find a balance between eliciting a healthy response rate and being over intrusive at events. It was decided that questionnaires would be handed to people at each venue with a request to 'tell us what they think.' At the end of each questionnaire, people will be asked if they would like to volunteer to be interviewed by a member of the team and invited to leave a contact address or telephone number.

At the time of writing this paper evaluation remains a focus for discussion and debate. Many problems relating to response rate and how best to elicit potentially sensitive data continue to be explored at planning meetings along with means by which extra funding can be sought.

Concluding comments

By the time this paper is presented at this conference, Breakthrough '91 will be a few days away. We will know the outcome of the range of issues still under debate and be able to describe these outcomes to Conference Delegates. At this point in time the planning of Breakthrough '91 remains a challenging, exciting and dynamic process. We look forward to it with some trepidation but with great enthusiasm.

Although we have not been able to describe our experiences of the event itself or the results of the evaluation, we hope that sharing our experiences of the planning process has provided food for thought for those who might be intending to organise similar initiatives.

We fully intend to make public the results of our evaluation along with our experiences of the event itself. That information, unfortunately, has to remain the subject for another time, perhaps another conference.

313

33   A better state of mind

B. Swallow

Abstract

This paper aims to examine how the writer's experience with the planning process of Mental Health Services in North Humberside and his research examining day services for people with mental health problems have influenced his view of mental health service planning and delivery. I will describe how this experience has shaped the work of the local MIND association. The paper will firstly offer a brief outline of community care provision in North Humberside. It will then propose an alternative model of service delivery. The role of the local MIND group will be discussed in relation to the guiding principles and functions of the proposed model. Finally, it will be argued that a promotional model of mental health can have two major advantages over a traditional reactive model: firstly as a preventative measure, and secondly as a way of removing stigma and hence assisting the integration of people with longer term mental health problems within the community. The paper will describe how the local MIND group is attempting to tackle the need for a greater emphasis on promotion, and new projects will be outlined.

Introduction

Mental health services in North Humberside

North Humberside has a population of approximately 500,000. Its two Health Districts of Hull and East Yorkshire have been served by two psychiatric hospitals, both sited in East Yorkshire. The 1985 East Yorkshire Health Authority Strategic Plan called for the closure of the psychiatric hospitals and the development of community services. The new services were planned to be local and accessible. New geographical boundaries called modules were established for both Health Authorities. One of the hospitals closed in 1989 and the other is due to close within the next six years. The mental health community services are provided from nine community teams - three in East Yorkshire and six in Hull. Humberside County Council provides mental health resource centres in four

315

modules and the North Humberside Association for Mental Health (MIND) provides a range of day care and accommodation services throughout the area.

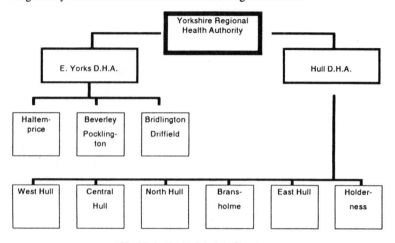

Health Authority Module Structure

Figure 1

Figure 1 looks at the structure of the Health Service provision.

In the 1985 strategy, it was intended that each module would provide services to meet its own needs. Laid down in the strategic plan was provision for a Community Mental Health Team and for a ten-bed residential unit in each module. Acute beds would be provided at district general hospitals. Within these broad criteria, it was intended that modules would determine their own staffing and service provision within available funding to meet the needs of the particular community.

The authorities established a planning structure which fed into the Joint Consultative Committee (JCC) (Figure 2).

The module planning teams were charged with the task of producing local plans which were then to be agreed by the higher tiers of the structure. The teams consisted of equal numbers of representatives from the Health Authority and the Social Services Department together with a MIND representative, the writer. Two of the Hull modules also held 'listening' meetings to which other organisations and professionals were invited. The last module to be planned, Haltemprice in East Yorkshire, had a slightly different approach. Following pressure from MIND, it was agreed to attempt to plan the module from a bottom-up approach and Humberside Polytechnic was commissioned to undertake a piece of research to identify the needs of users of mental health services within the module (see Golightley, 1989).

The other modules were all planned using a top-down approach and the plans were fairly standard. Often, the proposal looked like a 'shopping list' of staff and resources

316

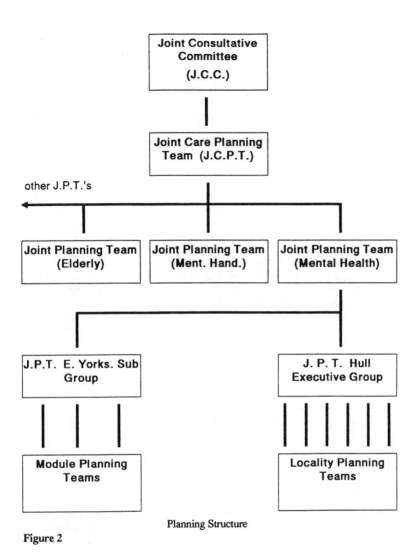

Planning Structure

Figure 2

required for each module but in reality funding allowed only certain staff to be employed. A typical list of staffing may consist of a consultant psychiatrist, a clinical assistant, a psychologist, four community psychiatric nurses, three nurses, two occupational or art therapists and possibly a social worker.

Three modules in Hull and one in East Yorkshire also had an injection of Social Services staffing funded through Social Services growth money and these developed a broader range of services.

Throughout this period, as the MIND representative on the Planning Teams the writer attempted to influence the planning away from the top-down approach of mental illness services towards a bottom-up approach for mental health. As the 1985 Short report states:

We have difficulty in hearing the authentic voice of the ultimate consumers of community care. There have been considerable advances in techniques designed to enable and encourage mentally ill or handicapped people to speak for themselves ..... but there is a long way to go. Services are still mainly designed by providers and not users, whether families or clients, and in response to blueprints rather than in answer to demand. Matching the service to the consumer rather than vice-versa should be the one central aim of community care in the future... (H.M.S.O., 1985)

This 'planning from the bottom-up' has been described by Dyer (1985) as beginning to plan for Ted, Ruth and Mary rather than for a glob of people called 'mentally ill'.

A second related concern appeared to be that staffing levels and disciplines were being decided in advance of considering the necessary tasks and skills required to provide the new service. It is self evident that staffing should have been determined after considering the skills required to undertake the tasks. Further, there was a missed opportunity to enter into partnership with the voluntary sector. I was the only voluntary sector representative on the planning teams - and at that time MIND was the largest provider of community mental health services in North Humberside. Finally, there were two major concerns about the outcome of the planning process - inadequate support and services for people with long term mental health problems and a lack of emphasis on preventative work and community development.

It was at this time, then, that the writer attempted to develop an alternative model of community services for people with mental health problems, based on a more social model.

Towards a comprehensive service: Guiding principles and functions

There is no shortage of suggestions offering a philosophy or principles for mental health services (see, for example, Brandon, 1986; HMSO, 1985; Patmore, 1985; Social Services Inspectorate, 1989; MIND, 1983; Wing & Furlong, 1986; Socialist Health Association, 1987; Shephard, 1988; Holloway, 1988; Richie *et al*, 1988). The fourteen principles listed below have been drawn from a review of this literature in conjunction with the writer's assessment of their relative merits. These principles are considered in two sections: major principles of service provision and principles relating to individuals.

Major principles for service provision

Comprehensive A full network of inter-connected complementary parts is needed to ensure the needs of individuals are met.

Accessible Services should be accessible, both physically and psychologically. They should be available during times when the users need them, including evening and weekend; locally based; be easily accessible using public transport; and responsive to the needs of users. Consideration needs to be given, for example to the nature of the building, the image conveyed by the service, the method of referral and initial contact, the management structure and the attitudes of the workers.

Friendly and informal Services should be friendly and welcoming. There should be no barriers, and they should be run on fairly informal lines. There should be a relatively open, unstructured relationship between staff and users, with a minimum of role differentiation.

Flexible Services should allow for change and adaptation in response to varying needs and wishes of individuals.

Non-stigmatising This is a primary theme of normalisation principles. The service should convey positive messages to users and the community, and not negative messages. For example, efforts should be made to ensure that signals about the clients' social status, their roles, and their competence are positive. The messages which services send to users or the community can be either explicit or implicit, and are conveyed through aspects such as the physical setting, the manner in which people are grouped together, the types of activities, the language and the labels used.

Integrated Services should strive for integration within the community, but include some specialist facilities. Integration means not only working with users, but also with community agencies, other statutory bodies, the Primary Health Care Team and relatives.

Social contacts Related to the principle of integration, is the need for services to foster contact between people; including opportunities to develop more intimate friendships. Probably the paramount need for people is that of friendship and close relationships.

Fully co-ordinated All services should be fully co-ordinated with easy access to all parts of the network. An initial contact with any one component of the service should open up access to the whole network.

Monitoring and Evaluation Services should be monitored and evaluated. External inspection should be introduced. Individual clients should have access to independent advocates.

Principles relating to individual service users

Dignity & Respect

Users should be valued as full citizens with rights and responsibilities. They should be offered full participation in their care plan and treated with dignity and respect.

Individual needs Services should be geared towards the needs of individuals, not groups of people. Each user should be seen as a unique person, with a range of normal human needs like love, friendship and feeling valued.

Empowerment

> The first task of a constructive mental health service must be to restore and develop people's confidence and ability to function successfully in the world ... mental health services ... should seek to empower, not further to disempower, as is currently the norm. (Socialist Health Association, 1987, p12).

Services should enhance users' competence, as it is devaluing to be incompetent. This

319

should be done through the use of effective, valued and relevant methods, and in a high quality environment.

The aim of services, therefore, should be to build confidence and enable users to make decisions based on realistic and informed choice. Rather than focus on symptoms and problems, services should concentrate on creating positive experiences using the users' own talents, strengths and interests. Problems should be seen within an overall context of health, rather than illness.

Choice It follows that if services are designed to meet individual needs there must be a degree of choice. Users may wish to attend a facility within their own locality, or in an area where they can maintain anonymity; to be involved with ordinary community facilities or to attend a specialist centre; to go to a voluntary sector run scheme or to one run by a statutory organisation.

Participation Users should be encouraged to participate in the planning and running of services. Services should help users develop their confidence to enable them to make decisions and exercise choice, and users should be given every opportunity and encouragement to offer comments, suggestions and criticisms of the service; and where their suggestions are not likely to affect the rights of other existing or future users, they should be acted upon.

Functions of the service

The guiding principles provide the philosophy of the service. This section considers the functions and tasks necessary for a comprehensive service. These have been developed by considering the needs of users, and by reviewing recent literature. Again, they are discussed below under two headings; general service functions and functions relating to the individual user.

General service functions

A range of residential provision is required which is capable of responding to the differing levels of support required by people experiencing mental health problems. The level of support available should be sufficiently flexible to respond to the needs of the individual's particular circumstances.

A key function of the service should be geared towards prevention and education. Many everyday experiences are known to produce emotional and psychological problems which can result in mental ill health. By providing help for the wider population in developing coping strategies in anticipation of such experiences some of the worst effects of these can be avoided.

The effects of mental ill health on a person's employment situation or prospects are variable. Some people may never return to or obtain work and require other opportunities or other forms of occupational activity. Others may require relatively short term support which will enable them to return to established employment. The particular skills, work experience, motivation, confidence and mental health of the individual must form the basis for decisions about the opportunities which need to be provided (Pilling, 1988).

A paramount need is for friendship, and the service should promote opportunities for meeting people. A drop-in social centre should be available seven days a week. As many users are on low incomes, food and refreshments should be provided at reduced rates. Smaller, separate social clubs may also be established run by volunteers or users themselves. A befriending scheme could be established with trained volunteers to accompany users to community facilities or simply talk (Richie et al, 1988).

Recreational, leisure and creative activities should be available. Users should be able to engage in a range of non-problem based activities, such as art, craft, drama and creative writing workshops, discussion groups, woodwork, pottery, darts, dominoes, table-tennis, photography and so on. Again, use should be made of ordinary community facilities if possible, mixing with the general population (Wainwright et al, 1988).

Outreach work is a crucial aspect of the service. Mental health services should be rooted in the community. A major task should be to enable users to use, for example, community centres, leisure services, adult education, voluntary bodies, public houses and so on. Staff will need detailed knowledge of the local community and the facilities available, and most of their time should be spent in the community rather than the centre. Links should be established with a range of other organisations, especially with the primary health care services. Training and support should be available to staff in other organisations, such as leisure services and adult education (Marks et al, 1988; Patmore, 1985; MIND, 1983).

Families paly a vital role, and they should be fully integrated into the caring programme. They often feel guilt and need support. The service should provide a rapid, practical and non-judgemental response to early appeals for help from relatives. Staff should be sensitive to the feelings of relatives, and interview in a manner which is unlikely to increase their level of guilt or anxiety. They should be provided with detailed information about the diagnosis and prognosis of the user and formal counselling should be offered. There will be occasions when families need relief, and short and long term in-care facilities must be provided (MacCarthy, 1988; Falloon et al, 1984).

An important element of the service should be on-going monitoring and evaluation, including an independent evaluation.

Functions relating to individual users

A thorough individual assessment should be an integral component. This should be based on the user's strengths and talents and not solely on the 'problem'. This should not be rushed; it is necessary to spend time with the client in order to obtain a full understanding of his/her strengths, talents and needs. Details about the user's family structure and network should be obtained, as well as information about the social circumstances and support systems, personal history and presenting problems. The assessment should be carried out with the user. Particular sensitivity and understanding of the needs and cultural circumstances of those from an ethnic origin should be exercised, and staff should have special training in this respect (Richie et al, 1988; Socialist Health Association, 1987).

Following the assessment, the individual care plan or rehabilitation programme should be devised, again in conjunction with the user. The individual plan is most important and forms the key to the whole service. Some degree of structure may be necessary for people, especially during their early contact with the service, and it should be remembered that some users have a higher chance of relapse if they are either over stimulated (for example, in an over-enthusiastic rehabilitation programme) or under stimulated (Holloway, 1988; Vaughan & Prechner, 1986).

Assessment is not a one-off process. It is important to hold periodic reviews to take account of the varying needs of the client.

Medical input may be required, especially during times of crises, when people may lose insight or be a danger to themselves or others. It may then be necessary to stabilise the condition using medication, and for some it may be necessary to maintain medication for longer periods (Marks *et al*, 1988). However, the aim should always be to minimise the use of drugs in favour of a more psycho-social approach. The consultant psychiatrist should have specific training in the use of psychotherapeutic techniques (Socialist Health Association, 1987; Richie *et al*, 1988). Mental health professionals need to develop close working relationships with colleagues involved in primary health care provision. This will enable earlier identification of difficulties leading to mental health problems, and provide opportunities for more appropriate help to be given at an earlier stage. The emphasis should always be towards enabling people to live without drugs.

There should be a 24 hour, seven day week facility to respond to crises. Staff time spent during the initial stages of crises can prevent relapse. A typical intervention may be to first stabilise the symptoms using medication and then prepare an individual programme including working with the client and his or her relatives in their own environment (Holloway, 1988; Marks *et al*, 1988).

The service should be focused towards preventing relapse, and this objective should run through all elements. Relapse may be avoided using appropriate day care, rehabilitation and work. However, staff will also need to work with users in their own home environment.

Individual counselling should be available. Behavioural approaches can be used for depression, anxiety, psychosis, family and emotional conflict (Falloon *et al*, 1984). Families can be taught to adopt a more positive style of coping which may reduce relapse rates. Using a network approach, the relationship between clients and their home situation may be improved. Information and support should also be available for neighbours, landlords, employers, police, shopkeepers and so on. It is also important to monitor the user's general health care. Finally, staff should make a determined effort actively to maintain contact and follow up users who fail to maintain their programme (Holloway, 1988; Marks *et al*, 1988).

The service should seek to empower people by helping them develop confidence and skills. Social skills should preferably be taught in situations in which they will be required; in shops, at home, in the local pub and so on (Stein & Test 1980; Marks *et al*, 1988). Training in self care, home management, the use of community facilities, literacy and numeracy should be available. Opportunities for people to talk through their difficulties in a group situation if appropriate and to develop confidence and self esteem should be provided. Training towards work is also a crucial element of the service (Pillin, 1988).

Users should have access to independent information and advice about issues such as mental health law, services, benefits, their rights and community facilities.

Advocacy refers to the process of pleading the cause and/or acting on behalf of persons with mental health problems to secure the services which they require and the enjoyment of their full rights. The service should ensure funding is made available for the establishment of an independent advocacy project. The project should develop a citizen advocacy scheme, which refers to the persuasive and supportive activities of trained, selected volunteers and co-ordinating staff. Citizen advocates are independent of those who provide direct services. They attempt to foster respect for the rights and dignity of vulnerable people. This may involve helping to express the individual's concerns and aspirations, obtaining services and providing other practical and emotional support for him or her. The project may also develop self advocacy schemes, which involve persons with mental health problems asserting their own rights expressing their needs and concerns, and assuming the duties of citizenship to the extent of their capabilities (North Humberside MIND, 1987).

Self advocacy and self help groups can be valuable in developing confidence and self esteem. However, such groups may act in opposition to normalisation principles. Problem based groups may be devaluing and become self stigmatising. Users may continue to hold on the their psychiatric label, and integration may be more difficult to achieve (Wainwright *et al*, 1988; Race, 1987).

The functions of the proposed service can be summarised in a form of a task triangle (figure 3). This looks at the services required along the base of the triangle. To the left are listed the skills required of practitioners and to the right are examples of staff. It is suggested that most of the input should be directed towards the base of the triangle in terms of support provided by the community and non-professional staff.

North Humberside MIND

Voluntary organisations can have up to three basic roles: to provide services, to represent the interests of consumers and to campaign for better service provision. North Humberside MIND attempts to fulfil all three roles. With regard to service provision, it has been providing community mental health services for fifteen years. There are a number of aspects which equip the Association to provide services to complement those provided by the statutory sector (see figure 4).

First, it is innovative. It is not bound by statutory responsibilities, it can experiment freely and does not have to seek approval through a complicated committee structure. When it identifies a need it can quickly develop projects to meet this need. It is flexible in the way it develops and changes services. It offers users a choice.

The Association offers services which are client-centred, friendly and accessible. Users have a major voice and participate in the day to day running of services: this helps them feel empowered by the service. It is welcoming and informal. Role differentiation between users, volunteers and staff is minimised. Its services are non-stigmatising. Accommodation looks like ordinary housing. Users do not need to see a G.P. before using the service: detailed records are not maintained and confidentiality is preserved.

Many of the Association's services attempt to meet some of the functions already discussed. For example, it provides a range of accommodation; it has a day centre and social clubs where people can build friendships, engage in leisure, educational and creative activities; it offers information and advice; runs a carers group; facilitates therapy groups and helps establish self help initiatives. Similarly, statutory services meet

323

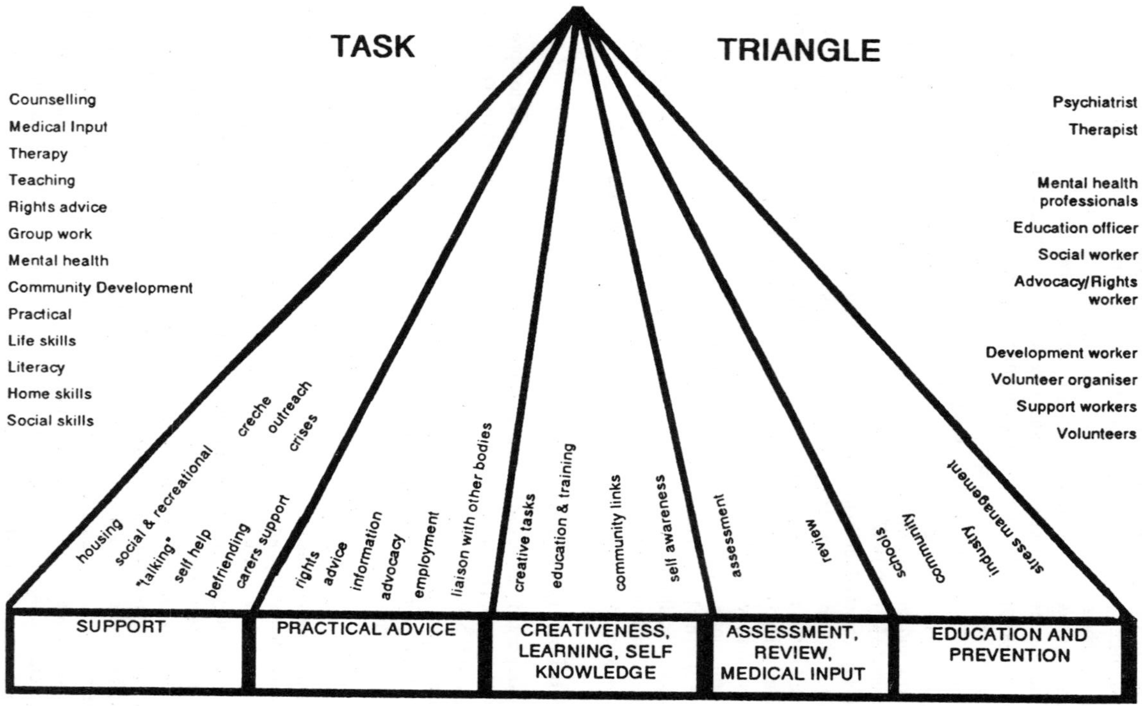

TRIANGLE

TASK

Counselling
Medical Input
Therapy
Teaching
Rights advice
Group work
Mental health
Community Development
Practical
Life skills
Literacy
Home skills
Social skills

Psychiatrist
Therapist

Mental health
professionals
Education officer
Social worker
Advocacy/Rights
worker

Development worker
Volunteer organiser
Support workers
Volunteers

SUPPORT

housing
social & recreational
"talking"
self help
befriending
carers support
crèche
outreach
crises

PRACTICAL ADVICE

rights advice
information
advocacy
employment
liaison with other bodies

CREATIVENESS,
LEARNING, SELF
KNOWLEDGE

creative tasks
education & training
community links
self awareness

ASSESSMENT,
REVIEW,
MEDICAL INPUT

assessment
review

EDUCATION AND
PREVENTION

schools
community
industry
stress management

Figure 3   Task triangle

324

other needs; such as medical and therapeutic.

It is not possible, nor arguably desirable, for a relatively small voluntary organisation

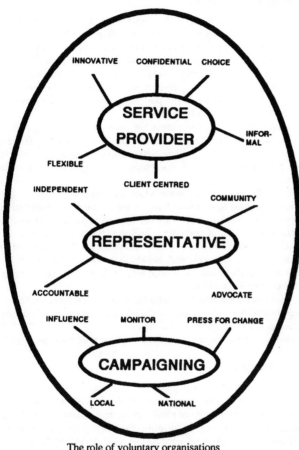

The role of voluntary organisations

Figure 4

to respond to all unmet needs. Funding restrictions force the Association to be selective about its projects. In making choices about developments, the Association considers existing provision, researches needs and attempts to develop imaginative ways to respond within available resources.

Of the functions listed above, one major short-fall in statutory provision is that of mental health promotion. MIND is in a good position to develop this work.

Mental Health Promotion

The task triangle recognises the need for mental health promotion, and this is an area which has become increasingly important in our work at MIND. Firstly, we aim to act upon factors which lead to poor mental health. Secondly, we hope to combat the prejudice and stigma associated with mental health in the population at large. Services should be more proactive and we urge a range of initiatives to further this; education in schools; community developments to encourage self help and an awareness of the range of ordinary community facilities; health promotion sessions including stress management; attempts to assist people into employment.

Through joint planning, the Association has attempted to encourage the statutory bodies to adopt a more promotional model of health. However, having failed to obtain any significant change in policy, the Association started to see how it could respond to these needs. First, we established a working party to investigate how to promote mental health in schools.

The definition of positive mental health which we used is as follows.

Embodying an attitude to ourselves which allows a sensible understanding of our limitations whilst being able to make the most creative use of our potential, unfettered by unrealistic expectations of ourselves. Such an attitude facilitates us in making satisfying relationships with others whilst maintaining a clear sense of our own boundaries and abilities. Being mentally healthy does not mean that we are immune to unhappiness or distress but enables us to cope with this important aspect of being human. (North Humberside MIND, 1986).

The conclusions of the working party called for the employment of a worker who would work alongside teaching staff to raise awareness about mental health and to discuss coping strategies to alleviate stress and anxiety.

Needless to say, funding has not been made available to develop this project further.

Mind your Health

The project which is perhaps achieving more success is our Mind your Health initiative which offers stress and anxiety management for members of the public. The project started in April 1990 with a series of stress management courses for working people. These courses were initially run as a pilot project in order to obtain an indication of future demand. However, it soon became apparent that the demand is there: all four courses completed at the time of writing have been full. But why do people attend our courses, which cost £37, when they could attend a course run by a community mental health team at no charge? There are probably a number of reasons. First, participants do not need to be referred through a doctor: this makes access easier. Second, there is less stigma attached to attending a Mind your Health course. Third, there is anonymity - few people will know that they are experiencing pressure. It will not be entered on their medical records. Finally, there is no fear of medication being prescribed.

The courses are run in a participatory manner. We believe that people have the key to their own health and our role is to enable them to develop their own skills and strengths to combat stress and anxiety.

So far, participants have come from a wide range of backgrounds and occupations. 62% have been female. Most have been professionals - we have had many managers and teachers - although there have been some manual workers such as builders and drivers. This leaves me with a feeling that it may be more difficult actively to promote the health of non professional people.

It is unfortunate that the Association does not have the resources to undertake any long term evaluation of the effectiveness of the courses. However, participants are asked to complete an evaluation form at the end of the course and, of those who have returned them, 98% felt the course had been helpful for their particular situation.

In April 1991 we extended this service and produced new publicity for our Mind your Health project. Our aim is to attract participants from a wider range of backgrounds and our programme now includes an anxiety management course and relaxation sessions. The first course has been successfully completed and has achieved our aim of attracting a broader spectrum of people -possibly because we offered concessionary rates to people on low income.

Interest has been growing and we are currently discussing the possibility of providing courses in G.P. surgeries with funding from the Family Health Services Authority.

Our next goal for the Mind you Health project is to offer individual counselling and therapy for the public. This ambitious project will use a pool of trained therapists, who will be registered by the Association. However, the interesting and unusual aspect of the project is that we intend to offer a range of alternative therapies, such as Bach flower remedies, aromatherapy and reflexology, in addition to more traditional approaches.

Workers in Mind

So far we have concentrated our efforts on members of the public. Some of our services are provided on a self financing basis, whereas others are subsidised through the Association's other income. The Workers in Mind project aims to offer a service to industry which will (a) maintain a healthy working population and (b) be self financing.

The project, launched in May 1991, offers stress management and counselling for industry and commerce. Industry is beginning to recognise the cost of stress.

> Up to 40% of absenteeism at work through illness can be attributable to mental or emotional problems (Health & Safety Executive, 1988).

> In Liverpool, the effects of employee stress are costing the ratepayers £3m per annum (Liverpool Environmental Health Officer, 1988).

> Around 30m days are lost at work for certified neurotic disorders. The cost equals £4bn per annum and excludes psychosomatic complaints and uncertified absence (Cooper et al, 1990).

> Approximately 33% of Civil Service Executive Officers had anxiety/depression problems of one kind or another (Jenkins, 1984).

> In England, G.P. consultation rates for mental disorders were 300 per 1000 population, exceeded only by coughs, colds and bronchitis (Cooper et al, 1990)

We have become more and more aware that users of our services have developed poor physical and mental health due to stress related factors. The effects of stress are well known.

In February, 1991, the Association commissioned a graphic artist to produce a logo and some publicity which would, hopefully, attract industry. The project was launched in May of this year and it is too soon to judge the effectiveness. However, we have received approaches from five companies in the Hull area who have expressed an interest in commissioning us to run stress management courses.

The service also aims to provide individual counselling for employees either on or off site to help them overcome their difficulties. In addition, whilst respecting individual confidentiality, the service will provide valuable feedback to management highlighting aspects of the work situation creating particular pressure.

Conclusions

The projects described aim to give a brief outline of some strategies adopted by North Humberside MIND to develop mental health promotion. Much greater flexibility and vision will be required to provide the kind of mental health services we will need in the future. What is actually needed is a radical shift in the way services are planned and delivered: we need a shift away from the medical model towards a social model; a shift away from treating people's problems towards looking at their skills, abilities and positive aspects; away from providing services for groups of people and towards looking at the needs of individuals. We must stop reacting to problems and move towards a proactive service which aims to maintain the health of the population.

References

Brandon, D. (1986, August 5). Pioneering heralds death of the hostel. *Social Work Today*. p. 9.

Brandon, D. (1987, December 21). Participation and choice: a worthwhile pilgrimage. *Social Work Today*. pp. 8-9.

Brandon, D. & Brandon, A. (1987). *Consumers as colleagues*. London: MIND.

Cooper, C.L., Sadri, G., Allison, T., & Reynolds, P (1990). Stress counselling in the Post Office. *Counselling Psychology Quarterly*. 3 (1) pp. 3-11.

Dyer, L. (1985). *Wrong end of the telescope*. London: MIND.

Falloon, I., Boyd, J. & McGill, C. (1984). *Family care of schizophrenia*. New York: Guildford.

Golightley, M. (1989). *If only they would listen. A study of the community mental health needs of people in the Haltemprice area of Humberside, Hull*. Humberside Polytechnic.

Health and Safety Executive (1988). *Mental health at work*. London: HMSO.

Holloway, F. (1988) Day care and community support. In A. Lavender, & F. Holloway, (Eds.). *Community care in practice: Services for the continuing care client*. Chichester: Wiley.

House of Commons Social Services Committee. (1985). Second Report: Sessions 1984-

1985. *Community care: with special reference to adult mentally ill and mentally handicapped people*. London: H.M.S.O.

Jenkins, R. (1984). *Report on survey of civil service executive officers*. Civil Service Occupational Health Service.

Liverpool Environmental Health Officer (1988, March). Article in *the Times*.

MacCarthy, B. (1988) The role of relatives. In A. Lavender, & F. Holloway, (Eds.)., *Community care in practice: Services for the continuing care client*. Chichester: Wiley.

Marks, I., Connolly, J. & Huijem, M. (1988, January). The Maudesley daily living programme. *Bulletin of the Royal College of Psychiatrists*. 12. pp. 22-24.

MIND. (1983). *Common concern*. London: MIND.

North Humberside MIND. (1986). *Education and training officer: Application for grant aid*. Hull: North Humberside MIND.

North Humberside MIND. (1987). *Application for grant aid to establish a citizen advocacy scheme and develop and support self help and user involvement initiatives*. Hull: North Humberside MIND.

Patmore, C. (1985, May 17). *Desirable directions for mental health day services*. Paper given at 'alternatives in day care' conference. London: MIND.

Pilling, S. (1988). Work and the continuing care client. In A. Lavender, & F. Holloway, (Eds.)., *Community care in practice: Services for the continuing care client*. Chichester: Wiley.

Race, D. (1987). Normalisation: Theory and practice. In N. Malin, (Ed.)., *Reassessing community care*. London: Croom Helm.

Richie, J., Morrissey, C. & Ward, K. (1988). *Keeping in touch with the talking. The community care needs of people with mental illness*. Birmingham: Social and Community Planning Research.

Shepherd, G. (1988). Evaluation and service planning. In A. Lavender, & F. Holloway, (Eds.)., *Community care in practice: Services for the continuing care client*. Chichester: Wiley.

Socialist Health Association. (1987). *Goodbuy to all that?: Re-thinking the politics of mental health*. London: Socialist Health Association.

Social Services Inspectorate. (1989). *Day services for people with long term mental health problems,* personal letter, 24th May, London: DHSS.

Stein, L. & Test, M. (1980). Alternatives to mental hospital treatment. *Archives of general psychiatry*. 37 pp.392-405.

Vaughan, P. & Prechner, M. (1986). A structured approach to psychiatric day care. *Occupational therapy*. 49 (1). pp. 10-12.

Wainwright, T., Holloway, F. & Brugha, J. (1988). Day care in inner cities. In A. Lavender, & F. Holloway, (Eds.)., *Community care in practice: Services for the continuing care client*. Chichester: Wiley.

Wing, J. & Furlong, R. (1986). A haven for the severeley disabled within the context of a comprehensive psychiatric community service. *Brit. J. of Psychiatry*. 149, pp. 449-457.

34 Use of the media and public lectures to publicise stress

J. White

Abstract

Although a good deal of information is currently available in the media about stress, much of this information is inaccurate, unrepresentative or sensationalised. There is a need for easily understandable, general information on stress to be made readily available to the large number of people who may not wish to 'medicalise' their problem by discussing it with their G.P. This project looked at the feasibility of publishing articles on stress in local newspapers and offering public lectures on stress management to coincide with these articles. Although evaluating the articles was not possible,. the lectures, which were well attended, did produce evidence suggesting that the project was successful.

Introduction

With the current unpopularity of benzodiazepines, there has been a great increase in interest directed towards creating new approaches to stress management. Clinical Psychologists have been in the forefront of this movement. Along with other professional and non-professional agencies, a range of creative methods has been developed. There has been no shortage of people willing to use these methods.

The extent of the problem

Espie and White (1986) reported that General Practitioners estimated that one in five patients seen in a primary care surgery presented with primarily a psychological complaint. Barlow, Cohen, Waddell et al. (1984) cite a Gallup survey in the United States which found marked anxiety in 30-40% of the general population. Lader (1975) found similar levels in a British study. Croft-Jeffries and Wilkinson (1989), estimating direct costs of treatment and care and indirect costs of lost productivity for neurotic disorders (classified according to ICD-9), established a minimal cost of £373 million (1985 costs) in general practice alone - equivalent to just over 9% of the total spent on the family practitioner services in 1984-85. In addition these workers quote government estimate costs of £219 million for secondary care, i.e. hospital in- and out-patient treatment. These sums in total are greater than the costs of treating heart disease - estimated at over £500 million per year (National Audit Office, 1989).

Developments in clinical psychology

During the 1970s and 80s, many clinical psychologists moved into the primary care field. Hall, Koch, Pilling and Winter (1986) noted that about one in four psychologists had some involvement in this area. Johnston (1978) suggested that one advantage of this move would be the opportunity of seeing patients earlier before the problem had become entrenched. The reality, however, has been quite different. The overall picture is of Clinical Psychology primary care services being 'swamped' with referrals and particularly those referrals for anxiety management. This has led to lengthy waiting times between referral and first appointment. It has also often been the experience that, far from being able to intervene with 'fresh' problems, psychologists are dealing with well-entrenched and severe difficulties.

Given the scarcity of trained therapists and resources, clinical psychologists, aware that they are only able to see a fraction of these problems. have increasingly looked at innovative methods of service delivery. Examples include self-help anxiety management packages (Donnan, Hutchison, Paxton, Grant and Firth, 1990); large group therapy (White and Keenan, 1990); walk-in clinics (Heller, Kear-Colwell and Beeken, 1986); adult education evening classes (Butler and de Clive-Lowe, 1985); training ex-clients (Milne, Jones and Walter, 1989); working with self-help groups (Long and Bourne, 1985); sharing psychological skills with other professional groups (Weinman and Medlic, 1985). In addition to these exciting developments, psychologists have increasingly used bibliotherapy, i.e. the use of reading material in the treatment of psychological problems. This interest may also be mirrored by that of the general population as the interest in D.I.Y. procedures may represent the growing ethos of self-help which leads people to seek help for a wide range of problems from a wide range of sources other than health and social services (Turvey, 1985). Dow (1982) suggests that the interest in bibliotherapy has been prompted by a number of potential advantages:

a) enhanced cost-effectiveness
b) increased accessibility of appropriate help
c) reduced feelings of 'standing alone'
d) increased privacy and reduced embarrassment.

In addition, Powell (1987) noted that, when asked to consider what they had found most useful about an anxiety management group therapy, patients rated 'information about anxiety and stress' more highly than they rated any active coping skill. Based on these findings, Powell argued that psychologists should place less emphasis on their role as individual therapists and more toward the position of educators. The present study aimed to take a tentative step in that direction.

The present study

Aims

The primary care clinical psychology service in Hamilton/East Kilbride Unit, in common with many services, is swamped with referrals. Typically an individual will wait six to eight months between referral and first appointment. General Practitioners, who provide the referrals, note that they refer only the 'tip of the iceberg' and that there are few alternative agencies providing appropriate help. This project was therefore seen as a pilot study looking at the feasibility of reaching a large number of individuals under stress and providing them with easily understandable information about stress and ways of handling it.

Background

This study comprised two related aspects:
1. The publishing of four, eight hundred word articles on stress which appeared on four consecutive weeks in two local newspapers.
2. In the week following the publication of the final article, a public lecture was given on the theme of 'Coping with Stress'. This lecture was given in three separate locations reflecting the three main population centres in the Health Service Unit.

It was not possible to evaluate the impact of the newspaper articles. However, a fifteen item evaluation questionnaire, developed by the author, was given to those who attended the public lectures.

The number of questions was kept reasonably low to enhance compliance and to allow the questionnaire to be quickly completed during the session. It was also decided to omit questions which would have been of interest but which would have unreasonably infringed upon the individual's privacy. Therefore questions about previous psychological/psychiatric treatment, psychotropic medication use, etc. were not included.

The questionnaire divided into three sections:
1. Demographic information (4 questions)
2. Evaluation of the articles (7 questions)
3. Evaluation of the lecture (4 questions)

There was a 90% return rate. Findings are given below.

The author wrote the articles and presented the lectures. I trained initially in behavioural therapy and more recently in cognitive therapy. Although relatively eclectic in outlook, the articles and lectures reflect a cognitive-behavioural perspective. As head of the primary care clinical psychology service in Hamilton/East Kilbride Unit of Lanarkshire Health Board, clinical and research interests are directed towards anxiety-management by the individual, group and bibliotherapy.

Hamilton/East Kilbride Unit divides into three main centres of population:
1. East Kilbride: a new town with a majority of the population coming originally from Glasgow. It has good health care facilities centred around modern health centres. Hi-tech industries flourish in the town.
2. Hamilton: a traditional country town. Unemployment has been high in the area

since the decline of heavy industry in Lanarkshire.

   3. Larkhall: an old mining village in more rural surroundings. The villages of
      Stonehouse and Strathaven are nearby.

The population of Hamilton/East Kilbride Unit is 191,000.

The newspapers

Two local newspapers are sold in the Unit:

   1. East Kilbride News - Covering only the new town, the circulation for the period
      July-December 1990 was 15,464 (Audit Bureau of Circulation Figures).
   2. Hamilton Advertiser - This paper is sold not only in town but also in the villages
      of Larkhall, Stonehouse and Strathaven. Circulation over the same period was
      32,906 (Audit Bureau of Circulation Figures).

Both papers are published weekly. Both, naturally, emphasise local issues. The
Hamilton Advertiser has a weekly 'Family Doctor' column. As 3.5 people read each
copy, there is a potentially large readership for information printed in these papers.

The articles: general

The author contacted both editors by phone, outlined the project to them and asked them
to consider four articles. On receipt of the articles, they agreed to publish them without
editing. They appeared in the East Kilbride News under the heading 'Beating Stress' and
in the Hamilton Advertiser under the heading 'Stress'. The sub-headings, provided by
the author were then provided. Layout in both papers was imaginative and eye-catching.
The articles were prominently placed in the top left hand corners of inside pages.

All four articles were 800 words in length and were published simultaneously in both
newspapers in four consecutive weekly issues. This size represents an above average
article in these papers.

Readability In order that the articles were easily understood by as large a readership
as possible, drafts of each article were submitted to the Flesch reading formula (Flesch,
1948). This formula indicates the level of difficulty in comprehending any text and also
indicates the percentage of the adult (U.S.) population who would be expected to
understand the test. The scores for all articles indicate that 80% of the population would
be expected to understand the text. Using Ley's 'cautious' IQ equivalents, an IQ of 84
is required (Ley, 1977).

Level of description This study was aimed towards the (presumed) large number of
people who were experiencing high levels of stress. Thus the description was placed at
a 'clinical' rather than a 'preventative' level.

As one of the aims was to transmit relevant information to as large a readership as
possible, the question of relevance became an important issue. Given the heterogeneity
of thoughts, symptoms and behaviour involved in stress, the articles had to be wide
enough to encompass a range of difficulties yet not become too diffuse and vague thus
losing relevance for the individual.

In addition, while it was of great importance to transmit accurate information, this had
to be done in an interesting manner in order to keep the reader's attention particulary those
readers who may not yet identify themselves as having a stress problem. 'Selling' the
articles to this group was of particular importance. Resolving the problem was aided by

reference to the excellent guidelines for bibliotherapy manuals presented by Turvey (1985).

Choosing the topics Having decided on a clinical level of description it was felt that a combination of information and advice was important. It was also felt that, in order to provide a sense of continuity, all four articles should be interrelated. As there are obvious marked restrictions on what information and advice can be transmitted in four relatively short pieces, the articles were ordered around generalised anxiety disorder and panic disorder - two very common forms of anxiety disorder. Articles 1 and 2 provided the background information while articles 3 and 4 provided the advice. Whenever possible, the advice was specific rather than general as there is evidence that this improves outcome (Bradshaw, Key, Kincey and Bradshaw, 1975).

The articles: specifics

Article 1: 'The Nature of Stress' Following a brief description of the author's affiliation and clinical interests, the article contains three 'quotes' for anxiety sufferers (written by the author):

'I just worry all the time. I can't sit at peace for two minutes and I can't relax at all. If my children are ten minutes late home from school, I'm round the bend with worry. I know I shouldn't get so uptight but I can't stop myself.'

'Work is getting worse. I always feel under pressure, I can't concentrate and I'm making a lot of daft mistakes. Although my friends say I look fine, I'm sure everyone can see how tense I am. I dread getting out of bed in the morning. I think I'm heading for a nervous breakdown.'

'It just comes on for no reason. I can be sitting there quite relaxed and next thing - bang - my head feels like its going to burst, my chest is so tight and I can hardly breathe. I'm sure I'm having a heart attack. This has happened about forty times now. My doctor has told me my heart is fine and that I'm having panic attacks. I know she is right but that reassurance goes right out the window when I feel like that.'

These quotes are intended to stimulate interest and, hopefully, to 'pull' people further into the articles. Common features of the quotes relate to a sense of losing control and apprehension - a feeling that something bad may be about to happen. This is described as the 'what if .....?' phenomenon.

Due to the lack of space in which to develop a rounded explanation of the various causes of stress, the article concentrates on the role of life events - i.e. if too many events, both good and bad, occur in a relatively short space of time, you may be more vulnerable to stress. The maintenance of stress is explained by means of the development of a vicious circle and highlights the influence of worry, avoidance, demoralisation and declining self-confidence.

The article ends by contrasting common myths about stress with the facts:

MYTH: Stress is a mental illness
FACT: Stress is not a mental illness. Stress is perfectly normal
MYTH: Too much stress will lead to mental illness
FACT: Too much stress will not lead to mental illness. At worst it will simply persist

MYTH	Stress only affects inadequate people
FACT	Stress affects anyone and everyone. It is a very common problem. If stress could be 'cured' by giving yourself a good shake, don't you think you would have happily done this?
MYTH	You are born with stress. It is in the blood so you have it for life.
FACT	Stress is caused by what happens to you in life - you are not born with it. It can be treated so you are not stuck with it.

Article 2: 'The Role of Stress' The main aim of this article was to make sense of the symptoms of stress by placing them into an evolutionary survival mechanism perspective. Seeing a contemporary stress reaction as being related to a more ancient means of protecting the individual may help the stress sufferer to alter his/her perception of the symptoms and to 'decatastrophise' anxious interpretations, i.e. a racing heart is a sign of an impending heart attack. Thus the concept of the 'fight/flight' response was detailed as a mechanism enabling the individual either to flee from danger or to fight it, thus enhancing survival.

A scene of a stone age man walking alone at night is built up. He is on his guard as he anticipates danger. To help him deal more effectively with any physical threat - wild animals, enemies - the following physical changes will occur:

His heart beats faster and stronger
His breathing quickens and deepens
His muscles tense
Sweating increases
Pupils dilate
Digestion and salivation slow down
Vigilance improves
Anticipation improves

The effect of each of these changes is described and why they may aid survival for the primitive man, e.g. sweating helps cool the muscles and also makes his skin more slippery and therefore less easy for a foe to grab. The side effects of these changes are also described, e.g. because blood is directed to where it is most needed - legs - so he can run faster - arms - so he can hit out more effectively and lungs - to improve his stamina, it has to be taken from places where it is less needed, e.g. skin, fingers and toes. This may cause coldness, numbness and tingling in these areas.

Readers are then invited to consider how stress affects them. Does this ancient inbuilt survival mechanism have anything to do with their stress response bearing in mind that psychological threats will trigger the response just as readily as physical threats, e.g. a car coming fast towards them while crossing the road? Stress is seen as causing the response to be triggered too readily and then, because of the secondary 'fear of the fear', the problem is exacerbated.

Article 3: 'Know your Enemy' The first task set in article 3 was for the reader to get to know more about his/her own reaction to stress. The reader is asked to respond to the following questions:

1. Is there a pattern to your stress? e.g. worse in the mornings, at weekends.
2. What things make it worse? e.g being in crowds, being alone, alcohol.
3. What things make it better? e.g. being with family, talking to friends, holidays.

336

4. What is the main thing you notice when stressful? e.g. heart racing, short-tempered, agitation.
5. What do others notice when you are stressful? (ask them), e.g. fidget, look ill, become withdrawn.
6. What aspects of your life are most affected by the stress? e.g. can't relax at night, can't sleep, loss of confidence in social situations.
7. What aspects of your life are least affected by the stress? e.g. work, being with the family.

The next step is to target the problem. The reader is asked to:
1. Write down all the problems which exist.
2. Discuss, if possible, these problems with family and friends.
3. Divide the problem into those that cannot be helped and those which can.

Confront the problems A range of simple behavioural strategies are suggested, e.g. expressing feelings, prioritising, learning from others, exercise, making time to relax, accepting personal limitations etc. It is pointed out that avoiding facing up to problems often helps in the short term but in order to achieve long term change, confronting the problem is essential.

Article 4: 'Panic Attacks' A description of someone having a panic attack begins this article, followed by a description of the signs and symptoms often involved in panic. Agoraphobia and its relationship to panic is briefly discussed.

A cognitive-behavioural explanation of panic, based on the model proposed by Clark (1986) is given. This model highlights the role of hyperventilation leading to a loss of carbon dioxide which in turn will trigger a range of sensations often described by a panic sufferer, e.g. breathlessness, heart pounding, sweating, dizziness etc. The catastrophic interpretation of these sensations is detailed - 'My heart is pounding - I am having a heart attack', 'I can't control myself, I'm cracking up' etc. Information on controlled breathing is given along with the factors which may heighten the risk of panic, e.g. tiredness, rapid postural change, low normal blood sugar, alcohol, illness, premenstrual phase, caffeine intake. Of importance is the highlighting of the fact that panics are, by their very nature, frightening but not dangerous.

The public lectures

Three (free) evening lectures were held - one in each of the three main population centres in the Health Board Unit. Non-NHS venues were chosen and were as follows:
1. East Kilbride Civic Centre (52 attended)
2. Larkhall Community Education Centre (33 attended)
3. Hamilton Town Hall (43 attended)

The meetings were held on consecutive nights in the week following the publication of the final article.

Advertising the lecture Adverts were inserted at the end of the articles three and four. Posters were sent to practice managers in all G.P. surgeries for display in waiting areas. Posters were also sent to social work departments, alcohol advice centres, community centres, libraries and sports centres. A notice appeared in a West of Scotland evening paper - The Evening Times - in its 'What's on' column on each of the three lecture nights. Similarly each of the lectures was announced in morning and early evening 'What's on' slots on the local radio station, Radio Clyde.

Format

In general, all three talks were based on the same format although inevitably the talk improved with practice. The format was based closely on the articles. One hour was set for the lecture with fifteen minutes for questions. In practice, questions or comments lasted for thirty minutes and would have lasted longer had more time been available. The lecture was kept reasonably informal with comments or questions accepted during the talk.

Introduction Opening comments described what the aims of the lecture were, the format of the session and a description of a psychologist's role and how this differed from that of a psychiatrist.

Using a slide projector, the quotes used in article 1 were shown. In addition three other quotes were given. These described each of the components of anxiety taken from three systems assessment:

> Cognition '..... the most upsetting thoughts hit me, especially in bed at night and even though I know they don't make sense, I just can't shift them'.

> Behaviour 'It was when I refused to go to my daughter's school concert that I realised how bad it had got to me. I had come up with yet another excuse to avoid going out.'

> Somatics '..... When I first went to the doctor, I thought I was ill - I would be covered in sweat, my heart would be racing and I was sure I was going to faint. I am sure that everyone can see how bad I am when I get into this state ....'.

A final slide looked at depression.

> '.... I don't see any light at the end of the tunnel. I thought I knew what depression was in the past but now I really know - the blackness that comes over me at times really frightens me.....'

The level of presentation was again at a clinical level. The aim was to help the audience identify with the problems and perhaps with each other by observing the verbal behaviour, 'I know how that feels', and the non-verbal behaviour - head nodding etc. produced by members of the audience.

Myths and facts

This section was based directly on the information presented in article 1.

Symptom lists Dividing stress again into the three components of cognition ('thoughts'), behaviour ('actions') and somatics ('body'), some time was spent on describing the range of symptoms found within these components.

The role of stress A slide presentation on the role of stress was based on article 2. A description of a clinical problem was given which highlighted the fight/flight response.

Different types of stress This segment looked at the various forms taken by stress and, in particular described:

1. Phobias (mainly agoraphobia and social phobia)
2. Post traumatic stress disorder
3. Obsessive compulsive disorder
4. Panic disorder

5. Depression
6. Generalised anxiety disorder

Particular attention was paid to the last disorder as G.A.D. has been described as the 'basic' anxiety disorder (Barlow, 1988) and, with the possible exception of simple phobias, is commonly found as a secondary complaint with all of the above disorders (Barlow, 1988). Therefore the four 'clusters' of G.A.D. - motor tension, autonomic excitability, apprehension, vigilance and scanning were described.

Coping with stress The role of relaxation was discussed and advice on obtaining tapes given. The coping strategies delineated in article 3 were highlighted.

Handouts Two handouts were available:

1. 'Describing your Stress' - an eight item form which guides the reader to analyse their reactions in order to determine whether a pattern exists. The aim is to divide problems up into more manageable segments.
2. Symptoms Lists - a two page list of symptoms divided into three components - cognitions, behaviour, somatics.

Both were devised by the author.

Audience characteristics and evaluation For all three lectures, impressions of giving the talk were very similar to running group therapies as part of the NHS clinical psychology service. Signs of anxiety were prominent in a significant number of people and this information was freely given by a number of individuals. The seats nearest the exits were quickly taken - presumably by those experiencing agoraphobic difficulties. About half of the audience came in pairs - often two women. A self-help agoraphobic group came en masse to one of the talks and commandeered all the back row seats (hopefully benefitting from the exposure). It was my impression that the vast majority of people had come to the lectures looking for information to help their own anxiety problem. Table 1 provides further information taken from the evaluation questionnaire. For ease of presentation, results from the three lectures have been merged.

The male:female ratio is similar to that found in the NHS Service (Espie and White, 1986). The age breakdown is less similar with fewer over 50s referred. With 70% of the audiences having consulted their G.P. because of stress and half describing themselves as very stressful, the decision to pitch the lectures and articles at a clinical level seems justified.

Table 2 suggests a generally positive evaluation of the articles. This is not surprising as anyone negatively evaluating them would have been less likely to attend the lecture. Of interest is the finding that most have tried out some of the ideas with the vast majority obtaining at least some help from them.

The results from table 3 seem to echo those found in table 2. It does appear that the level of description employed and the range of topics included in the talk have been appropriate given the high ratings for relevance. The strong impression of the lecturer was that the audience had found them positive.

Question section

On each of the three occasions, a great many questions were received. One common concern to many related to panic attacks and some time was devoted to offering advice on controlling these. The role of tranquillisers was brought up along with questions about other forms of stress management techniques e.g. hypnosis, meditation, herbal remedies, acupuncture etc. A surprisingly high number of people had unsuccessfully tried these approaches. A large number had read at least one book on anxiety - Claire Weeks seemed to the most widely read and appreciated.

Sex	Male	27%
	Female	73%
Age	Up to 18	2%
	18 - 30	15%
	31 - 50	57%
	Over 50	26%
Consulted GP with stress problem recently	Yes	70%
	No	30%
Stress level	Not at all stressful	4%
	A bit stressful	20%
	Moderately stressful	27%
	Very Stressful	49%

Audience characteristics
(n=115)

Table 1

Ending the session

Due to the lack of time, not all questions could be answered and the sessions ended, after the questionnaires were completed, with a series of cartoon slides on the subject of stress. The vast majority took the handouts and a sizeable number of people stayed behind to ask for specific advice. Of this number, at least three stated that they believed their problems to be physical until reading the articles and attending the lecture. Two of these individuals have now been referred to the clinical psychology department.

Conclusions

This project looked at the feasibility of reaching the expected large number of people in the community experiencing high levels of stress; to provide them with information about their problem and to offer advice on ways of coping. It appears to have been successful. The number of people attending the lectures was encouraging as their evaluation of the project was positive. One unexpected effect of the project has become apparent as NHS patients attend for their first appointment having been on the waiting list during the time when the project ran. Practically all had read the articles and several had attended the lectures. All reported that they had found this useful particularly during the frustrating time when no help would normally be offered by the clinical psychology department. Similarly, the project has shown the NHS to be pro-active instead of reactive

Did you read the articles on stress in your local paper?	Yes	75%
	No	25%
If yes, did you find them	Boring	0%
	Interesting	30%
	Very interesting	70%
Did you find them	Useless	0%
	Useful	58%
	Very useful	42%
Having read them, do you feel you know more about stress?	Very much more	27%
	More	56%
	About the same	17%
Have you tried out any of the ideas for reducing stress?	Yes	68%
	No	32%
If yes, what effect has this had?	No help at all	9%
	Helpful	65%
	Very helpful	26%
Would you like to see more articles on stress in the paper?	Yes	95%
	No	5%

Audience evaluation of newspaper articles
(n=115)

Table 2

Have you found this talk	Boring	0%
	Interesting	34%
	Very interesting	66%
Have you found this talk	Not at all relevant	0%
	Relevant	43%
	Very relevant	57%
Do you feel you know more about stress after the talk?	About the same	19%
	More	47%
	Very much more	34%
Would you like to hear more talks on stress?	Yes	98%
	No	2%

Audience evaluation of the lecture
Table 3 (n=115)

341

and this may enhance the reputation of mental health services in the area.

The project was simple to set up and run. In terms of time and expense, it was extremely economical. In view of the fact that psychology departments appear only to be getting at the 'tip of the iceberg', this project, in line with the many other innovative developments referred to earlier, may provide a way to significantly increase the number of people it can reach while not significantly stretching limited resources. Further forays into the use of local media and lectures are being explored.

References

Barlow, D. H. (1988). *Anxiety and its disorders.* New York: Guilford Press.

Barlow, D. H., Cohen, A. S., & Waddell, M. T. et al. (1984). Panic and generalised anxiety disorders: Nature and treatment. *Behavior Therapy* 15, 431-449

Bradshaw, P. W., Ley, P., Kincey, J. & Bradshaw, J. (1985). Recall of medical advice. *British Journal of Social and Clinical Psychology* 14, 55-62

Butler, P. & de Clive-Lowe (1985). Strategies for living: Teaching psychological self-help as adult education. *British Journal of Medical Psychology* 8, 275-283

Clark, D. M. (1986). A cognitive approach to panic. *Behaviour Research and Therapy* 24, 461-470

Croft-Jeffries, C. & Wilkinson, G. (1989). Estimated costs of neurotic disorder in UK general practice 1985. *Psychological Medicine* 19, 549-558

Donnan, P., Hutchinson, A., & Paxton, R. et al. (1990). Self-help materials for anxiety: A randomised controlled trial in general practice. *British Journal of General Practice.*

Dow, M. G. T. (1982). Behavioural bibliotherapy: Theoretical and methodological issues in outcome research into self-help programmes. In C. J. Main (Ed.), *Clinical psychology and medicine.* New York: Plenum Press

Espie, C. A. & White, J. (1986). Clinical psychology and general practice: A four year review. *Health Bulletin* 44/5, 266-273

Flesch, R. (1948). A new readability yardstick. *Journal of Applied Psychology* 32, 221-233

Hall, J., Kock, H., Pilling, S. & Winter, K. (1986). Health Services information and clinical psychology. *Bulletin of the British Psychological Society* 39, 126-130

Heller, M. B., Kear-Colwell, J. & Beeken, J. (1986). The 'walk-in' clinic for adult psychology services: A pilot project. *Division of Clinical Psychology Newsletter,* 27-31

Johnson, M. (1978). The work of a clinical psychologist in primary care. *Journal of the Royal College of General Practitioners* 28, 661-667

Lader, M. (1975). Benzodiazepines - the opium of the masses? *Neuroscience* 3, 159-165

Ley, P. (1977). Psychological studies of doctor-patient communication. In S. Rachmin. (Ed.), *Contributions to Medical Psychology,* Vol. 1. Oxford: Pergamon

Long, C. G. & Bourne, V. (1987). Linking professional and self-help resources for anxiety management: A community project. *Journal of the Royal College of General*

Practitioners 37, 199-201

Milne, D., Jones, R. & Walters, P. (1989). Anxiety Management in the community: A social support model. *Behavioural Psychotherapy* 17, 221-237

National Audit Office (1989). *National Health Service: Coronary heart disease.* HMSO: London

Powell, T. J. (1987). Anxiety Management groups in clinical practice: A preliminary report. *Behavioural Psychotherapy* 15, 181-187

Turvey, A. (1985). Treatment Manuals. In F. N. Watts. (Ed.), *New developments in clinical psychology.* British Psychological Society

Weinman, J. & Meduk, l. (1985). Sharing psychological skills in the general practice setting. *British Journal of Medical Psychology* 58, 223-230

White, J. & Keenan, M. (1990). Stress Control: A pilot study of large group therapy for generalised anxiety disorder. *Behavioral Psychotherapy* 18, 143-146